T0372021

Plants of Central Asia

Volume 8c

Plants of Central Asia

Plant Collections from China and Mongolia

(*Editor-in-Chief:* V.I. Grubov)

Volume 8c

Astragalus L.

N. Ulzijchutag

Science Publishers, Inc.

Enfield (NH), USA   Plymouth, UK

ACADEMIA SCIENTIARUM ROSSICA
INSTITUTUM BOTANICUM nomine V.L. KOMAROVII
PLANTAE ASIAE CENTRALIS
(secus materies Instituti botanici nomine V.L. Komarovii)
Fasciculus 8c
Leguminosae (Fabaceae)
Genus Astragalus L.
Confecit: N. Ulzijchutag

SCIENCE PUBLISHERS, INC.
Post Office Box 699
Enfield, New Hampshire 03748
United States of America

Internet site: *http://www.scipub.net*

ISBN 1-57808-341-9 (Volume 8c)
ISBN 1-57808-062-2 (Set)

Library of Congress Cataloging-in-Publication Data

Rasteniia TSentral'noĭ Azii. English
Plants of Central Asia: plant collections from China and Mongolia /[editor-in-chief. V.I. Grubov].
p. cm.
Research based on the collections of the V.L. Komarov Botanical Institute.
Includes bibliographical references.
Contents: V.8c. Legumes. Genus: Astragalus L.
ISBN 1-57808-341-9(V. 8c)
1. Botany-Asia, Central. I. Grubov, V.I. II. Botanicheskiĭ institut im. V.L. Komarova. III. Title.
QK374, R23613 2002
581.958-dc21 99-36729
CIP

Translation of: Rasteniya Tsentral'noi Asii, vol. 8c, 2000
Mir i Sem'ya, St.-Petersburg

Published by Science Publishers, Inc., USA
Printed in India

ANNOTATION

Volume 8c of the illustrated list of vascular plants of Central Asia (within the People's Republics of China and Mongolia) treats the large and very complex genus *Astragalus* L. of the family Leguminosae. The species of this genus enjoy considerable importance as fodder and medicinal plants as well as in the formation of coenosis. Keys to species are given under each subgenus and references to nomenclature, information on habitat and geographic distribution under each species.

The original layout was sponsored by Russian Foundation for Basic Research (Grant 94-04-62118).

Editor-in-Chief
V.I. Grubov

PREFACE

Volume 8c of "Plants of Central Asia" covers the largest and taxonomically complex genus *Astragalus* L. with 306 species inhabiting the Chinese and Mongolian parts of Central Asia. Keys and text also include 42 unnumbered (asterisked) species reported from the immediately adjoining regions and are likely to be detected in the Central Asian territory under consideration. The census of species inhabiting the Central Asian part of Kazakhstan, Tajikistan and Kirgizstan would add 60–70 more species. Thus, the total number of species under genus *Astragalus* in the entire Central Asian territory totals roughly 400.

In the flora of Central Asia, genus *Astragalus* is important not only in the abundance of species but also in phytocoenosis and economy.

Many species are extensively and massively distributed (*A. tenuis, A. adsurgens, A. mongolicus, A. dahuricus*), some are assectators and even characteristic plants of desert and dry steppe associations and deserts (e.g. *A. vallestris* forms nearly pure associations over vast expanses along trails in Valley of Lakes and *A. pavlovii* is an assectator in subshrubs of Alashan Gobi deserts). Some (like *A. dahuricus*) actively spread as weeds. In economic terms, they are of interest as fodder—*A. adsurgens, A. laguroides, A. melilotoides, A. miniatus, A. tenuis*—although some of them are highly toxic, specially during anthesis, like *A. galactites* and *A. variabilis*. Fleshy, thick and long roots of *A. membranaceus* and *A. mongolicus* are valued in Chinese medicine as tonics and common remedies and were formerly exported from Mongolia in large quantities. These also find use in the food of locals.

In the territory under study, genus *Astragalus* L. includes 9 subgenera: *Cercidothrix* Bunge 132 species (49 of them endemics), *Phaca* L. 72 (18 endemics), *Astragalus* (*Caprinus* Bunge) 45 (7 endemics), *Calycocystis* Bunge 40 (17 endemics), *Trimeniaeus* Bunge 15 (1 endemic), *Hypoglottis* Bunge 13 (6 endemics), *Pogonophaca* Bunge 12 (4 endemics), *Calycophysa* Bunge 6 (1 endemic) and *Monodelphus* Ching fil. 1 (introduced from south-west. China).

Thus, the total number of endemics of this genus in the Central Asian territory under consideration is 104 species (31% of total number of species of the genus). Such a high degree of endemism suggests that

Central Asia, along with Fore Asia, is the most important centre of speciation of *Astragalus*.

Analysis of area-wise distribution of genus *Astragalus* L. shows that species of Junggar subprovince predominate in the flora of Central Asia, they forming 56.2% (189 species) of the total number of *Astragalus* species. Next come species distributed in Mongolian subprovince and Tibet province at 34.2% and 25.0% (115 and 84 species, respectively), followed at the end by species from Kashgar and Qaidam subprovinces at 16.1% and 2.4% (54 and 8 species, respectively).

Phytogeographic analysis reveals that species of Tien Shan mountain districts (78 species) predominate in the composition of Central Asian *Astragalus* flora. These are followed by Mongolian Altay (62 species), Tarbagatai (46 species), Nanshan (42 species), South. Tibet (35 species), and desert districts: Junggar Gobi (59 species) and Zaisan basin (40 species). The next important category in this analysis is: desert and montane-desert districts of Jarkent (32 species), Eastern Gobi (30 species), Eastern Pamir (28 species) and Gobi Altay (25 species). Qaidam (2–6 species), Takla Makan in Kashgar (2 species) and Balkhash-Alakul' (4 species) districts are of least importance in the distribution of the species of *Astragalus*.

In Central Asian territory, the major secondary centres of speciation of genus *Astragalus* L. are Tien Shan mountain range and intermontane desert depressions.

It is interesting to note that the following members of subgenus *Pogonophaca* Bunge, *Astragalus tengriensis* Ni et P.C. Li, *A. tribulifolius* Benth. ex Beg., *A. tanguticus* Bat., *A. hendersonii* Baker and *A. heydei* Baker are distributed only in Qinghai and Tibet subprovinces.

In subgenus *Astragalus*, most species of section *Aegacantha* (Nevski) Gontsch. (*A. oplites* Benth. ex Parker, *A. bicuspis* Fisch., *A. rhizanthus* Royle ex Benth. and others) and species of section *Astenolobium* Bunge (*A. webbianus* Grah. ex Benth., *A. royleanus* Bunge) are distributed in Tibet while species of section *Skythropos* Simps. (*A. smithianus* Peter-Stib., *A. fenzelianus* Peter-Stib., *A. licentianus* Hand.-Mazz., *A. weigoldianus* Hand.-Mazz., *A. tatsienensis* Bureau et Franch. et al.) are distributed in Tibet province and many species of section *Myobroma* Bunge, in Junggar province.

In subgenus *Phaca* (L.) Bunge, members of section *Melilotropsis* Gontsch. inhabit Mongolian subprovince with reports from Manchuria and nor. Chinese regions.

The geographic distribution of the following 3 closely-related *Astragalus* species (placing them in 2 oligotypical sections, in our opinion, is not quite logical—V.G.) *A. dshinensis* (Junggar and West.

Mongolia), *A. hoantchy* (East. Mongolia) and *A. hedinii* (Tibet), which form a natural series, is of interest as they demonstrate close floristic relations between all 3 subprovinces of Central Asia: Junggar, Mongolia and Tibet.

Mention should also be made of the following group of Gobi desert endemics: *A. baitagensis* Sancz. ex Ulzij., *A. valerii* Ulzij., *A. zacharensis* Bunge, *A. chrysopteris* Bunge, *A. alaschanus* Bunge, *A. pavlovii* B. Fedtsch. et N. Basil., *A. discolor* Bunge, *A. variabilis* Bunge ex Maxim., *A. miniatus* Bunge, *A. grubovii* Sancz., *A. junatovii* Sancz., *A. pseudoscaberrimus* Wang et Tang, *A. scaberrimus* Ledeb., *A. glomeratus* Ledeb., *A. galactites* Pall., *A. parvicarinatus* S.B. Ho, *A. jiuguanensis* S.B. Ho, *A. pseudohypogaeus* S.B. Ho, *A. koburensis* Bunge, *A. ordosicus* H.C. Fu, *A. hsinbaticus* P.Y. Fu et Y.A. Chen, *A. monophyllus* Bunge, *A. gubanovii* Ulzij., *A. macrotrichoides* Peter-Stib., *A. baischanticus* Ulzij., *A. efoliolatus* Hand.-Mazz., *A. vallestris* R. Kam., *A. ochrias* Bunge, *A. gobi-altaicus* Ulzij., *A. baotouensis* H.C. Fu, *A. koslovii*, B. Fedtsch. et N. Basil. ex Ulzij.

Plant drawings in the plates presented in this volume have been prepared by artrist O.V. Zaitseva and maps of distribution ranges by the author N. Ulzijchutag.

O.I. Starikova translated the Chinese references and herbarium labels.

In the course of editing the manuscript, V.I. Grubov effected certain improvements and modifications in citations of geographic origin of type specimens of plants as well as geographic distribution of species.

V.I. Grubov, N. Ulzijchutag

CONTENTS

TAXONOMY

SPECIAL ABBREVIATIONS

Abbreviations of Names of Collectors

Bar.	—	V.I. Baranov
Chaff.	—	J. Chaffanjon
Chaney	—	R.W. Chaney
Chen and Chou	—	Chen Tszin-shen and Chou Guan-yui (1957)
Ching	—	R.C. Ching
Chu	—	C.N. Chu
Czet.	—	S.S. Czetyrkin
Divn.	—	D.A. Divnogorskaya
Fedtsch.	—	B.A. Fedtschenko
Fet.	—	A.M. Fetisov
Franch.	—	A. Franchet
Glag.	—	S.A. Glagolev
Gr.-Grzh.	—	G.E. Grum-Grzhimailo
Grombch.	—	B.L. Grombchevski
Grub.	—	V.I. Grubov
Gub.	—	I.A. Gubanov
Gus.	—	V.A. Gusev
Hand.-Mazz.	—	H. Handel-Mazzetti
Hao	—	Hao Kin-Shen
Ik.-Gal.	—	N.P. Ikonnikov-Galitzkij
Isach.	—	E.A. Isachenko (also known as E.A. Volkova)
Ivan.	—	A.F. Ivanov
Kal.	—	A.V. Kalinina
Kam.	—	R.V. Kamelin
Karam.	—	Z.V. Karamysheva
Klem.	—	E.N. and D.A. Klements
Knorr.	—	O.E. Knorring
Kozl.	—	P.K. Kozlov

Krasch.	— I.M. Krascheninnikov
Krasn.	— A.N. Krasnov
Kryl.	— P.N. Krylov
Kuan	— K.C. Kuan
Lad.	— V.F. Ladygin
Lavr.	— E.M. Lavrenko
Liou	— Liou Tchen-ngo
Lis.	— Lisovsky
Li Sh.-i	— Li Shi-in
Li Sh.-s et al.	— S.H. Li et al. (1951)
Litw.	— D.I. Litwinow
Lom.	— A.M. Lomonossov
Martin	— J. Martin
Merzb.	— G. Merzbacher
Mois.	— V.S. Moiseenko
Nov.	— V.F. Novitski
Pal.	— I.V. Palibin
Pavl.	— N.V. Pavlov
Petr.	— M.P. Petrov
Pevts.	— M.V. Pevtsov
Pias.	— P.Ya. Piassezki
Pob.	— E.G. Pobedimova
Pop.	— M.G. Popov
Pot.	— G.N. Potanin
Prokh.	— Ya.I. Prokhanov
Przew.	— N.M. Przewalsky
Rachk.	— E.I. Rachkovskaya
Reg. A.	— A. Regel
Rob.	— V.I. Roborowsky
Safr.	— I.N. Safronova
Sap.	— V.V. Sapozhnikov
Schischk.	— B.K. Schischkin
Serp.	— V.M. Serpukhov
Sold.	— V.V. Soldatov
Tug.	— A.Ya. Tugarinov
Ulzij.	— N. Ulzijchutag [Ulzijkhutag]
Volk.	— E.A. Volkova (also known as E.A. Isachenko)

Wang Ch.-f.	—	Wang Chao-feng
Wang K.-S.	—	K.S. Wang
Yuan	—	Yuan' I-fen'
Yun.	—	A.A. Yunatov
Zab.	—	D.K. Zabolotnyi
Zam.	—	B.M. Zamatkinov

Abbreviated Names of Herbaria

A	—	Herbarium, Arnold Arboretum of Harvard University, Cambridge, Massachusetts, USA
AA	—	Herbarium of the Botanical Institute of Academy of Sciences of Kazakhstan, Alma Ata
B	—	Botanisches Garten und Botanisches Museum, Berlin-Dahlem
BM	—	British Museum (Natural History), London
BP	—	Botanical Department of the Hungarian History Museum, Budapest
C	—	Copenhagen Botanical Museum and Herbarium, Copenhagen
E	—	Royal Botanic Garden, Edinburgh
G	—	Conservatoire et Jardin botaniques de la Ville de Geneve, Geneva
GAT	—	Gatersleben: Zentral Institut für Genetik und Kulturpflanzenforschung
GH	—	Gray Herbarium of Harvard University, Cambridge, Massachusetts, USA
H	—	University of Helsinki, Helsinki, Finland
HAL	—	Herbarium, Martin-Luther-Universität, Halle, Germany
HIMC	—	Herbarium, Department of Biology, University of Inner Mongolia, Huhehot
K	—	The Herbarium, Royal Botanic Gardens, Kew, Richmond, Surrey, London
KUN	—	Herbarium of Kunming Institute of Botany, Academia Sinica, Kunming
L	—	Rijksherbarium, Leiden
LE	—	V.L. Komarov Botanical Institute, St. Petersburg, Russia

LINN	—	Herbarium, The Linnean Society of London, London
LIV	—	Herbarium, Merseyside County Museum, Liverpool
LY	—	Herbiers de l'Universite de Lyon, Department de Biologie Végétale, Villeurbanne, France
LZDI	—	Herbarium, Institute of Desert Research, Academia Sinica, Gansu, Lanzhou
LZU	—	Herbarium of the Lanshou University, Gansu, Lanzhou
MICH	—	Herbarium of the University of Michigan, Ann Arbor, Michigan, USA
MO	—	Herbarium, Missouri Botanical Garden, St. Louis, Missouri, USA
MW	—	Herbarium of the Moscow State University, Moscow
NS	—	Novosibirsk: The Central Siberian Botanical Garden of the Siberian Division of the Russian Academy of Sciences
NWBI	—	Herbarium, North-Western Plateau Institute of Biology, Academia Sinica, Shaanxi, Wugung
NY	—	Herbarium, New York Botanical Garden, Bronx, New York
O	—	Oslo, Botanical Museum, Norway
OXF	—	Fielding-Druce Herbarium, Department of Botany, University of Oxford, Botany School, Oxford, England
P	—	Museum National d'Histoire Naturelle, Laboratoire de Phanerogamie, Paris
PE	—	Herbarium, Institute of Botany, Academia Sinica, Beijing
TI	—	Botanical Institute, University of Tokyo, Tokyo
TK	—	Krylov Herbarium of the State University, Tomsk
UBA	—	Herbarium, Institute of Botany, Mongolian Academy of Sciences, Ulan Bator
UBU	—	Herbarium, Department of Botany, Mongolian National University, Ulan Bator
US	—	United States National Herbarium, Department of Botany, Smithsonian Institute, Washington
W	—	Naturhistorisches Museum, Botanische Abteilung, Wien [Vienna]
XJBI	—	Herbarium of the Institute of Biology, Soil and Desert Sciences, Xinjiang, Acad. Sin., Urumqi [Urumchi]

YNFI — Herbarium, Yunnang Institute of Forestry, Yunnang [Yunnan]

Z — Institut für Systematische Botanik der Universität, Zürich, Switzerland

32. **Astragalus** L.

Sp. Pl. (1753) 755;
idem, Gen. Pl. ed. 5 (1754) 335.

Key to Subgenera

1. Perennial plant with woody root neck or, more often, with shortened, predominantly short-branched subsurface caudex. Rather shrubs, subshrubs or small shrubs pubescent with simple or double-ended hairs .... 2.
\+ Annuals or biennials with slender roots pubescent with simple hairs .... Subgenus 6. **Trimeniaeus** Bunge.
2. Plant pubescent with simple (affixed at one end) hairs, more rarely glabrous .... 3.
\+ Plant pubescent with double-ended hairs (medifixed; sometimes, hairs affixed close to their end, thus appearing simple); sometimes, plants subglabrous (stray, double-ended hairs seen only on petiole or on calyx).................................... 8.
3. All 10 stamens connate into a single tube (monodelphous). Ovary pilose .... Subgenus 1. **Monodelphus** Cheng fil.
\+ Only 9 stamens connate, 1 free (diadelphous) .... 4.
4. Style and stigma covered with long hairs or only stigma with long brush-like (barbate) hairs .... Subgenus 3. **Pogonophaca** Bunge (*Trichostylus* Baker).
\+ Style and stigma without pubescence or with numerous papillae or covered with extremely short hairs .... 5.
5. Flowers in short or long loose racemes; in case of capitate racemes, calyx considerably smaller or plant with shortened stems; wings and keel free at base .... 6.
\+ Flowers in dense large globose or somewhat oblong inflorescence; calyx inflated, specially at the beginning of fruiting, villous, 15–30 mm long, teeth as long as its tube, more rarely smaller; wings and keel connate with androphore at base. Pods small, enclosed in inflated calyx, sometimes slightly piercing it. Leaves long, with 15–25 pairs of leaflets; smaller

leaflets 3–6 cm long. Plant large (30–90 cm tall), with patent hairs .... Subgenus 7. **Calycophysa** Bunge.

6. Plant usually with well-developed stems; pods membranous, scarious or leptodermatus with slender, usually semitransparent valves on long stalks; calyx small, campanulate or tubular-campanulate, more rarely large, tubular; in latter case, pods membranous. Stipules free or adnate to petiole only at base, more rarely up to 1/2 and connate above, specially of lower leaves. Inflorescence on well-developed peduncle .... Subgenus 2. **Phaca** (L.) Bunge.

\+ Plant acauline or with shortened stems or sometimes stems well-developed; pods coriaceous, with stiff strong valves, sessile; calyx large, tubular, more rarely campanulate but then pods coriaceous. Stipules usually distinctly adnate to petiole or connate. Inflorescence on short peduncle or sessile, more rarely on long peduncle .... 7.

7. Plant usually with shortened stems or subacauline; sometimes, spiny shrubs or subshrubs with woody petiole and rachis. Stipules usually distinctly adnate to petiole, usually for much of the length (if stipules adnate only at base, plants usually with well-developed pubescence and hard, stiff-coriaceous pods). Inflorescence usually racemose, lax, sometimes subsessile; corolla usually yellow, more rarely violet or blue, sometimes reddish; calyx tubular, saccate-inflated at base. Pods oval or oblong-oval with hard, dense, thick coriaceous valves .... Subgenus 5. **Astragalus** (s. str.)=*Caprinus* Bunge.

\+ Plant with well-developed stems. Stipules connate but not adnate to petiole. Inflorescence dense, capitate or ovate; corolla sky-blue or violet, more rarely yellow; calyx symmetrical at base. Pods linear-oblong, with slender, flexible, coriaceous valves .... Subgenus 4. **Hypoglottis** Bunge.

8. Calyx not inflated after anthesis or somewhat enlarged in fruit .... Subgenus 8. **Carcidothrix** Bunge.

\+ Calyx vesicularly inflated and enveloping pod .... Subgenus 9. **Calycocystis** Bunge.

Subgenus 1. **Monodelphus** Cheng fil. ex P.C. Li et C.C. Ni

1. Rachis white hairy. Stems rather thick, erect, up to 60 cm tall. Stipules large, leaflike, rather oblong, brownish, or somewhat light-green, almost herbaceous. Leaflets (5) 5–9 pairs, oblong-lanceolate or oblong-ovate, 10–18 mm long, 5–9 mm broad.

Bracts 2–3 times longer than pedicels. Raceme with 8–11 flowers, elongated. Corolla yellow or yellowish, later erubescent. Calyx teeth subulate, as long as tube. Pods flattened, unilocular (section 1. **Monodelphia** K.T. Fu) .... 1. **A. monodelphus** Bunge ex Maxim.

\+ Rachis with black pubescence and sparse, short, soft hairs. Stems rather slender, up to 30 cm tall. Stipules small, herbaceous, triangular or deltoid. Corolla blue or violet; calyx teeth triangular or lanceolate, shorter than tube (section 2. **Parvistipula** K.T. Fu) .... 2.

2. Leaflets 5–6 (7) pairs, obovate, 3–8 mm long, 4–5 mm broad, with broad notch at tip, pubescent beneath. Raceme with 1–3 flowers. Calyx 7–8 mm long, teeth triangular, 1/2 as long as tube. Standard 13 mm long, with orbicular blade; ovary and style without hairs .... *__A. yatungensis__ Ni et P.C. Li.

\+ Leaflets 7–11 pairs, oblong, 6–10 mm long, 2–4 mm broad, with rounded and obtuse tip and sparse hairs on both sides. Raceme with 1–7 flowers. Calyx 5 mm long, teeth lanceolate, 2/3 as long as tube. Standard 12 mm long, with oblong-oval blade; style pilose .... *__A. changmuicus__ Ni et P.C. Li.

Section 1 (1). **Monodelphia** K.T. Fu

1. **A. monodelphus** Bunge ex Maxim. in Mel. Biol. Ac. Sci. St.-Petersb. 10 (1877) 52; id. in Bull. Ac. Sci. St.-Petersb. 24 (1878) 32; Simps. in Not. Bot. Gard. Edinb. 8 (1915) 255; Peter-Stib. in Acta Horti Gotoburg, 12 (1937) 45; Wang and Tang in Ill. treatm. princip. I. China, Legum. (1955) 410; K.T. Fu in Acta Bot. Bor.-Occ. Sinica, 1, 2 (1981) 16.—*A. luteus* Ulbr. in Report. Nov. Sp. Beih. 12 (1922) 419.

—**Ic.:** Wang and Tang l.c. fig. 405.

Described from Qinghai (Nanshan). Type in St.-Petersburg (LE).

In alpine meadows along river banks.

IIIA. Qinghai: *Nanshan* (South Tetung mountain range, Tetung river, forest belt in high mountains at level 3048 m [10,000 ft] July 2–17 [14–29], 1872—Przew., typus !; Gansu; Kuku-Nor-Peter-Stib. l.c.; K.T. Fu l.c.).

General distribution: China (? North-West: East. Gansu; South-West.: Sichuan).

Subgenus 2. **Phaca** (L.) Bunge

1. Flower in addition to bract with 2 small bracteoles at base of calyx, deciduous in fruit, leaving behind distinct scars at point of their attachment. Pods suspended, narrowed at base, on up to 20 mm long pedicels .... 2.

\+ Flowers without bracteoles; if present, pods not suspended and more inflated .... 7.

2\. Corolla yellow or pale-yellowish .... 3.

\+ Corolla violet or greenish-brown .... 4.

3\. Pods unilocular; calyx 7–8 mm long, teeth lanceolate-subulate, 1/4–1/3 of tube length; standard 13–15 mm long, blade obovate. Leaflets oblong-ovate, subacute at tip, glabrous above, white-hairy beneath (section 1 (2). **Alexandri** Ulzij.) .... 2. **A. ulziykhutagii** Sytin.

\+ Pods bilocular; calyx 8–10 mm long, teeth lanceolate, 1/2 as long as tube; standard 20 mm long, blade orbicular-oval. Leaflets orbicular-obovate, broadly and shallowly truncate-emarginate at tip, glabrous on both surfaces (section 2 (3). **Robusti** Peter-Stib.) .... 3. **A. dshinensis** Gontsch.

4\. Calyx 4–7 mm long, teeth less than 1/3 as long as tube. Pods unilocular (section 3 (4). **Monotheca** Ulzij.) .... 5.

\+ Calyx 11–13 mm long, teeth 1/2 as long as tube. Pods semi-bilocular (section 4 (5). **Diplotheca** Hochst) .... 6.

5\. Calyx about 7 mm long, teeth narrow-deltoid, 1.5 mm long, i.e. 1/3 as long as tube. Pods equilateral, elliptical-oblong, acuminate toward both ends, 20 mm long, 9 mm broad. Leaflets linear or linear-lanceolate, 15–30 mm long, 3–5 mm broad, tip rounded, base circular, glabrous above, with short pubescence beneath. Plant up to 60 cm tall .... 4. **A. przewalskii** Bunge.

\+ Calyx 4–6 mm long, teeth shortly-deltoid, 0.5–1 mm long, 1/10–1/6 as long as tube. Pods asymmetrical, semioval or semioval-oblong, with cusp at tip; gradually narrowed at base, 30–40 mm long, 9–12 mm broad. Leaflets oblong or oblong-ovate, (8) 10–15 mm long, (3.5) 4–6 mm broad, with appressed or semi-appressed white hairs on both surfaces. Plant (60) 70–90 cm tall .... 5. **A. petrovii** Ulzij.

6\. Pods distinctly symmetrical, oblong, 25–30 (32) mm long, 4–5 (7) mm broad, on long pedicels. Calyx teeth deltoid-lanceolate. Leaflets 8–10 pairs, broadly-oval, broadly-obcordate (-ovate), sometimes suborbicular, up to 22 mm long, up to 18 mm broad, emarginate at tip and with short cusp, sparse white hairs along margin and veins. Plant large, up to 1 m tall .... 6. **A. hoantchy** Franch.

\+ Pods distinctly asymmetrical, semioval or nearly oblong, 30–40 mm long, 8–10 mm broad. Calyx teeth linear-lanceolate. Leaflets 7–8 pairs, elliptical or oblong-ovate, 15–22 mm long,

10–15 mm broad, subacute at tip, sparse hairs at base of blade. Plant large, 1–1.7 m tall .... 7. **A. hedinii** Ulbr.

7. Plant with withered leaf petioles; if persistent, not spiny. Pedicels generally developed. Flowers in racemes on distinct or fairly long peduncles .... 8.

\+ Plant with persistent, rigescent, spiny or more rarely inermous petioles. Pedicels short, not developed, up to 3 cm long. Flowers in shortened, subsessile inflorescences, 2–5 each in leaf axils, yellow (section 6 (7). **Lithophilus** Bunge) .... 9.

8. Plant acauline, rarely stems 2–3 cm long. Flowers on developed leafless, 10–60 cm long peduncles. Bracts 3–5 mm long. Calyx tubular, with appressed white and black hairs, teeth very short, almost invisible, deltoid. Corolla yellow, standard 16–20 mm long. Leaflets 7–12 pairs, hispid, 10–20 (24) mm long, 2–8 mm broad, elliptical, oblong-elliptical or lanceolate. Pods unilocular, oblong-elliptical, 15–20 mm long, 5–8 mm broad (section 5 (6). **Scheremeteviana** O. et B. Fedtsch.) .... *__A. scheremetevianus__ B. Fedtsch.

\+ Plant with well developed at least 3–10 cm tall stems .... 12.

9. Pods compressed, oval-ovate, up to 10 mm long, patently white-hairy. Leaflets 5–15 mm long, with long white hairs on both surfaces .... 8. **A. dalaiensis** Kitag.

\+ Pods inflated, more than 10 mm long. Leaflets glabrous or pilose on one surface .... 10.

10. Plants herbaceous, with stems up to 35 cm tall. Calyx glabrous. Pods hard-membraned, oval, 13–15 mm long, almost bilocular. Leaflets 10–17 pairs, 2.5–4 mm long, obovate or oblong-obcordate, rather thick, subglabrous, sparsely ciliate along margin .... *__A. olgae__ Bunge.

\+ Plants woody. Calyx hairy. Leaflets more than 5 mm long .... 11.

11. Leaflets 12–14 pairs, oval, oblong-lanceolate or oblong-oval, 8–14 mm long, glabrous or generally pilose beneath. Pods entirely bilocular. Calyx brown-hairy .... 9. **A. lithophilus** Kar. et Kir.

\+ Leaflets 7–11 (12) pairs, oblong-linear, 15–25 mm long, 2–4 mm broad, glabrous above, long-hairy beneath. Pods incompletely bilocular. Calyx with dense white pubescence .... 10. **A. munroi** Benth. ex Bunge.

12. Stipules leaflike or herbaceous, free, very rarely connate but then large. Racemes lax, many-flowered; corolla pale- or

bright-yellow or blue, rose-red, 14–23 mm long. Pods on slender long pedicels. Sturdy mesophilic herbs .... 13.

\+ Stipules not leaflike-herbaceous, more often connate or very small, less than 5 mm long, sometimes up to 8 mm long. In doubtful cases, either wings bilobed at tip or pods small, 6–7 mm long, subtrigonous, glabrous or with patent pubescence. Racemes usually dense, more rarely somewhat lax; corolla lilac-coloured, light-violet, rose, more rarely albescent, sometimes yellowish, often with very dark tip of keel, usually less than 15 mm long, more rarely 16–17 mm long .... 26.

13\. Pods nodding, oval, inflated, (9) 10–14 mm long, 4–5 mm broad, 7–9 mm thick, skin hard and chondroid, nut-shaped, rugose-nervate in cross-section, nearly completely bilocular. Calyx campanulate. Corolla 14–15 mm long, wings shorter than keel, latter shorter than standard (section 7 (8). **Nuculiella** Gontsch.) .... 11. **A. chinensis** L. fil.

\+ Pods pendent, rather oblong, elliptical, lanceolate or almost hemispherical, slightly inflated, finely-membranous, unilocular. Calyx tubular-campanulate. Corolla 15–23 mm long, wings shorter than standard and longer than keel (section 8 (9). **Cenantrum** Koch) .... 14.

14\. Corolla blue, purple-violet or rose-red. Pods ovate-lanceolate, 1.5–2 cm long, 5 mm broad .... 15.

\+ Corolla yellow or light-yellow .... 16.

15\. Flowers 10–12 mm long; calyx teeth shorter than tube .... 12. **A. degensis** Ulbr.

\+ Flowers 13–14 mm long; calyx teeth longer than tube or as long .... 12. **A. degensis** var. **rockianus** Peter-Stib.

16\. Stipules large, leaflike or leaflike-scaly, oblong-lanceolate, (2) 3–5 mm long, 1.3–1.5 cm broad, glabrous on both sides. Calyx glabrous or subglabrous outside, densely covered inside with short, black hairs. Pods oblong-lanceolate, 2–3 cm long, densely covered with long, soft, black hairs, unilocular .... 13. **A. tongolensis** Ulbr. var. **glaber** Peter-Stib.

\+ Stipules small, not leaflike, less than 2 cm long, deltoid, lanceolate or coiled, covered with sparse or dense pubescence of long or short soft hairs. Calyx densely-pubescent outside .... 17.

17\. Leaflets 2–8 pairs. Pods elliptical or oblong-elliptical to lanceolate, usually symmetrical, rarely slightly asymmetrical .... 18.

+ Leaflets (7) 10–21 pairs. Pods usually semioval or semiorbicular, rarely asymmetrical, sometimes almost oblong .... 22.

18. Pedicels and inflorescence axis covered with dense patent or semipatent black hairs. Calyx 7–12 mm long, patently pilose allover surface. Corolla lemon-yellow. Inflorescence with many flowers; racemes lax, 4–7 mm long. Leaflets (4) 6–7 (8) pairs, (15) 20–35 (40) mm long, (5) 10–15 (20) mm broad, oblong-ovate or lanceolate, bright-green, glabrous above; canescent, silver-hairy below. Pods asymmetrically lanceolate-elliptical, (13) 15–25 mm long, inflated, acute at base and tip, on slender, 8–10 mm long pedicels. Plant 20–50 cm tall .... 14. **A. lepsensis** Bunge.

+ Pedicels and inflorescence axis as well as calyx glabrous or covered with sparse appressed hairs in upper portion .... 17.

19. Ovary and pods generally with fine, black hairs .... 20.

+ Ovary and pods totally glabrous .... 21.

20. Corolla ivory-white, 14–16 mm long. Calyx about 7 mm long, green, somewhat mowed down, its teeth broadly-deltoid, 1/7–1/6 of tube length, usually pubescent on both sides. Leaflets oblong-ovate or elliptical, 20–40 mm long, 8–20 mm broad .... 15. **A. frigidus** (L.) A. Gray.

+ Corolla yellowish, 10–11 mm long. Calyx about 5 mm long, dark-purple at base, teeth lanceolate, about 2 mm long, black-hairy inside. Leaflets ovate or oblong, 10–20 mm long, 4–10 mm broad .... 16. **A. chilienshanensis** Y.C. Ho

21. Pods symmetrical, oblong or lanceolate-elliptical, 14–20 mm long, inflated. Corolla ivory-white, standard 12–15 mm long. Calyx shortly-tubular, 5–7 mm long, teeth broadly-deltoid, acute, not more than 0.5 mm long, glabrous or sparsely-hairy only along margin of teeth. Leaflets 5–7 pairs, oblong-ovate, 12–40 (50) mm long .... 17. **A. secundus** DC.

+ Pods asymmetrical, broadly- or oblong-elliptical, (20) 25–30 (35) mm long. Corolla pale yellow, standard 18–22 mm long. Calyx shortly-tubular, 6–8 mm long, teeth linear-subulate, 1/6–1/4 of tube length, glabrous or with sparse hairs. Leaflets (2) 3–4 pairs, oblong-ovate, 30–50 mm long .... 18. **A. aksuensis** Bunge.

22. Pods semiorbicular or semioval, 1 cm long .... 23.

+ Pods rather oblong or elongated, 2–2.5 cm long, densely covered with patent, long, soft, black hairs. Leaflets 9–21 pairs, narrowly-oblong or lanceolate-oblong, 12–20 mm long, 4–6 mm broad, glabrous or sparsely hairy above, densely covered with appressed, long, soft, white hairs beneath. Standard oblong, barely longer than keel and wing .... 19. **A. floridus** Benth. ex Bunge.

23. Leaves relatively small, sparse; leaflets usually less than 10 mm long, somewhat thick, (6) 10–18 pairs. Pods and ovary totally glabrous .... 24.

+ Leaves large, numerous, densely covering stems; leaflets usually more than 15 mm long, slender, 10–14 pairs. Pods and ovary pubescent with black hairs, very rarely glabrous. Calyx 5–7 (8) mm long. Corolla 15–17 mm long .... 25.

24. Calyx 8–9 mm long. Corolla 18–20 mm long. Pedicel 2–3 mm long, i.e. shorter than calyx. Stipules small, lanceolate or ovate, 3–7 mm long, 2–3.5 mm broad. Leaflets 12–18 pairs, oblong-obovate, oval or oblong-ovate .... 20. **A. mongolicus** Bunge.

+ Calyx about 5 mm long. Corolla 10–12 mm long. Pedicel longer than calyx. Stipules large, ovate-deltoid, or deltoid, 8–12 mm long, 5–9 mm broad. Leaflets 8–17 pairs, oblong .... 21. **A. lucidus** Tsai et Yu

25. Calyx about 8 mm long, with appressed black hairs allover surface, campanulate-tubular, teeth 1–3 (5) mm long, narrowly-deltoid. Leaflets 10–12 pairs, 10–35 mm long, 5–12 mm broad, ovate-elliptical or somewhat oblong, subglabrous above, pilose beneath. Stems, generally pilose at least in lower part, rarely subglabrous .... 22. **A. propinquus** Schischk.

+ Calyx 5–7 mm long, broadly-campanulate, subglabrous, pilose only on teeth, latter 0.5–1 mm long, broadly-deltoid. Leaflets 10–14 pairs, 10–20 mm long, 2–7 mm broad, elliptical or oblong-ovate, obtuse, glabrous above, diffusely hairy along margins of midrib beneath .... 23. **A. membranaceus** (Fisch.) Bunge.

26 (12). Flowers in dense capitate, oval or broadly-cylindrical inflorescences on long peduncles, small; standard 6–8 (10) mm long, wings undivided; calyx shortly-campanulate, 3–5 mm long. Pods sessile, pilose or more rarely glabrous, ovate or globose, small, 3–5 (8) mm long. Rather short alpine plant with slender, weak, ascending or procumbent stem (section 9 (10). **Brachycarpus** Boriss.) .... 27.

+ Plant with different characteristics: flowers in lax or slightly lax, elongated, more rarely short inflorescences on long peduncles .... 41.

27. Corolla violet or sky-blue, sometimes white .... 28.
+ Corolla yellowish or albescent, sometimes light-sky-blue, yellowish when dry .... 34.
28. Calyx teeth 1/2 as long as tube, dissimilar; deltoid and lanceolate or linear. Corolla intense-violet. Pods angularly-globose, 3–4 mm long, deeply-sulcate and transversely-rugose .... 29.
+ Calyx teeth as long as tube and almost similar. Corolla red- or dirty-violet. Pods glabrous or indistinctly rugose .... 30.
29. Bracts linear, 1–2 mm long, with short black pubescence. Standard 6–8 mm long, wings 5–6 mm long, keel 4–5 mm long. Ovary and pods with black and white pubescence or glabrous. Leaflets rather oblong or elliptical, subglabrous above, with short white pubescence mixed with black hairs beneath .... 24. **A. heterodontus** Boriss.
+ Stipules lanceolate, 3–4 mm long, glabrous or black-hairy above. Standard 9–10 mm long, wings 8–9 mm long, keel 5–6 mm long. Ovary and pods glabrous. Leaflets ovate or oblong, with short, white pubescence on both surfaces .... 25. **A. golmunensis** Y.C. Ho
30. Leaflets 4–7 (8) pairs, sparsely pilose beneath. Bracts 2–6 mm long .... 31.
+ Leaflets 7–10 pairs, oval or oblong-ovate, 3–16 mm long, 2–8 mm broad, with dense white pubescence beneath, acuminate or obtuse at tip, rounded at base. Bracts 1.5–2 mm long, lanceolate. Flowers in dense, spicate, 1–2.5 cm long racemes. Blade of standard obcordate, 7–8 mm long, 3.5 mm broad, wings shorter than standard; keel extremely short. Pods orbicular-globose, about 3 mm long, emarginate at tip, with short recurved beak in notch .... 26. **A. mahoschanicus** Hand.-Mazz.
31. Bracts as long as calyx tube. Pods without beak at tip, pubescent with white and black hairs .... 32.
+ Bracts longer than calyx tube. Pods with beak at tip, black-hairy .... 33.
32. Leaflets 4–6 pairs, oblong or ovate-oblong, 3–8 mm long, 1–3 mm broad. Racemes dense, capitate, rather oblong, more rarely spicate, 10–30 mm long. Bracts linear-lanceolate, 3–4 mm long. Corolla dirty-violet, standard 7 mm long, wings 6 mm long. Pods about 3 mm long .... 27. **A. densiflorus** Kar. et Kir.

+ Leaflets 7–9 pairs, linear-oblong or lanceolate, (7) 9–27 mm long, (2.5) 3–7 mm broad. Racemes dense, spicate or cylindrical, (2) 3–5 (7) cm long. Bracts lanceolate, 2–3 mm long. Corolla pale-pink or light-violet, even white, standard 8–10 (11) mm long, wings 7–8 mm long. Pods 4–5 mm long .... 28. **A. longiracemosus** Ulzij.

33. Bracts 4–6 mm long, ovate-lanceolate. Calyx 4–8 mm long. Corolla red or violet. Pods 4–5 mm long, 3.5–4.5 mm broad, ovate. Leaflets 3–5 (8) mm long, more rarely up to 18 mm long, 3–6 mm broad, rather oblong or obcordate, more rarely linear-lanceolate, emarginate or obtuse .... 29. **A. melanostachys** Benth. ex Bunge.

+ Bracts 2–3 (4) mm long, subulate- or lanceolate-linear. Calyx 2.5–3 (4) mm long. Corolla pale-violet, later flavescent. Pods (5) 6–8 mm long, 3–4 mm broad, obtusely-trigonous-ovate or trigonous-oblong. Leaflets 5–12 mm long, (2) 3–7 mm broad, orbicular-obovate, oblong or oblong-obovate, rounded or somewhat emarginate at tip .... 30. **A. baitagensis** Sancz. ex Ulzij.

34 (27). Leaflets somewhat oblong to lanceolate or linear-lanceolate .... 35.

+ Leaflets oval, obovate, oblong-obovate or oblong-elliptical .... 38.

35. Stems and leaflets canescent or silvery; leaflets with dense semipatent or patent, long, white shaggy hairs or woolly on both surfaces or beneath .... 36.

+ Stems and leaflets green; leaflets glabrous on both surfaces or with scattered short, appressed hairs only beneath .... 37.

36. Inflorescence long, cylindrical-spicate, 2.5–4 cm long. Calyx and bracts densely covered with long, predominantly white hairs mixed with black hairs. Leaflets covered on both surfaces with semipatent, silvery-white, long hairs. Bracts deltoid-lanceolate, 2–3.5 mm long, as long as calyx tube or slightly longer. Calyx (3.5) 4–5 mm long, teeth 1/2–2/3 of tube length .... 31. **A. luteoflorus** Ulzij.

+ Inflorescence capitate or ovate, 2.5 cm long. Calyx and bracts densely covered with predominantly black hairs mixed with sparse white hairs. Leaflets rather densely covered beneath with semiappressed or appressed white bristly hairs. Bracts linear-lanceolate, 4–6 mm long, twice as long as calyx tube or cover calyx. Latter 5–6 mm long, teeth as long as tube .... 32. **A. valerii** Ulzij.

37. Calyx teeth 1/3–1/2 as long as tube. Bracts as long as calyx tube or slightly shorter. Leaflets linear-lanceolate, 10–18 mm long, 3–5 mm broad, subacute or subobtuse, often with very short cusp, glabrous above, with scattered short, appressed, white hairs beneath. Peduncles erect, 15–30 cm tall. Racemes globose-capitate, about 1 cm in diam., later elongating to 2–3 cm. Subacauline or short-stemmed plant .... 33. **A. subscaposus** M. Pop. ex Boriss.

\+ Calyx teeth as long as tube. Bracts as long as calyx or longer. Leaflets oblong or sublanceolate, 8–18 mm long, 2–3 (4) mm broad, acute at tip, round-cuneate, glabrous toward base. Peduncles axillary, 5–10 cm long. Racemes dense, spicate, oblong or globose, 1–3 cm long. Plant with well developed stem .... ***A. fetissovii** B. Fedtsch.

38. Pods tuberculate-rugose, up to 5 mm long, 2–2.5 mm broad, inflated, elliptical. Flowers light-sky-blue, yellowish when dry. Bracts ovate. Leaflets 7–9 pairs, 7–15 (20) mm long, oblong-obovate or oblong-elliptical .... 34. **A. jagnobicus** Lipsky.

\+ Pods glabrous. Flowers albescent. Bracts lanceolate .... 39.

39. Pods trigonous, rather oblong or ovate, 4–5 mm long, beaked. Bracts longer than calyx tube. Leaflets 4–8 (10) pairs, cordate- or orbicular-obovate, emarginate, 3–9 mm long. Corolla albescent (flavescent when dry) or pale-violet with violet spot on keel .... ***A. schugrnanicus** B. Fedtsch.

\+ Pods globose or oval, about 3 mm long, without beak. Bracts as long as calyx tube. Leaflets 3–6 pairs, oblong-elliptical or oblong .... 40.

40. Inflorescence capitate, 1–2 (3) cm long. Corolla 7–8 mm long, standard with distinct claw (about 1.5 mm broad) at base. Calyx teeth lanceolate-subulate. Pods black-hairy, more rarely with insignificant mixture of white hairs. Leaflets 3–5 pairs. Plant subglabrous, with 1.5–9 cm tall ascending stems .... 35. **A. tulinovii** B. Fedtsch.

\+ Inflorescence cylindrical, 2–8 cm long. Corolla 6–7 mm long, standard with broadly-cuneate base, without distinct claw. Calyx teeth subulate. Pods white-hairy, more rarely with insignificant mixture of black hairs. Leaflets 5–6 pairs. Plant quite densely pubescent, with numerous stems (10–15 cm tall) branched from base .... 36. **A. imetensis** Boriss.

41 (26). Leaves with 3–15 leaflets somewhat approximated flabellately or pinnate. Flowers small, 4–6 (7) mm long, in long, lax

racemes. Pods very small, (2) 3–6 mm long, globose or elliptical (section 10 (11). **Melilotopsis** Gontsch) .... 42.

\+ Leaves pinnate, with several distant pairs of leaflets. Combination of characteristics different .... 45.

42. Leaflets 7–15 .... 37. **A. satoi** Kitag.

\+ Leaflets 3–9 .... 43.

43. Pods globose-ovate, 4–6 mm long, with curved beak. Leaflets 3–4 pairs, oval-oblong, or oblong-obovate, 5–20 mm long, 3–10 mm broad, rounded at tip, obtuse, with short cusp. Calyx teeth 1/5–1/4 as long as tube. Standard 5.5–7 mm long. Plant 30–60 cm tall .... 38. **A. capilipes** Fisch. ex Bunge.

\+ Pods 2.5–4 mm long, obcordate or globose-ovate. Leaflets (1) 2–4 pairs, narrow, filiform-linear or oblong-narrowly-cuneate, up to 30 (40) mm long, 0.5–4 (7) mm broad .... 44.

44. Leaflets 3–4 pairs, oblong-narrowly-cuneate, 7–15 (25) mm long, 2–4 (7) mm broad, obtuse or emarginate. Flowers white-pink, albescent, in lax racemes. Pods about 3 mm long, 3 mm broad, obcordate. Plant 40–90 cm tall, usually densely covered with appressed hairs .... 39. **A. melilotoides** Pall.

\+ Leaflets 1–2 pairs, usually in triplets, narrowly-, often almost filiform-linear, 10–30 (40) mm long, 0.5–2 (2.5) mm broad, acute. Flowers violet or pink-violet, in lax long racemes. Pods 3–4 mm long, about 3 mm broad, globose-ovate or sub-obovate. Plant 25–45 cm tall, subglabrous .... 40. **A. tenuis** Turcz.

45. Ovary and pods pilose; if glabrous, wings of corolla rounded at tip, undivided or slightly emarginate .... 46.

\+ Ovary and pods glabrous; if pilose, wings at tip deeply bila-ciniate .... 56.

46. Stipules connate at base or up to 1/2, very short. Pods on 3–5 mm long stalk, latter as long as calyx tube. Inflorescence subcapitate, racemes contracted .... 47.

\+ Stipules free, 5–8 mm long. Pods on short stalk, about 0.5 mm long, much shorter than calyx tube. Inflorescence lax, elongated raceme (section 13 (14). **Orobella** Gontsch.) .... 55.

47. Pods unilocular or subunilocular but then wall very narrow (section 11 (12). **Polycladus** Y.C. Ho) .... 48.

\+ Pods almost or not completely bilocular (section 12 (13). **Komaroviella** Gontsch.) .... 53.

48. Plant with slender ascending or procumbent stems; latter up to 15 (20) cm tall. Inflorescence few-flowered (but sometimes up to 12 flowers) .... 49.

\+ Plant densely caespitose; however, stray slender decumbent branches seen. Inflorescence with 6–10 flowers .... 51.

49. Calyx teeth slightly longer than tube or as long. Pods subsessile, trigonous-semioblong, dorsal suture with narrow wall. Racemes densely capitate, later elongated and ovate. Standard broadly-rhomboid-obovate .... 41. **A. polycladus** Bur. et Franch.

\+ Calyx teeth shorter than tube. Pods on distinct stalk, dorsal suture without wall .... 50.

50. Calyx 3–4 mm long; corolla bluish-white, blade of standard obcordate. Leaflets 1–2 mm broad, oblong-ovate or oblong, more rarely lanceolate, tip subobtuse. Pods 3–6 mm long, asymmetrically-oblong, on stalk as long as calyx, usually mutant .... 42. **A. zacharensis** Bunge.

\+ Calyx about 3 mm long; corolla violet, blade of its standard suborbicular. Leaflets 2–3 mm broad, elliptical or oblong-obovate, with cuneate base, subobtuse or somewhat emarginate at tip, densely grey-hairy beneath, more sparsely pilose above. Pods 7–8 mm long, stalked, drooping, trigonous-oblong, with projected keel .... 43. **A. mongutensis** Lipsky

51. Pods distinctly asymmetrical, suboval or oblong-subovate, 6–7 mm long. Bracts lanceolate, nearly as long as pedicels. Racemes with 5–10 flowers. Corolla about 8 mm long, light-sky-blue with dark spot at tip of keel, wings 6–7 mm long, shorter than keel. Calyx (2.5) 3–4 mm long, teeth subulate, 1.5–2 times shorter than tube. Leaflets 6–9 pairs, 2–5 (7) mm long, 1.3 mm broad, largely distant, elliptical or oval-oblong, subglabrous above, greyish densely appressed hairs beneath .... 44. **A. kuschakewiczii** B. Fedtsch. ex O. Fedtsch.

\+ Pods symmetrical, oval or oblong, up to 5 mm long .... 52.

52. Leaflets 5–7 (8) pairs, oblong, 10–20 mm long, 0.5–1 mm broad. Inflorescence subumbellate, with 6–8 flowers. Corolla 7–8 mm broad, pale-blue, wings longer than keel. Calyx about 3 mm long, teeth broadly-deltoid, 1/3 as long as tube. Pods rather oblong, somewhat falcate, 4–5 mm long .... 45. **A. confertus** Benth. ex Bunge.

\+ Leaflets 8–10 pairs, oval or ovate, 4–7 mm long, 2–3 mm broad. Inflorescence with 8–12 (15) flowers, globose. Corolla about 10 mm long, standard oblong-ovate, somewhat emarginate at tip, wings as long as keel. Calyx 4 mm long, teeth lanceolate, slightly longer than tube or nearly as long. Pods suboval .... 46. **A. saxorum** N.D. Simpson

53. Corolla bluish or light-violet .... 54.

\+ Corolla pale-yellowish with purple keel; standard orbicular-obovate, 11–13 mm long. Leaflets 4–8 pairs, obovate, oblong or oval, 4–10 mm long, 3–6 mm broad. Pods trigonous, oblong-ovate, 7–9 mm long, 4–5 mm broad, usually with black hairs. Racemes compact, 1.5–2 cm long. Plant 5–15 cm tall .... 47. **A. changaicus** Sancz. ex Ulzij.

54. Pods 7–11 (12) mm long, 2–4 mm broad, asymmetrically oblong, slightly curved, with black puberulence, on slender, 3–4 mm long stalk, with 1.2 mm long beak. Corolla white, bluish or sky-bluish with a dark-blue spot on keel. Calyx 3–6 mm long, teeth linear-subulate, longer than tube or nearly as long. Leaflets 9–12 pairs, elliptical, oblong-elliptical or orbicular, 5–17 mm long, 4–7 (10) mm broad .... 48. **A. alpinus** L.

\+ Pods 4–7 mm long, 3–5 mm broad, oblong-elliptical, nutant, with black and white hairs, on 1 mm long stalks, with falcate beak. Coralla light- or yellowish-violet. Calyx 5–7 mm long, teeth short, 2/5–2/3 of tube length, deltoid-lanceolate. Leaflets 5–8 pairs, ovate, oblong-elliptical or upper ones somewhat oblong or lanceolate, 5–20 mm long, 3–5 mm broad .... 49. **A. abramovii** Gontsch.

55. Corolla 20–22 mm long, keel pale-violet or pale-yellow with violet, blade of standard obovate-oblong, emarginate at tip, wing blades spathulate. Calyx about 7 mm long. Leaflets 5–6 pairs, oblong, up to 25 mm long, about 7 mm broad, glabrous .... 50. **A. luxurians** Bunge.

\+ Corolla 13–14 (15) mm long, tip of standard yellowish with lilac, oblong-obovate, somewhat emarginate, wing blades linear-oblong. Calyx 5–6 mm long. Leaflets 6–7 pairs, oblong-elliptical or oblong, obtuse or slightly emarginate, (11) 10–15 (24) mm long, 4–7 mm broad, glabrous on both sides .... 51. **A. politovii** Kryl.

56 (45). Stipules free, lanceolate. Keel longer than wings and standard. Latter 12–14 mm long. Pods papery, unilocular, semioval or semioblong, 8 mm long, 4 mm broad, stalked, slightly longer than calyx, with long cusp at tip. Leaflets 7–10 pairs, rather oblong or broadly-oval, 7–19 mm long, 3–9 mm broad, with very rare appressed hairs (section 14 (15). **Chrysopteris** Y.C. Ho) .... 52. **A. chrysopteris** Bunge.

\+ Stipules connate. Keel usually shorter than or as long as wings and standard. Pods membranous or scarious .... 57.

57. Wing tip deeply bilaciniate. Pods (12) 14–40 mm long, nutant, stalked, as long as or longer than calyx tube, more rarely shorter, 2–5 mm long. Bracts membranous, usually not surpassing calyx (section 15 (16). **Hemiphragmium** Koch) .... 58.

+ Wings undivided, rounded or somewhat emarginate; if bilaciniate, pods sessile, not nutant. Pods (4) 5–11 (12) mm long, obliquely erect, more rarely (in *A. multicaulis* Ledeb.) horizontally declinate or lower ones somewhat nutant, sessile, i.e. stalk not longer than 0.5 (1) mm. Bracts often very large, surpassing calyx and even flower, sometimes as long as calyx .... 62.

58. Stems well developed, erect or procumbent. Corolla yellow, light-yellow, bluish or albescent with violet tip of keel, more rarely violet. Pods asymmetrical, semiovate, lanceolate and linear-oblong, laterally compressed, barely inflated .... 59.

+ Dwarf or nearly acauline plant; sometimes, stems erect but dwarf. Stems 1–7 (10) cm tall. Corolla violet, bluish-lilac or rose-red. Pods vesicularly-inflated, subglobose, broadly-oval or broadly-ovate, usually glabrous, unilocular .... 60.

59. Pods bilocular or semibilocular, glabrous, oblong or lanceolate, drooping, on long stalk (not less than 6 mm long), glabrous, compressed-trigonous in cross-section, about 3 mm in diam. Standard 11–14 mm long, wings bilobed at tip; keel shorter than standard and wings; calyx teeth nearly 1/2 of tube length. Lower stipules connate at base, upper ones free. Leaflets 6–9 pairs, elliptical or somewhat lanceolate, initially generally puberulent on both surfaces, greyish .... 53. **A. vaginatus** Pall.

+ Pods unilocular, asymmetrical, nutant, oblong-ovate, finely membranous, short-pointed at both ends. Corolla light-yellow, with dark-violet tip of keel; standard 9–10 mm long. Calyx teeth linear-subulate, 2/3 as long as tube. Leaflets 5–6 pairs, oblong-ovate, more rarely ovate-lanceolate, acute with semipatent white hairs beneath, more rarely on both surfaces .... *__A. sarchanensis__ Gontsch.

60. Corolla lilac-violet, standard 14–16 (17) mm long. Pods oblong-ovate or asymmetrically-ovate, with reddish spots, speckled, 15–25 (30) mm long. Racemes globose or globose-ovate, with 8–17 flowers, 15–30 mm long. Leaflets 5–7 pairs, ovate- or lanceolate-oblong, 5–8 (10) mm long, 1–3 (5) mm broad, glabrous above, appressed or with semipatent greyish hairs beneath, more rarely on both surfaces .... 54. **A. beketovii** (Krassn.) B. Fedtsch.

\+ Corolla violet, 12–15 mm long. Pods ovate or globose, subglobose, without red spots. Leaflets (5) 6–9 pairs, very small, 4–9 mm long. Dwarf 5–10 cm tall plant, subacauline, i.e. stems 1–5 cm tall .... 61.

61\. Wings as long as standard. Calyx teeth slightly shorter than tube. Standard obovate, 12–15 mm long. Leaflets 6–8 pairs, oblong-ovate or elliptical, (3) 4–7 mm long, obtuse-acuminate, grey-pubescent beneath. Peduncles slightly longer than leaves, more rarely as long .... 55. **A. tschuensis** Bunge.

\+ Wings invariably shorter than standard. Calyx teeth distinctly shorter (usually 1/2) than tube. Standard broadly-ovate, 14–18 mm long. Leaflets 5–7 pairs, lanceolate or narrowly-elliptical, acute, white-hairy beneath. Peduncles 2–4 (5) times longer than leaves .... ***A. pseudochorinensis** Ulzij.

62\. Bracts leaflike, usually large, surpassing calyx and even flower but at times barely shorter than calyx. Pods sessile, unilocular or almost unilocular, pubescent, more rarely glabrous (section 16 (17). **Hemiphaca** Bunge) .... 63.

\+ Bracts usually small, membranous or herbaceous, linear, linear-lanceolate, more rarely broadly-lanceolate. Pods almost bilocular, glabrous, cross-section trigonous. Tall or moderately tall, erect plant (section 17 (18). **Paraphaca** R. Kam.) .... 67.

63\. Ovary glabrous. Pods broadly ovate, 8–12 mm long .... 64.

\+ Ovary pubescent .... 65.

64\. Stipules free, leaflike, ovate, (4) 7–12 mm long. Bracts oblong-ovate, 5–10 (14) mm long, leaflike, green or reddish-green. Calyx 8–9 mm long. Corolla pale-violet or albescent with violet spot on keel, 13–16 mm long, wings 12–13 mm long. Pods vesicular, ovate, curvipointed .... 56. **A. laceratus** Lipsky

\+ Stipules connate, membranous, lanceolate, 6–10 mm long. Bracts lanceolate-linear or linear, about 3 mm long. Calyx 4–5 mm long. Corolla violet, 11–14 mm long, wings 8–11 mm broad. Pods nearly vesicular-inflated, acute .... ***A. hemiphaca** Kar. et Kir.

65\. Plant subacauline. Peduncles longer than leaves. Racemes very dense, many-flowered, globose-capitate .... 66.

\+ Plant dwarf, 3–10 cm tall, with shortened stems. Peduncles shorter than leaves or as long. Racemes with 10–12 flowers, somewhat lax, globose. Corolla about 10 mm long, pale-violet, standard oblong-obovate, emarginate at tip, wings 2–3 mm longer than keel, tip of wings laciniate. Calyx asymmetrically-campanulate, about 3 mm long, its teeth dissimilar; upper 2 shorter than rest, deltoid, rest 3 lanceolate, 1/3–2/5 as long as tube. Leaflets 3–8 pairs, oval or obovate, 3–7 mm long, 2–5 mm broad .... 57. **A. alaschanus** Bunge.

66. Stipules connate at base .... ***A. aurantiacus** Hand-Mazz.

+ Stipules totally free .... 58. **A. dependens** Bunge.

67. Ovary and pods glabrous or pods diffusely-pilose but then pubescence shedding early .... 68.

+ Ovary and pods pilose. Calyx 2.5 mm long. Wings undivided at tip. Pods small, with transversely-rugose nervation, asymmetrically-globose-ovate, 4–5 mm long, with extremely fine, appressed white hairs. Leaflets 3–5 pairs, linear-lanceolate or linear, 8–20 mm long, 2–2.5 mm broad, greyish-hairy. Plant multicaulis, 8–15 cm tall .... 59. **A. rytidocarpus** Ledeb.

68. Wing blades nearly as long as standard or slightly shorter, undivided at tip, obtuse .... 69.

+ Wing blades barely shorter than standard, emarginate or laciniate at tip .... 70.

69. Leaflets (3) 4–6 (7) pairs, linear-oblong, 3–4 times longer than broad, cuneately-narrowed at base, 10–15 (20) mm long. Peduncles delicate, only 2 (3) times longer than subtending leaves. Corolla 9–10 mm long, calyx 2.5–3 mm long. Bracts subulate. Pods 7–9 mm long, about 3 mm broad, semiovate or oblong-ovate, trigonous, erect. Plant (30) 40–90 cm tall .... 60. **A. macropteris** DC.

+ Leaflets 7–10 pairs, rather oblong or ovate-oblong, obtuse at tip, rounded at base, 6–11 mm long, 2–5 mm broad. Peduncles strong, 5–6 times longer than subtending leaves. Corolla 10–11 mm long, calyx 3–4 mm long. Bracts linear-lanceolate. Pods 11–13 mm long, 4–4.5 mm broad, ovate-oblong, trigonous, obliquely erect. Plant 30–40 cm tall .... 61. **A. longipes** Kar. et Kir.

70. Leaflets glabrous or sparsely hairy beneath, (6) 7–10 pairs, 7–13 mm long, (0.5) 1–2 (2.5) mm broad, linear, filiform or narrowly-oblong. Bracts linear-lanceolate, 2–3 mm long. Calyx 3.5–4 mm long, campanulate, with short and sparse pubescence mostly of white hairs. Corolla violet, rarely white with violet keel, 8–11 mm long, pods sessile, erect, ovate or oblong, compressed, (7) 8–10 mm long, (2.5) 3–4 mm broad, membranous. Stems few,

slender, up to 0.9 (1) mm thick. Plant with tap root, lax and finely caespitose, (15) 20–50 cm tall .... 62. **A. versicolor** Pall.

\+ Leaflets pubescent on both surfaces or only beneath, sometimes hairy only along midrib beneath .... 71.

71. Leaflets 2–5 pairs .... 72.

\+ Leaflets 6–18 pairs .... 73.

72. Leaflets 3–4 (5) pairs, obovate, deeply and broadly emarginate at tip, cuneately narrowed toward base, 5–10 (18) mm long, 3–5 (7) mm broad, covered with short, flat, white dense hairs beneath, less dense above. Pods subsessile, glabrous, with distinct reticulate nervation, oblong or oblong-lanceolate, 7–12 mm long, up to 3 mm broad, acute. Racemes with 15–25 flowers. Corolla 8–9 mm long, violet, standard suborbicular or orbicular-obovate; tip of wings undivided (subsp. *gobicus* Ulzij.) or deeply laciniate or emarginate (subsp. *songaricus* Ulzij.). Few-flowered ..... 63. **A. pavlovii** B. Fedtsch. et N. Basil.

\+ Leaflets 2–3 pairs, oblanceolate, tips acuminate, 3–10 mm long, 1.5–2.5 mm broad, densely covered on both surfaces with ash-grey hairs. Pods densely covered with white and black hairs, oblong, 5–6 mm long. Racemes with 6–12 flowers. Corolla about 8 mm long, yellowish, standard rather oblong; wing tip undivided. Perennial with woody stem base .... 64. **A. qingheensis** Liou f.

73. Racemes lax, elongated, 5–15 cm long. Leaflets 6–9 pairs, linear or linear-oblong, 5–12 mm long, 1.5–3 mm broad, obtuse or slightly emarginate with fine appressed white pubescence diffuse above and dense beneath. Calyx broadly campanulate, 2–2.5 mm long. Corolla pale-lilac, more rarely pale-yellow (var. *flavescens* Schischk.), 5–7 mm long. Pods erect, semiovate or oblong-ovate, rather obtuse, with distinct reticulate nervation. Plant multicaulis, 20–45 cm tall .... 65. **A. puberulus** Ledeb.

\+ Racemes rather lax, capitate or subglobose, 1.5–2 cm long. Leaflets (6) 7–18 pairs, oblong-ovate or oblong-oval, 3–8 mm long, 1–4 mm broad, usually emarginate at tip, glabrous above, sometimes with short appressed hairs only along midrib beneath. Calyx campanulate, (3) 4–4.5 mm long. Corolla pale-violet, 8–10 mm long. Pods horizontally declinate or slightly nutant, oblong-ovate, acute. Plant multicaulis, 5–15 cm tall .... 66. **A. multicaulis** Ledeb.

Section 1 (2). **Alexandri** Ulzij.

2. **A. ulziykhutagii** Sytin in Kew. Bull. 51, 2 (1996) 376.—*A. alexandri* Ulzij. in Bull. Soc. Natur. Moscou, Ser. Biol. 95, 1 (1990) 107, non Kharadze 1948.

Described from Mong. Altay. Type in St.-Petersburg (LE).

In larch forests.

IA. Mongolia: ***Mong. Alt.*** (Khobdo. ajmaq—administrative territorial unit in Mongolia—Bulga somon, upper course of Kharagaitu-gol river, left bank tributary of Bulgan river. Larch forest, No. 12990, Aug. 24, 1947—Yun., typus !).

General distribution: endemic.

Section 2 (3). **Robusti** Peter-Stib.

3. **A. dshinensis** Gontsch. in Not. Syst. (Leningrad) 10 (1947) 30 ("errore dshimensis"); idem in Fl. SSSR, 12 (1946) 23, Fl. Kazakhst. 5 (1961) 95; Bait. Astrag. Tyan'-Shanya (1947) 35; Opred. rast. Sr. Azii [Key to Plants of Mid. Asia] 6 (1981) 89; Gub. in Byull. Mosk. obshch. ispyt. prir., biol. 78, 1 (1982) 127; K.T. Fu in Bull. Bot. Research, 2, 1 (1982) 132; Sanczir in Grub. Opred. rast. Mong. [Key to Plants of Mongolia] (1982) 157; Ulzij. in Tr. Inst. bot. AN MNR, 8 (1982) 16; C.Y. Yang in Claves pl. Xinjiang, 3 (1985) 122.—*A. hoagtschy* auct. non Franch.: O. et B. Fedtsch. Konsp. fl. Turk. 2 (1909) 193.

—**Ic.:** Fl. Kazakhst. 5, Plate 11, fig. 3; Bait. l.c. fig. 1; Grub. 1982. l.c. Plate 83, fig. 381; C.Y. Yang l.c. tab. 7, fig. 2.

Described from Sinkiang (Jung. Ala Tau). Type in St.-Petersburg (LE). Map 1.

On rocky meadow-steppe slopes, along river valleys, in lower and middle belts of mountains, along arid gorges, in rock shadows, among boulders in river gorges.

IA. Mongolia: ***Mong. Alt.*** (along road to Altay somon from Bugat somon, Gazhingiin-gol river, arid gorge, No. 165, July 3, 1973—Golubkova and Tsogt; Adzhi-Bogdo mountain range, southern macro slope, Ikhe-gol river, gorge, left bank, 2200–2300 m, tansi-feather grass steppe, No. 1631, Aug. 22, 1979—Grub. et al; 10 km south-west of Bugat somon, Ulyastain-gol gorge, on pebble beds, No. 148, July 5; same locality, Ulyastain-gol river valley, midportion, along valley, No. 444, July 13, 1984, Kam. and Dariima).

IIA. Junggar: ***Jung. Ala Tau*** ("near Kul'dzha boundary"—Gontsch. l.c. (1946) 24), Tien Shan (Uital from Karol' to Bedel' pass, June 27, 1908—Divn.; "Boro-Khoro mountain range"—Bait. l.c. 36; Piluchi gorge, 915–1525 m, April 24, 1879—A. Reg.; Taldy gorge (Turgen, Dzhin-khe) in Irenkhabirga mountains, 1525-2440 m, May 15, 1879—A. Reg., typus !; Oberer Taldy, 2438 m, May 17; Bainamun bis Dschin, 1524-1830 m, June 7–1879, A. Reg., paratypus !; midcourse of Dzhin-Tsagan-tunge, 1830–1920 m, June 7, 1879, pass to Khomote valley from descent through Tsin-shuikhe river banks, 1445 m, No. 7636, July 28; hill road to timber works in Khomote from Bartu, 6939 m, Aug. 3–1958, A.R. Lee (1958); Sinkiang, No. 403, July 17, 1979—Chinese collector [PE];

"south of Uruchi town" —C.Y. Yang l.c.), ***Jung. Gobi*** (Baitag-Bogdo mountain range, east. macro slope, Budun-Kharangaityn-gol river valley, on rock outcrops, No. 7074, July 29, 1979—Gub. [MW]).

General distribution: endemic.

Section 3 (4). **Monotheca** Ulzij.

4. **A. przewalskii** Bunge in Mel. Biol. Ac. Sci. St.-Petersb. 10 (1877) 52; id. in Bull. Ac. Sci. St.-Petersb. 24 (1878) 32; Peter-stib. in Acta Horti Gotob. 12 (1937) 50; Wang and Tang in Ill. treatm. princip. pl. China, Legum. (1955) 412; Y.C. Ho in Bull. Bot. Lab. North-East. Forest Inst. 8 (1980) 52.

—**Ic.:** Wang and Tang l.c. fig. 407.

Described from Qinghai (Nanshan). Type in St.-Petersburg (LE). Plate 1, fig. 3.

In alpine meadows and in spruce forest.

IC. Qaidam: ***Mount*** (Dulan-khit temple. On humus in spruce forest, 3353 m, No. 378, Aug. 8, 1901—Lad.).

IIIA. Qinghai: ***Nanshan*** (Alpine zone south of Tetung river, No. 263—Przew., typus !; up to Rako-gol river, 3050–3355 m, No. 540, July 22, 1880—up to Yusun-Khatym river, 2745–3050 m, No. 2, July 23—Przew.; "Kukunor, Fenzel, 1257", "Kansu, Ta Hwa, near Pingfar, Ching, 540"—Peter-Stib.).

General distribution: China (North-West: Gansu east. ?; South-West, Sichuan).

5. **A. petrovii** Ulzij. in Novit. syst. pl. vasc. 30 (1996) 109.

Described from Qinghai (Nanshan mountain range). Type in St.-Petersburg (LE). Map 1.

Among scrubs in mountain valley.

IIIA. Qinghai: ***Nanshan*** (Regio Tangut ad fl. Yussun-Chatyma, 9000–10,000 ft. (2743–3048 m), subfruticubus in humo frequens, July 12 (24), 1880, No. 566, fl. et fr.—Przew.; 70 km south-east of Dzhan'e town, Matisy temple, Nanshan hills, Tsilyan'shan', scrubs with small meadows in hilly valley, 2600 m alt., flowers—Petr.—typus ! Qinghai, Gansu—K.T. Fu l.c.).

IIIB. Tibet: ***Weitzan*** (valley of Alyk-Norin-gol river, 1900–1901, No. 568—Lad.).

General distribution: endemic.

Section 4 (5). **Diplotheca** Hochst.

6. **A. hoantchy** Franch. in Nouv. Arch. Mus. Hist. Nat. Paris, ser. 2, 5 (1883) 238; id. in Pl. David. 1 (1884) 86; Peter-Stib. in Acta Horti Gotoburg, 12 (1937) 60; Wang and Tang in Ill. treatm. princip. pl. China, Legum. (1955) 388; K.T. Fu in Bull. Bot. Research 2, 1 (1982) 133; Pl. vasc. Helanshan (1986) 152; H.C. Fu in Fl. Intramong. ed. 1, 3 (1977) 195; and ed. 2, 3 (1989) 267.

—**Ic.:** Wang and Tang l.c. fig. 375; H.C. Fu l.c. 1977, tab. 98, fig. 1–8; and ed. 2, 3 (1989), tab. 103, fig. 14–18.

Described from East. Mongolia. Type in Paris (P), isotype in St.-Petersburg (LE).

On rocky slopes, among rocks in gorges.

IA. Mongolia: ***East. Mong.*** (Ourato, vallis picrrenus Chine (Mongolia orientale), No. 276a, July 1866—A. David), ***Alash, Gobi*** (Alashan mountain range: Khelan'shan', in Shui Tigou gorge, 2300 m, No. 2129, June 9, 1980—Liou [HIMC]); "Holanshan-hing, 87"—Peter-Stib. l.c.).

IB. Kashgar: ***East.*** (Turfan, 10 km nor. of Kalangou village, 2300 m, No. 5811, June 23, 1958—A.R. Lee (1958)).

General distribution: endemic.

7. **A. hedinii** Ulbr. in Bot. Jahrb. 35 (1905) 679; K.T. Fu in Bull. Bot. Research, 2, 1 (1982) 132; P.C. Li et Ni in Fl. Xizang, 2 (1985) 830.

—**Ic.:** Fl. Xizang, 2, tab. 268, fig. 8.

Described from Tibet. Type in Cambridge (GH).

In ploughed fields, along banks of canals and irrigation ditches, at 3200–3600 m alt.

IIIB. Tibet: ***Chang Tang*** ("Tibet, Fundortsangabe unleslich, 1903, leg. Sven Hedin"—E. Ulbrich l.c.; "Tibet" 3500 m, No. 8083, June 18, 1976—P.-q. Li [PE]; "Nor. Tibet" K.T. Fu l.c.), ***South.*** ("Chzhada" P.C. Li et Ni l.c.).

General distribution: endemic.

Section 5 (6). **Scheremeteviana** O. et B. Fedtsch.

***A. scheremetevianus** B. Fedtsch. in Trav. Mus. Bot. Ac. Petersb. 1 (1902) 125; idem in Tr. SPb. bot. sada, 31, 3 (1915) 455; O. et B. Fedtsch. Konsp. fl. Turk. 2 (1909) 202; Boriss. in Fl. Tadzhik. 5 (1937) 305; idem in Fl. SSSR, 12 (1946) 15; Kitamura, Fl. Afgh. (1960) 217; Ikonn. Opred. rast. Pam. [Key to Plants of Pamir] (1963) 164; idem, Opred. rast. Badakhsh. [Key to Plants of Badakhshan] (1979) 230; Podlech et Anders. in Mitt. Bot. Staatssamml. München, 13 (1977) 442; Fl. Tadzhik. 6 (1981) 38; Opred. rast. Sr. Azii [Key to Plants of Mid. Asia] 6 (1981) 91.—*A. lipskyanus* Freyn in Bull Herb. Boiss. 2, ser. 4 (1904) 755.

—**Ic.:** Fl. SSSR, 12, Plate 1, fig. 3; Fl. Tadzhik. 6 (1981), Plate 1, fig. 12–16.

Described from Mid. Asia (Shugnan). Type in St.-Petersburg (LE).

On rocky and rubbly slopes, rocky debris cones and washed moraines in upper hill belt (up to 4300 m).

Reports likely from Sinkiang in East. Pamir.

Section 6 (7). **Lithophilus** Bunge

8. **A. dalaiensis** Kitag. in J. Jap. Bot. 22 (1948) 172; Fl. pl. herb. Chinae bor.-or. 5 (1976) 91; Y.C. Ho in Bull. Bot. Lab. North-East. Forest. Inst.

8 (1980) 66; Rast. pokrov Vn. Mong. [Plants in the Vegetational Cover of Inner Mongolia] (1985) 135; H.C. Fu in Fl. Intramong. ed. 2, 3 (1989) 257.

Described from China (Dunbei). Type in Tokyo (TI).

In steppe and meadow-steppe associations.

IA. Monoglia: ***East. Mong.*** ("Khulunbuir, Shilin-gol"—H.C. Fu l.c.).

General distribution: China (Dunbei), Korean Peninsula.

***A. olgae** Bunge in Izv. Obshch. lyubit. estestv. antr. i etnogr. 26, 2 (1880) 223; Lipsky in Acta Horti Petrop. 18 (1901) 33; emend. O. et B. Fedtsch. Konsp. fl. Turk. 2 (1909) 204, excl. pl. e Tianschan occid.; Gontsch. in Fl. Tadzhik. 5 (1937) 316; idem in Fl. SSSR, 12 (1946) 21; Fl. Kirgiz. 7 (1957) 218; Ikonn. Opred. rast. Badakhsh. [Key to Plants of Badakhshan] (1979) 231; Rasul. in Fl. Tadzhik. 6 (1981) 45; Opred. rast. Sr. Azii [Key to Plants of Mid. Asia] 6 (1981) 87.

Described from Mid. Asia (Alay mountain range). Type in St.-Petersburg (LE).

On rubbly and rocky slopes, pebble beds, moraines in middle and lower mountain belts.

Reports possible in Sinkiang in the eastern part of Pamir.

General distribution: Mid. Asia (Pamiro-Alay).

9. **A. lithophilus** Kar. et Kir. in Bull. Soc. Natur. Moscou, 15, 2 (1842) 344; Bunge Gen. Astrag. Sp. Geront. L (1868) 30 and 2 (1869) 35; id. in Izv. Obshch. lyub. estestv., antr. i etnogr. 26, 2 (1880) 225; O. et B. Fedtsch. Konsp. fl. Turk. 2 (1909) 204; Gontsch. in Fl. Tadzhik. 5 (1937) 312; idem in Fl. SSSR, 12 (1946) 19; Fl. Kirgiz. 7 (1957) 217; Fl. Kazakhst. 5 (1961) 94; Bait. Astr. Tyan-Shanya (1977) 35; Y.C. Ho in Bull. Bot. Lab. North-East. Forest. Inst. 8 (1980) 67; Opred. rast. Sr. Azii [Key to Plants of Mid. Asia] 6 (1981) 89; Rasul. in Fl. Tadzhik. 5 (1981) 42; C.Y. Yang in Claves pl. Xinjiang, 3 (1985) 122.—*A. dicystis* Bunge in Izv. obshch. lyub. estestv., antr. i etnogr. 26, 2 (1880) 225; O. et B. Fedtsch. Konsp. fl. Turk. 2 (1909) 204.

—**Ic.:** Fl. Kazakhst. 5, Plate 11, fig. 1; Fl. Tadzhik. 5 (1981), Plate 2, fig. 4.

Described from East. Kazakhstan (Jung. Ala Tau). Type in St.-Petersburg (LE). Plate I, fig. 4.

On rocky and rubbly, more rarely clayey slopes, pebble beds, moraines, talus, grasslands in middle and upper hill belts.

IIA. Junggar: ***Jung. Ala Tau*** (Borotala river basin, southern macro slope of Junggar Ala Tau, before Koktau pass, No. 2029, July 21, 1909—Lipsky), Tien Shan ("Ili"—Y. C. Ho l.c.; "Inlin"—C.Y. Yang l.c.).

General distribution: Mid. Asia (Pamiro-Alay west).

Note. Our plant differs from type in the following respects: peduncles with long patent-white-hairs, leaflets lanceolate, oblong-lanceolate, etc.

10. **A. munroi** Benth. ex Bunge in Gen. Astrag. Sp. Geront. 1 and 2 in Mém. Ac. Sci. St.-Petersb. ser. 7, 11, 16 (1868) 30 and 15, 1 (1869) 35; Baker in Hook. f. Fl. Brit. Ind. 2 (1879) 128; Ali in Nasir. Fl. West. Pakistan, 100, Papilionac. (1977) 180; Y.C. Ho in Bull. Bot. Lab. North-East. Forest Inst. 8 (1080) 66; P.C. Li et Ni in Fl. Xizang, 2 (1985) 829.—*A. longicalyx* Ni et P.C. Li in Acta phytotax. sin. 17 (1979) 110; in Fl. Xizang, 2 (1985) 829.

—**Ic.:** Fl. Xizang, 2, tab. 270, fig. 1–9.

Described from Himalayas (Ladakh). Type in London (K).

On rocky and rubbly slopes of high mountains 3000–4000 m.

IB. Kashgar:—P.C. Li et Ni l.c.?

IIIB. Tibet: ***Chang Tang*** (Tsata, 3600 m, June 30, 1976, 70–8116, Chinghai-Tibetan Complex Exp. [PE]—typus !; *A. longicalyx* Ni et P.C. Li ! "West. Tibet" P.C. Li et Ni l.c.), ***South.*** ("Chzhada" P.C. Li et Ni l.c.).

General distribution: Himalayas (west., Kashmir).

Section 7 (8). **Nuculiella** Gontsch.

11. **A. chinensis** L. fil. Pl. Rar. Hort. Ups. 1, 5 (1762) t. 3; Pall. Sp. Astrag. (1800) 36; DC. Astrag. (1802) 134; id. Prodr. (1825) 294; Maxim. Prim. Fl. Amur. (1859) 80; Bunge Gen. Astrag. Sp. Geront. 2 (1869) 32; Forbes and Hemsley in J. Linn. Soc. Bot. 23 (1887) 165; Kom. Fl. Man'chzh. 2 (1904) 585; Kitag. Lin. Fl. Mansh. (1939) 280; Boriss. in Fl. SSSR, 12 (1946) 24; Wang and Tang in Ill. treatm. princip. pl. China, Legum. (1955) 380; Ic. cormoph. Sin. 2 (1972) 423; Dashnyam, Fl. i rast. Vost. Mong. [Flora and Plants of East. Mong.] (1974) 44; Fl. pl. herb. Chinae bor.-or. 5 (1976) 92; H.C. Fu in Fl. Intramong. 3 (1977) 189 and ed. 2, 3 (1989) 255; Y.C. Ho in Bull. Bot. Research 1, 3 (1981) 104; Rast. pokrov Vn. Mong. [Vegetational Cover of Inner Mongolia] (1985) 134; Sanczir in Grub. Opred. rast. Mong. [Key to Plants of Mongolia] (1982) 157; Ulzij. in Tr. Inst. bot. AN MNR, 8 (1982) 16; Liou fil. in Fl. desert Sin. 2 (1987) 252.—*Glycyrrhiza costulata* Hand.-Mazz. Osterr. Bot. Zeitschr. 82 (1933) 248 and 85 (1936) 215.

—**Ic.:** Ic. cormoph. Sin. fig. 2576; Fl. pl. herb. Chinae bor-or. 5, tab. 42, fig. 7–12; Fl. Intramong. 3, tab. 95, fig. 1–7 and 2, 3, tab. 99, fig. 1–7.

Described from China. Type in London (LINN). Plate I, Fig. 1.

On sandy and rocky river banks, mostly among sparse scrubs.

IA. Mongolia: ***East. Mong.*** (Ortous and Ourato, Guillet No. 2726—David; Durbet base halt, July 13, 1903—Rudnev; in bottomland deciduous forest of Khalkhin-gol river in Khamardaban region, No. 274, Aug. 9; Dashbalbar somon 20 km beyond confluence of

Ulsaz river in Dood-Dure-nur lake, No. 302 Aug. 13, 1971, Dashnyam; "Shilin-gol", "Ulantsab (east)", "Ulashan'"—H.C. Fu l.c.), ***Ordos*** ("Ordos–Licent, No. 5554"—Peter-Stib. l.c., "East. Ordos"—H.C. Fu l.c.).

General distribution: Far East (Primor., West. Amur), Nor. Mong. (Cis-Hing.), China (Dunbei, North-West, Central).

Section 8 (9). **Cenantrum** Koch

12. **A. degensis** Ulbr. in Feddes Repert. 12 (1922) 418; Peter-Stib. in Acta Horti Gotoburg, 12 (1937–38) 44; Wang and Tang in Ill. treatm. princip. pl. China, Legum. (1955) 382; Y.C. Ho in Bull. Bot. Lab. North-East. Forest Inst. 8, 8 (1980) 54; P.C. Li and Ni in Fl. Xizang, 2 (1985) 826.—*A. degensis* Ulbr. var. *rockianus* Peter-Stib. in Acta Horti Gotoburg, 12 (1938) 44; P.C. Li et Ni, l.c. 827.

Described from China (Sichuan). Type in Cambridge (GH).

In alpine meadows, at 3600 m.

IIIB. Tibet: ***Weitzan*** (Mekong basin, Chok-chyu river, 3460–3660 m, No. 336, Aug. 1900—Lad.; "East. Tibet"—Y.C. Ho l.c.; "Tszyanda"—P.C. Li et Ni l.c.), ***South.*** ("Chayui", 3500 m—P.C. Li et Ni l.c.).

General distribution: China (South-West: Sichuan, Yunnan).

13. **A. tongolensis** Ulbr. in Bot. Jahrb. 1, Beibl. 110 (1931) 12; Simps. in Not. Bot. Gard. Edinb. 8 (1915) 258; Peter-Stib. in Acta Horti Gotoburg, 12 (1938) 48; Wang and Tang in Ill. treatm. princip. pl. China, Legum. (1955) 406; Y.C. Ho in Bull. Bot. Lab. North-East. Forest Inst. 8, 8 (1980) 55; P.C. Li et Ni in Fl. Xizang, 2 (1985) 829.—*A. tongolensis* Ulbr. var. *glaber* Peter-Stib. in Acta Horti Gotoburg, 12 (1938) 49; Fl. Xizang, 2 (1985) 825.—*A. potaninii* Kom. in Feddes Repert. 13 (1915) 231.—*A. veichianus* Simps. in Feddes Repert. 13 (1915) 247.

—**Ic.:** Ulbr. l.c., fig.; Wang and Tang l.c. fig. 399; Fl. Xizang, 2, tab. 271, fig. 1–3.

Described from South-West China (Sichuan). Type in Cambridge (GH).

In forest meadows, among shrubs on slopes.

IIIA. Qinghai: *Nanshan* (Kokonor, No. 12508, Sep. 7, 1975, Chin. collector, PE); ***Amdo*** ("Inter Kweit and Labrang, Fenzel, No. 2485"—Peter-Stib., l.c.).

IIIB. Tibet: *Weitzan* ("Amnyi Machen range, No. 14420—Rock, Peter-Stib." l.c.; Yan-tszy-tszyan basin (Goluboi river); Donra area on Dyne-chyu river (Khi-chyu river), 3962 m, July 16, 1900—Lad.).

General distribution: China (South-West).

14. **A. lepsensis** Bunge Gen. Astrag. Sp. Geront. 1 (1868) 25 and 2 (1869) 29; id. Astrag. Turk. in Izv. Obshch. lyubit. estestv., antr. i etnogr. 26, 2 (1880) 217; Fedtsch. Konsp. fl. Turk. 2 (1909) 292; Gontsch. and Boriss. in Fl. SSSR, 12 (1946) 32; Fl. Kirgiz. 7 (1957) 221; Bait, Astrag. (1977) 36; Fl. Kazakhst. 5 (1961) 97; Y.C. Ho in Bull. Bot. Lab. North-

East. Forest Inst. 8 (1980) 53; Opred. rast. Sr. Azii [Key to Plants of Mid. Asia] 6 (1981) 88; C.Y. Yang in Claves pl. Xinjiang, 3 (1985) 124.—*A. frigidus* auct. non L.: Bunge Astrag. Turk. (1980) 217; O. et B. Fedtsch. Konsp. fl. Turk. 2 (1909) 201, excl. pl. e Pamiro-Alaj.—*A. propinquus* auct. non Schischk.: Sanczir in Grub. Opred. rast. Mong. [Key to Plants of Mongolia] (1982) ex parte pl. e Mongol.-Altai.

—**Ic.:** Fl. Kazakhst. 5, Plate 11, fig. 4.

Described from East. Kazakhstan (Jung. Ala Tau). Type in St.-Petersburg (LE). Map 8.

In spruce and larch forests, among shrubs, in subalpine grasslands at upper forest limit, along forest borders.

IA. Mongolia: *Mong. Alt.* (Bulgan river upper courses, Kosho-tin-gol valley near Kudzhirtu settlement, left bank, Artelin-sala creek valley, on south. slope of Shara-Khamryn-Ora mountain range 3 km beyond Kudzhirtu, larch forest along slope exposed nothward, July 3; Kobdo river 2 km beyond estuary of Zhalanda river, right bank of Gurtyn-ama creek valley 1 km beyond estuary, larch forest along slope exposed northward, 2200–2300 m, July 11–1971, Grub., Ulzij. et al.).

IB. Kashgar: *Nor.* (Uch-Turfan, Airi gorge, along brook between rocks, June 4, 1908—Divn.).

IIA. Junggar: *Cis-Alt.* (Khalaun river valley, Ch. Irtysh system, forest, July 7, 1908—Sap.), *Jung. Ala Tau* (on road from syata (Shaty) village up to Ven'tsyuan' [Arasan] town, Aug. 13, 1957—Shen-Tyan'; from Ulastai to Yakou, on slope, No. 3982, Aug. 30, 1957—Kuan), *Tien Shan* (Khanakhai south-east of Kul'dzha, 1500–2100 m, June 16; Ili river, 1500–1700 m, July 16; Chubaty [Sairam] valley, 2440-2700 m, Aug. 2–1878; Usinsthecho between Borborogussun and Dzhinkho, April 29; Bagaduslung-Bainamun, tributary of Dzhin river, 2100–2700 m, June 4; up to Borborogussun, 2700 m, June 15—1879, A. Reg.; up to Sairam lake, Urtak-sary [Sairam] south of Borotal, July 20—1878, Fet.; Urumchi region, Tasenku river upper courses, Biankou locality, in spruce forest, Sep. 24, 1929—Pop.; nor. slopes of Tien Shan, along Danu river, steppe slope, 2700 m, No. 2170 m, July 22, 1957, Kuan; "Tien Shan"—common, C.Y. Yang l.c.).

General distribution: Jung.-Tarb., Cen. Tien Shan (east. part).

15. **A. frigidus** (L.) A. Gray in Proc. Amer. Ac. Arts. Sci. 6 (1864) 219; Bunge Gen. Astrag. Sp. Geront. 2, in Mém. Ac. Sci. St.-Petersb. ser. 7, 15, 1 (1869) 28; Baker in Fl. Brit. Ind. 2 (1879) 130; Simps. in Not. Bot. Gard. Edinb. 8 (1915) 258; Kryl. Fl. Zap. Sib. 7 (1933) 1655; Hand.-Mazz. Symb. Sin. 7 (1933) 557; Peter-Stib. in Acta Horti Gotoburg, 12 (1937–38) 46; Gontsch. and Boriss. in Fl. SSSR, 12 (1946) 33; Boriss. in Fl. Zabaik. 6 (1954) 577; Wang and Tang in Ill. treatm. princip. pl. China, Legum. (1955) 409; Grub. Konsp. fl. MNR, (1955) 184; M. Pop. Fl. Sr. Sib. 1 (1957) 327; Fl. Krasnoyar. kr. 6 (1960) 24; Fl. Kazakhst. 5 (1961) 97; Malysh. Vysokogorn. fl. Vost. Sayana [Alpine Flora of East. Sayan] (1965) 172; idem, Opred. vysokogorn. rast. Yuzhn. Sib. [Key to Alpine Plants of South. Siberia] (1968) 180; Ulzij. in Opred. rast. Okrestn. Ulan-Batora [Key to Plants in the Vicinity of Ulan Bator] (1972) 171; Krasnob. Vysokogorn. fl. Zap. Sayana [Alpine Flora of West. Sayan] (1976) 153;

Ali in Nasir Fl. West. Pakistan, No. 100, (Papilionac.) (1977) 178; Fl. Tsentr. Sib. 2 (1979) 600; Y.C. Ho in Bull. Bot. Lab. North-East. Forest Inst. 8 (1980) 50; Sanczir in Grub. Opred. rast. Mong. [Key to Plants of Mongolia] (1982) 157; Ulzij. in Tr. Inst. bot. AN MNR, 9 (1982) 17; idem, opred. korm. rast. MNR [Key to Forage Plants of Mongolian People's Republic] (1985) 304; Opred. rast. Tuv. ASSR [Key to Plants of Tuva Autonomous Soviet Socialist Republic] (1984) 174; C.Y. Yang in Claves pl. Xinjiang, 3 (1985) 124; Ulzij. and Gub. in Byull. Mosk. obshch. ispyt. prir., otd. biol. 92, 5 (1987) 116.—*Phaca frigida* L. Syst. nat. ed. 10 (1759) 1143; DC. Prodr. 2 (1825) 273; Ledeb. F1. Alt. 3 (1831) 268; id. Fl. Ross. 1 (1842) 575.

—**Ic.:** Wang and Tang l.c. fig. 404; Ulzij. 1972, l.c. fig. 69.

Described from Scandinavia. Type in London (LINN).

In larch forests, willow groves and bottomland deciduous forests, humid, humid shrubs, banks of mountain brooks in forest and subalpine belts.

IA. Mongolia: ***Khobd.*** (Turgen mountain range, Turgen-gol valley 7 km beyond estuary, right bank slope beyond first creek valley, larch grove with grass park, July 17, 1971—Grub., Ulzij. et al.; Tszusylan west of Ulangom, in forest, July 13, 1879—Pot.), ***Mong. Alt.*** (upper Kobdo river, Dayan-nur, nor. slope of Yamanyn-ul town, 2350–2500 m, larch forest, July 9, 1971—Grub., Ulzij. et al.), ***Gobi-Alt.*** (Baga-Bogdo, moist upper canyons, 2135–2590 m, No. 259, 1925–Chaney; Dzun-Saikhan mountain, on top of Yalo-ama creek valley [Elynama] among willow and birch groves, Aug. 26, 1931—Ik.-Gal.).

IIA. Junggar: ***Cis-Alt.*** ("Altay"—C.Y. Yang l.c.), ***Jung. Ala Tau*** (around Chzhaosu, Syada [Syata]—Ven'tsyuan' [Arasan], in forest, 2000 m, No. 3388, Aug. 13, 1957—Shen-Tyan'), ***Tien Shan*** (Y.C. Ho l.c.), ***Zaisan*** ("Burchum-Kaba-Khe"—C.Y. Yang l.c.).

General distribution: Arct. (nor., Asian), Europe (Cen., East.), West. Sib. (Altay), East. Sib. (Sayans, Daur.), Far East, Nor. Mong. (Fore Hubs., Hent., Hang.), China (Altay).

16. **A. chilienshanensis** Y.C. Ho in Bull. Bot. Lab. North-East. Forest Inst. 8 (1980) 51.

—**Ic.:** Y.C. Ho l.c., tab. 2, fig. 1–9.

Described from Qinghai (Tsilinshan' mountain range). Type in Beijing (PE).

Habitat not known.

IIIA. Qinghai: ***Nanshan*** (Tsilinshan' mountain range, Niouxin-Shan, 3500 m, No. 8621, July 29, 1958—P.C. Tsoong, typus ! [PE] Menyuan, 3600 m, No. 12247, P.C. Kuo).

General distribution: endemic.

17. **A. secundus** DC. Astrag. (1802) 128; Boriss. and Gontsch. in Fl. SSSR, 12 (1946) 32; Boriss. in Fl. Zabaik. 6 (1954) 576; M. Pop., Fl. Sr. Sib. 1 (1957) 327; Fl. Tsentr. Sib. 2 (1979) 604.—*A. exaltatus* Bunge Gen. Astrag. Sp. Geront. 1 (1868) 25 and 2 (1869) 28 p.p.; Pavl. in Byull. Mosk. obshch. ispyt. prir., otd. biol. 38, 1–2 (1929) 91.

Described from Siberia. Type in Paris [P].

In humid forests, shrubs and coastal meadows.

IA. Mongolia: ***Gobi-Alt.*** (Ikhe-Bogdo mountain, nor. macro slope, 2800 m, in *Cobresia* grove, No. 3595, July 1, 1972—Banzragch et al.).

General distribution: West. Sib. (Alt.), East. Sib. (Sayans, Daur.), Far East (West. and East. Amur), Nor. Mong. (Fore Hubs, Hang.) ?.

Note. Bunge (op. cit. 2 (1869) 28 (*A. exaltatus* Bunge) cited specimens from Irtysh valley in Altay.

18. **A. aksuensis** Bunge Gen. Astrag. Sp. Geront. 1 in Mém. Ac. Sci. St.-Petersb. 7 ser. 11, 16 (1868) 25 and 2 op. cit. 15, 1 (1969) 30; id. Astrag. Turk. in Izv. Obshch. lyubit. estestv. antr. i etnogr. 26, 2 (1880) 217; Lipsky in Acta Horti Petrop. 18 (1901) 30; O. et B. Fedtsch. Consp. Fl. Turk. 2 (1909) 201; Fedtsch. in Rast. Turk. [Plants of Turkmenia] (1915) 519; Fl. Tadzh. 5 (1937) 290; Gontsch. and Boriss. in Fl. SSSR, 12 (1946) 30; Fl. Kirgiz. 7 (1957) 218; Fl. Kazakhst. 5 (1961) 96; Podlech in Mitt. Bot. Staatssamml. München, 11 (1973) 289; Bait. Astrag. Tyan'-Shanya (1977) 36; Y.C. Ho in Bull. Bot. Lab. North-East. Forest. Inst. 8 (1980) 48; Opred. rast. Sr. Azii [Key to Plants of Mid. Asia] 6 (1981) 88; Fl. Tadzhik. 8 (1981) 51; C.Y. Yang in Claves pl. Xinjiang, 3 (1985) 124.—*Phaca bracteosa* Kar. et Kir. in Bull. Soc. Natur. Moscou, 15, 2 (1842) 323.

—**Ic.:** Fl. Tadzhik. 5 (1937), Plate 30 and 6 (1981), Plate 3, fig. 3 and 4; Fl. Kazakhst. 5 (1961), Plate 11, fig. 5; Y.C. Yang l.c., tab. 8, fig. 1.

Described from East. Kazakhstan. Type in St.-Petersburg (LE).

On rubbly slopes, in broad-leaved and coniferous forests, juniper groves, river valleys, middle and lower parts of upper belt of mountains.

IIA. Junggar: Tarb. (Manrak mountain range, 1800 m, upper Taldy river (beyond Kegetas town) from east. slope, Aug. 4, 1986—Rakityanskaya), ***Tien Shan*** (Tianschan, prope Hami, July 31, 1876—Pias.; Bogdo mountain range, 1800–2100 m, July 1878—A. Reg.; in Dastazymyao region, No. 760, July 23, 1957—Shen-Tyan'; "at many places in Tien Shan"—C.Y. Yang l.c.).

General distribution: Jung.-Tarb., Nor. and Cen. Tien Shan, East. Pamir; Mid. Asia (Pamiro-Alay).

Note. Specimen from Khami region differs distinctly from type. Pods are subsymmetrical, broadly-elliptical. Calyx teeth very short, (1/10) 1/8–1/6 of tube length, filiform.

19. **A. floridus** Benth. ex Bunge in Mém. Acad. Sci. St.-Peters., ser. 7, 15, 1 (1869) 28; Baker in Fl. Brit. Ind. 2 (1876) 127; Dunn. in J. Linn. Soc. Bot. 36 (1911) 421; Simps. in Not. Bot. Gard. Edinb. 8 (1913) 258; Peter-Stib. in Acta Horti Gotoburg, 12 (1937–38) 45; Wang and Tang in Ill. treatm. princip. pl. China, Legum. (1955) 413; Y.C. Ho in Bull. Bot. Lab. North-East. Forest Inst. 8 (1980) 53; P.C. Li et Ni in Fl. Xizang, 2 (1985) 830.—*A. przewalskii* (?) Hand.-Mazz. Symb. Sin. 7 (1933) 556, p.p., non Bunge, 1877.

—**Ic.:** Wang and Tang l.c. fig. 409.

Described from Himalayas (Sikkim). Type in London [K].

On meadow slopes, scrubs, at 3700-4300 m in alpine belt.

IIIA. Qinghai: ***Nanshan*** (Rakool river, alpine belt, 3000–3300 m, July 22, 1880—Przew.; Koknor, 3650 m, No. 1044, June 25, 1956—Yan Tsen-chzhan [PE]; "Gansu"— Y.C. Ho, l.c.), ***Amdo*** (alpine belt of Dzhakhar-Dzhargyn hills, 3150 m, June 21, 1880— Przew.).

IIIB. Tibet: ***Weitzan*** ("Sosyan', Leinyaotszi"—P.C. Li et Ni, l.c.), ***South.*** ("Tszyantszy"—P.C. Li et Ni, l.c.).

General distribution: China (South-West), Himalayas.

20. **A. mongolicus** Bunge Gen. Astrag. Sp. Geront. 1 (1868) 25 and 2 (1869) 30; Palib. in Tr. Troitskosav.-Kyakht. otd. rus. geogr. obshch. 8, 3 (1906) 48; Pavl. in Byull. Mosk. obshch. ispyt. prirod., biol. 38, 1–2 (1929) 91; Kryl. Fl. Zap. Sib. 7 (1933) 1658; Peter-Stib. in Acta Horti Gotoburg, 12 (1937–38) 46; Gontsch. and Boriss. in Fl. SSSR, 12 (1946) 37; Grub. Konsp. fl. MNR (1955) 185, p. max. p.; Wang and Tang in Ill. treatm. princip. pl. China, Legum. (1955) 381; M. Pop. Fl. Sr. Sib. 1 (1957) 328; Fl. Kazakhst. 5 (1961) 98; Ulzij. in Opred. rast. okrestn. Ulan-Batora [Key to Plants in the Vicinity of Ulan Bator] (1972) 171; H.C. Fu. Fl. Intramong. 3 (1977) 189; Fl. Tsentr. Sib. 2 (1979) 603; Sanczir in Grub. Opred. rast. Mong. [Key to Plants of Mongolia] (1982) 157; Ulzij. in Tr. Inst. bot. AN MNR, 8 (1982) 17.—*A. membranaceus* var. *mongolicus* (Bunge) Hsio in Acta Pharmac. Sin. 11, 2 (1964) 117; Fl. pl. herb. Chinae bor.-or. 5 (1976) 89; Y.C. Ho in Bull. Bot. Lab. North-East. Forest Inst. 8 (1980) 54; H.C. Fu in Fl. Intramong. ed. 2, 3 (1989) 259.—*Phaca macrostachys* Turcz. in Bull. Soc. Natur Moscou, 13 (1840) 66, non DC.

—**Ic.:** Fl. pl. herb. Chinae bor.-or. 5 (1976), tab. 38, fig. 7–8; H.C. Fu l.c. 3 (1977), tab. 94, fig. 1–7.

Described from East. Mongolia. Type in St.-Petersburg (LE). Plate I, fig. 2.

On sand, sandy steppes, pebble bed terraces, sandy floors of gorges, rocky slopes in steppes, fallow lands, stone talus and rocks.

IA. Mongolia: ***Mong. Alt.*** (Adzhi-Bogdo mountain range, Urtengol river gorge, June 30, 1877—Pot.; same locality, southern macro slope, Ikhe-gol brook, gorge, 2500–2550 m, Aug. 22, 1979—Grub. et al.), ***Cen. Khalkha*** (Ulan-Khada mountains, on sand, more common on dunes, July 7, 1891—Levin; along road to Tsakharyn-tal area from Tsagan-tolga well, June 10, 1909—Czet.; between Borokhchin lake and Suchzh river, July 8, 1924 —Pavl.; Dzhargalant river basin, waterdivide between Ara-Dzhargalant and Uber Dzhargalant rivers, rubbly sand, July 10, 1925—Krasch.; Choiren station, July 24, 1928—Tug.; 30 km south of Munkh-khan somon, high hillocky area, June 20; same locality, 19 km east of Bayan-terem somon, June 23; 34 km east of Byan-terem somon, granitic hillocky area, June 22, 1977, Dashnyam, Isach. et al.; Undzhul somon, feather grass steppe, July 1; Munkh-khan somon, Munkh-khan-ula hill, 1607 m, July 25—1974, Golubkova, Tsogt, Tsetsegma; 80 km south-east-east of Underkhan town, Zaan-shire hill, June 19, 1987—Gub., Kam. et al.), ***East. Mong.*** (in montosis lapidosis Mongolia chinensis, 1831; Mongolia chinensis, 1841—Kirilov; between Kulusutaevsk settlement and Dolon-nor lake, 1870—Lom.; Suma-khada hills, May 22; between Kalgan and Yinshan,

May–June 1871, Przew.; midcourse of Kerulen river, Bain-khan mountain, granitic montane slopes, 1899—Pal.; Inner Mongolia, grasslands, No. 590, 1925—Chaney; Shilin-khoto town, true steppe, 1959—Ivanov; Erdene-tsagan somon, Nukhutyn-daban pass 25 km south of somon, July 27, 1962—Yun.; Shiliin-Bogdo mountain 62 km south-east of Dariganga somon, July 8, 1971—Dashnyam, Karam. et al.; same locality, Molotsog-els sand 12 km south-east-east of Dariganga settlement, July 8, 1985, Gub. [MW]; "Shilin-gol, Ulashan'"—Y.C. Fu l.c.), ***Depr. Lakes*** (Iter and Kobdo, long frossula, June 17, 1870—Kflning; Dzun-Dzharglant mountain range, south-west. slope, Ulyastain-gol gorge, 1850–2800 m, June 28, 1971—Grub. et al.), ***Val. Lakes*** (South. foothill of Hangay between Ongiin-gol river and Tsagan-Tek-tala valleys, July 21, 1926—Glag.; 60–80 km west of Dzag-Baidarig somon, steppe, Aug. 27, 1943—Tsebigmid; Bain-bulak somon, garage on Dzag—Tsagan-ol road, 40 km east of Bayan khongor, July 11, 1947—Yun.; Narin-tel' somon 8 km nor. of somon on right bank of Tatsin-gol river, upper part of south. slope of Dungindeg-nur mountain, montane steppe, July 30, 1952—Davazamč; Tatsyn-gol—Tuin-gol interfluvine zone in Abzag-ul region and Adagiin-khara-khuduk well, Lutaryn ama creek valley, June 13, 1971—Grub., Ulzij.), ***Gobi-Alt.*** (Dundu-Saikhan hills, June 5, 1909—Czet.; Ikhe-Bogdo mountain range, Bityuten-ama, montane slopes, July 12, 1927—Simukova; Bayan-Tsagan hills, Subulyur creek valley, Aug. 5; Dundu-Saikhan mountains, in Ulan-khuzhir creek valley, Aug. 16; Dzun-Saikhan top of Yalo [Elyn-ama] creek valley, Aug. 26, 1931, Ik.-Gal.; pass between Dundu and Dzun-Saikhan, 1 km north of pass, July 22; Khongor-Obo somon, pass between Dzun- and Dundu-Saikhan, lower hill belt, July 22, 1943; Dzun-Saikhan mountain range, middle and lower belts, June 19, 1945—Yun.; Baga-Bogdo mountain range, nor. slope, July 15, 1963—Sanzhid [UBA]; Ikhe-Bogdo mountain range, Ar-Nokhoityn khundii valley, nor. slope, Aug. 20, 1967—Tsagaanmaam; Dzun-Saikhan mountain range, nor. slope on pass; Dund-Saikhan mountain range, south. slope under peak, 2825 m, July 25—Grub., Ulzij. et al.; 30 km esat-north-east of Bayan-Dalai, Dundu-Saikhan mountain range, 2300 m, July 22, 1972—Guricheva, Rachk.; Bayan-Tsagan mountain range, Dzhargalant-gol river, on south. slopes, July 8; Ikhe-Bogdo mountain range, south. slope, Dzhargalantyn-ama gorge, 2600 m, July 9, 1973, Golub-kova, Tsogt; Ikhe-Bogdo mountain range, south. macro slope, on plateau-like peak, Aug. 4, 1973—Isach., Rachk.), ***East. Gobi*** ("Ulantsab, Yinshan"—H.C. Fu l.c.), ***Ordos*** ("Ordos"—H.C. Fu l.c.).

General distribution: East. Sib. (Daur.), Nor. Mong. (except Cis-Hing.), China (Dunbei, North).

21. **A. lucidus** Tsai et Yu in Bull. Fan. Mem. Inst. Biol., Bot. ser., 11 (1939) 262; Y.C. Ho in Bull. Bot. Research, 1, 3 (1981) 105; P.C. Li et Ni in Fl. Xizang, 2 (1985) 832.

—**Ic.:** Fl. Xizang, 2, tab. 269, fig. 10–17.

Described from South-West China (Mill). Type in Yunnan (YNFI).

In forest meadows and borders, around water, usually 2000–3500 m.

IIIB. Tibet: ***Weitzan*** ("Tszyacha"—P.C. Li et Ni l.c.; "East. Tibet"—Y.C. Ho l.c.), ***South.*** ("Tszyanda"—P.C. Li et Ni l.c.).

General distribution: China (South-West).

Note. The authors of this species placed it in section **Nigricantes**.

22. **A. propinquus** Schischk. in Fl. Zap. Sib. 7 (1933) 1657; Pavl. in Byull. Mosk. obshch. ispyt. prir., otd. biol. 38, 1–2 (1929) 91; Gontsch. and Boriss. in Fl. SSSR, 12 (1946) 38; Grub. Konsp. fl. MNR (1955) 186, p.p.; M. Pop. Fl. Sr. Sib. 1 (1957) 328; Fl. Kazakhst. 5 (1961) 100; Ulzij. in Opred. rast. okrestn. Ulan-Batora [Key to Plants in the Vicinity of

Ulan Bator] (1972) 171; Fl. Tsentr. Sib. 2 (1979) 603.—*A. penduliflorus* Bunge Gen. Astrag. Sp. Geront. 2 (1869) 30 non Lam., p.p.; Ulzij. in Tr. Inst. bot. AN MNR, 8 (1982) 17; Opred. rast. Tuv. ASSR [Key to Plants of Tuva Autonomous Soviet Socialist Republic] (1984) 147; C.Y. Yang in Claves pl. Xinjiang, 3 (1985) 125.—*Phaca abbreviata* Ledeb. Fl. Alt. 3 (1831) 268, non *Astragalus abbreviatus* Kar. et Kir.

—**Ic.:** Fl. SSSR, 12, Plate 2, fig. 1; Fl. Kazakhst. 5, Plate 91, fig. 1.

Described from Altay. Type in St.-Petersburg (LE).

In montane forests, forest borders, shrubs and forest meadows, along banks of rivers, more rarely in steppe meadows.

IA. Mongolia: ***Khobd.*** (Achit-nur lake, arid sandy gorge, Aug. 6, 1963; Sagil somon, Elyn-sair, July 1963—Tumurkhoyag [UBA]; Turgen mountain range, Turgen-gol valley 7 km beyond estuary, right bank slope, herbaceous larch grove, July 17, 1971—Grub., Ulzij., Dariima), ***Mong. Alt.*** (Bulgan-gol upper course, Koshetyn-gol valley near Kudzhirtu settlement, left bank, Artelin-sal creek valley, on south. slope of Shara-Khamryn-Oroi mountain range 3 km beyond Kudzhirtu, larch forest on slope exposed northward, July 3; Kobdo river 2 km beyond Zhalandy river estuary, right bank, Gurtyn-ama creek valley 1 km beyond estuary, 2200–2300 m, larch forest, July 11, 1971. Grub., Ulzij., Dariima), ***Depr. Lakes*** (around Ak-Karasuka river on south. descent of Tannu-Ol, in meadows, July 6, 1892—Kryl.).

IIA. Junggar: ***Cis-Alt.*** (Y.C. Yang l.c.), ***Tarb.*** (Saur mountain range, south. slope of Karagaitu river valley, subalpine belt, June 23, 1957—Yun., I-f. Yuan'; Tarbagatai mountain range, north of Dachen town, on slope, 1200 m, No. 2938, Aug. 13, 1957—Kuan), ***Jung. Ala Tau*** (Toli district, Albakzin mountains, on slope, No. 2576, Aug. 7, 1957—Kuan), ***Tien shan*** (Piluchi, 1000–1300 m, July 23; Kasan pass, 2440 m, Aug.—1978, A. Reg.).

General distribution: West. Sib. (Alt., Irt., south-east), East. Sib. (Sayans, Daur.), Nor. Mong. (Fore Hubs. east., Hent., Hang., Mong.-Daur.), China (Altay).

23. **A. membranaceus** (Fisch.) Bunge Gen. Astrag. Sp. Geront. 1 (1868) 25 and 2 (1869) 30; Kom. in Acta Horti Petrop. 22 (1904) 586; Nakai, Fl. Kor. 1 (1909) 150; Peter-Stib. in Acta Horti Gotoburg, 12 (1937–38) 47; Kitag. Lin. Fl. Mansh. (1939) 281; Gontsch. and Boriss. in Fl. SSSR, 12 (1946) 38; Boriss. in Fl. Zabaik. 6 (1954) 577, p.p.; Wang and Tang in Ill. treatm. princip. pl. China, Legum. (1955) 414; M. Pop. Fl. Sr. Sib. 1 (1957) 328; Fl. Krasnoyarsk. kr. 6 (1960) 26, p.p.; Dashnyam in Bot. zh. 11, 50 (1965) 1638; Grub. in Novosti sist. vyssh. rast. 9 (1972) 279; Krasnov. Vysokogorn. fl. Vost. Sayana [Alpine Flora of Eastern Sayan] (1976) 154, p.p.; H.C. Fu in Fl. Intramong. 3 (1977) 187, p.p.; Fl. pl. herb. Chinae bor.-or. 5 (1976) 87; Fl. Tsentr. Sib. 2 (1979) 602, p.p.; Y.C. Ho in Bull. Bot. Lab. North-East. Forest Inst. 8 (1980) 53; Sanczir in Grub. Opred. rast. Mong. [Key to Plants of Mongolia] (1982) 157 p.p.; Ulzij. in Tr. Inst. bot. AN MNR, 8 (1982) 18; H.C. Fu in Fl. Intramong. ed 2, 3 (1989) 259.—*Phaca membranacea* Fisch. in DC. Prodr. 2 (1825) 273.—*Phaca alpina* β *dahurica* Fisch. (1825) 1, p. 273.—*Phaca alpina* Ledeb. Fl. Ross. 1 (1842) 576 ex p.—*Astragalus penduliflorus* auct. non Lam.: Kom. in Acta Horti Petrop. 22 (1904) 587 p.p.

—**Ic.:** Fl. Zabaik. 6, fig. 295; Wang and Tang l.c., fig. 410; H.C. Fu l.c. 3 (1977) tab. 94, fig. 8–12.

Described from Dauria. Type in St.-Petersburg (LE).

On meadow slopes, forest meadows, borders of larch groves, in willow groves, birch stands and scrubs, along slopes and floors of creek valleys, in forest belt and lower part of alpine belt.

IA. Mongolia: ***East. Mong.*** ("Datsinshan', Ulashan'"—H.C. Fu 1977, 1989, l.c.).

General distribution: East. Sib. (Daur.), Far East, Nor. Mong. (Hent., Mong.-Daur.), China (Dunbei), Korean peninsula.

Section 9 (10). **Brachycarpus** Boriss.

24. **A. heterodontus** Boriss. in Tr. Tadzhik. bazy AN SSSR, 2 (1936) 161; idem in Fl. Tadzhik. 5 (1937) 279; idem in Fl. SSSR, 12 (1946) 61; Fl. Kirgiz. 7 (1957) 233; Ikonn. Opred. rast. Pam. [Key to Plants of Pamir] (1963) 167; Y.C. Ho in Bull. Bot. Lab. North-East. Forest Inst. 8 (1980) 67; Opred. rast. Sr. Azii [Key to Plants of Mid. Asia], 6 (1981) 108. —*A. porphyrocalyx* Y.C. Ho in Bull. Bot. Lab. North-East. Forest Inst. 8 (1980) 67; P.C. Li et Ni in Fl. Xizang, 2 (1985) 824.

—**Ic.:** Fl. Tadzhik. 5 (1937), Plate 27 and 6 (1981), Plate 6, fig. 24–29.

Described from Pamir. Type in St.-Petersburg (LE).

Along banks of rivers and lakes, on rocky and pebble-bed coastal zones, rubble-melkozem slopes, more rarely in meadows and grasslands as well as cryophyte deserts in alpine belt, 3800–4700 m.

IIIA. Qinghai: ***Nanshan*** (Choibsen-khit temple, No. 76, 1901—Lad.).

IIIB. Tibet: Chang Tang ("Ban'ge"—P.C. Li et Ni l.c.), ***Weitzan*** (upper Huang He river, on coastal pebble beds, 2440–2740 m, May 31, 1880; upper Yangtze river, left bank of Dy-cho river, 3962 m, June 23—Przew.; Burkhan-Budda mountain range, south. slope, 3870 m, dry and moist beds of brooks and high water, May 30; valley of Alyk-norin-gol river, on sandy banks of river, 3810 m, June 2; bank of Russkoe lake and Yellow River, 4115 m, No. 76, latter half of June—1900; Burkhan-Budda mountain range, south. slope, beds and brooks running in Alyk-norsk valley, 3810 m, June 9, 1901—Lad.).

IIIC. Pamir (Ulug-tuz gorge in Charlym river basin, around shrubs along brook and Ulug-Rabat pass, along descent—1909, Divn.).

General distribution: Mid. Asia (Pamir), China (South-West: Sichuan).

Note. *A. porphyrocalyx* Y.C. Ho described recently from Sichuan (Litan) evidently represents the eastern form of highly variable *A. heterodontus* Boriss., with which it resembles in habitat and structure of fruit but differs in very short wings slightly emarginate at tip. Based on the description of Ho Ye-Chi l.c., variety *A. heterodontus* var. *porphyrocalyx* (Y.C. Ho) Ulzij. can be recognised.

25. **A. golmunensis** Y.C. Ho in Bull. Bot. Lab. North-East. Forest Inst. 8 (1980) 61.

—**Ic.:** Y.C. Ho l.c., tab. 5, fig. 1–9.

Described from Qinghai. Type in Wugung [NWBI] (in Herb. Inst. Biol. Wugung, Shaanxi, conservatur).

Habitat not known.

IC. Qaidam (Golmo, 4100 m, No. 452, June 16, 1959.—Qinghai-Gansu expedition, typus !, non vidi).

General distribution: endemic.

Note. Judging from the high altitude of the record of this species, the location possibly lies not in the territory of Qaidam basin but on northern slope of Burkhan-Budda mountain range or in the territory of Chang Tang district of Tibet subprovince. The author of this species (Y.C. Ho) clearly erred in relegating it to section **Orobella** Gontsch.

26. **A. mahoschanicus** Hand.-Mazz. in Oesterr. Bot. Zeitschr. 82 (1933) 247; Peter-Stib. in Acta Horti Gotoburg, 12 (1937–38) 31; Wang and Tang in Ill. treatm. princip. pl. China, Legum. (1955) 398; Y.C. Ho in Bull. Bot. Lab. North-East. Forest. Inst. 8 (1980) 69; H.C. Fu in Fl. Intramong. ed. 2, 3 (1989) 263; C.Y. Yang in Claves pl. Xinjiang, 3 (1985) 125; Pl. vasc. Helanshan (1986) 152.

—**Ic.:** Wang and Tang l.c., fig. 383; Ic. cormoph. Sin. 2, fig. 2570; H.C. Fu l.c. tab. 102, fig. 1–5.

Described from China (West. Gansu: Makhoshan' mountain range). Type in Wien [Vienna] (W).

IA. Mongolia: ***West. Gobi*** (Gansu, vicinity of Dinsi [Din-sin'] hill, along slopes of ravine, June 20, 1957—Kabanov; "Mahoschan, Licent, 4208"—Peter-Stib. l.c.; "Gansu" Y.C. Ho l.c.), ***Alash. Gobi*** ("Khelan'shan'"—H.C. Fu l.c.), ***Ordos*** ("Ninsya"—Y.C. Ho l.c.).

IIIA. Qinghai ("Qinghai"—C.Y. Yang l.c.).

General distribution: China (North-West: Gansu).

27. **A. densiflorus** Kar. et Kir. in Bull. Soc. Natur. Moscou 15 (1842) 329; Bunge Gen. Astrag. Sp. Geront. 1 (1868) 21 and 2 (1869) 22; id. in Izv. Obshch. lyub. estestv., antr. i etnogr. 26, 2 (1880) 214; Baker in Hook. f. Fl. Brit. Ind. 2 (1879) 125; O. et B. Fedtsch. Konsp. fl. Turk. 2 (1909) 198, excl. pl. e Zeravschan et Pamir; Boriss. in Fl. SSSR, 12 (1946) 59; Fl. Kirgiz. 7 (1957) 229; Fl. Kazakhst. 5 (1961) 104; Bait. Astrag. Tyan'-Shanya (1977) 39; Ali in Nasir, Fl. West. Pakistan, No. 100 (Papilionac.) (1977) 161; Y.C. Ho in Bull. Bot. Lab. North-East. Forest Inst. 8 (1980) 68; Opred. rast. Sr. Azii [Key to Plants of Mid. Asia] 6 (1981) 107; P.C. Li et Ni in Fl. Xizang, 2 (1985) 825; C.Y. Yang in Claves pl. Xinjiang, 3 (1985) 126, p.p.

—**Ic.:** Fl. Kazakhst. 5, Plate 12, fig. 5; Fl. Xizang, 2, tab. 269, fig. 1–9.

Described from East. Kazakhstan (Jung. Ala Tau). Type in St.-Petersburg (LE).

IB. Kashgar: ***West.*** (nor. Slope of Tokhta-khon mountains, 3050–3660 m, in meadows in spruce forest, in recesses of gorges among shrubs, July 19 and 22, 1989, Rob.; Sarykol'sk mountain range, Bostan-Terek locality, July 10, 1929—Pop.).

IIA. Junggar: ***Tien Shan*** (Sudliches Kuikonik Tal, beim Lager unter Tschon Yailak Pass, June 15, 1908—Merzb.; Manas river basin, valley of Ulan-Usu river valley 45 km beyond its confluence into Dzhartas, alpine meadow, July 18, 1957—Yun. and I-f. Yuan';

from Danyu for 6–7 km south on alluvium, 3400–2600 m, No. 459, July 21; south of Barkul' lake, No. 2216, Sep. 27, 1957, Shen-Tyan'; Khalangao in Khomote, on nor. slope, 2540 m, No. 7676, Aug. 11, 1958—A.R. Lee (1958)).

IIIB. Tibet: ***Chang Tang*** (Tokus-daban mountain range, nor. slope, Tuzlyk river, 3960 m, Aug. 15; Przewalsky mountain range, nor. slope, 4270 m, Aug. 21–1890, Rob.; "Kunlun"—C.Y. Yang l.c.; "Ban'ge, Gentsi Shuankhu"—P.C. Li et Ni l.c.), ***Weitzan*** (Dzhagyn-gol river, 4200 m, July 15, 1884—Przew.; Yantszy-tszyan river basin [Goluboi river], Nru-Chyu, 3650 m, along conglomerate cliffs, July 25, 1900—Lad., "Sosyan"— P.C. Li et Ni l.c.), ***South.*** ("Dintsze, Chzhada, Pulan'"—P.C. Li et Ni l.c.).

General distribution: Jung.-Tarb. (Jung. Ala Tau), Nor. Tien Shan, Trans-Ili and Tersk Ala Tau, Atoinek mountain range).

28. **A. longiracemosus** Ulzij. in Novit. syst. pl. vasc. 30 (1996) 114.

Described from Qinghai (Nanshan). Type in St.-Petersburg (LE). Map 3.

Along banks of lakes, on coastal pebble beds and meadows.

IIIA. Qinghai: ***Nanshan*** (desert at nor. foot of mountain range to the south of Kukunor lake, 10,000 ft (3048 m) on rubble, common, No. 449, June 23; some locality, on coastal sand of lake, 10,200 ft (3109 m), No. 463, flowers, June 27 [July 9] 1880, Prezew.—typus !; Kukunor lake, along bank, on sand, 12,000 ft (3658 m), Aug. 29, 1908—Czet.; same locality, meadow on eastern bank of lake, 3210 m, Aug. 5, 1959—Petr.).

General distribution: endemic.

29. **A. melanostachys** Benth. ex Bunge Gen. Astrag. Sp. Geront. 1 (1868) 21 and 2 (1869) 22; Baker in Hook. f. Fl. Brit. Ind. 2 (1876) 125; Boriss. and Schischkin in Fl. Tadzhik. 5 (1937) 277; idem, Fl. SSSR, 12 (1946) 54; Ikonn. Opred. rast. Pam. [Key to Plants of Pamir] (1963) 167; idem, Opred. rast. Badakhsh. [Key to Plants of Badakhshan] (1979) 231; Kitamura, Pl. West. Pakist. and Afgh. (1964) 89; Ali in Nasir, Fl. West Pakistan, No. 100 (1977) 159; Opred. rast. Sr. Azii [Key to Plants of Mid. Asia] 6 (1981) 106; Fl. Tadzhik. 6 (1981) 60; K.T. Fu in Bull. Bot. Research, 2, 4 (1982) 70; P.C. Li et Ni in Fl. Xizang, 2 (1985) 824.—*A. supraglaber* Kitam. in Acta Phytotax. et Geobot. 16 (1956) 138.—*A. macrostegius* Rech. in K. Danske Vid. Selsk. Biol. Skrift. 9, 3 (1958) 37, t. 29, 30.—*A. debilis* Ovcz. et Rassul. in Dokl. AN Tadzhik. 20, 1 (1977) 62, non A. Gray (1864).—*A. bibracteatus* Ovcz. et Rassul. in Dokl. AN Tadzhik. 20, 1 (1977) 61.

—**Ic.:** Fl. Tadzhik. 6 (1981) Plate 6, fig. 1–6.

Described from West. Himalayas. Type in London [K].

In humid meadows, grassy slopes, standing moraines, pebble beds and along banks of springs in alpine belt, 1700–4600 m.

IIIA. Qinghai: ***Nanshan*** (Kadiger monastery, May 26, 1885—Pot.).

IIIB. Tibet: ***Chang Tang*** ("Tibet"—P.C. Li et Ni l.c.).

General distribution: East. Pamir; Mid. Asia (Pamiro-Alay), Himalayas (west., Kashmir), Fore Asia (East.).

Note. Judging from reference in the flora of Tajikistan, Afghanistan and other adjoining regions, this species may be found in Sinkiang in Pamir territory.

30. **A. baitagensis** Sancz. ex Ulzij. in Bull. Soc. Natur. Moscou, Ser. biol., 95, 1 (1990) 109; Sanczir in Grub. Opred. rast. Mong. [Key to Plants of Mongolia] (1982) 157, descr. ross. in clave; Grub. in Novosti sist. vyssh. rast. 21 (1984) 206.

Described from Mongolia (Jung. Gobi). Type in St.-Petersburg (LE). Isotype in Ulan Bator (UBA).

Along rocky and rubbly slopes of arid hills.

IIA. Junggar: ***Jung.*** Gobi (on northern slope of Baitag-Bogdo hill 110 km south-west of Bugat somon in Khobdo ajmaq, No. 7293, Aug. 8, 1977—Isach. and Rachk., typus !; Ikhe-Khabtag-ula mountain range 130 km south-east of Bugat somon, Aug. 12, 1977; idem, same locality, macro slope of mountain range 80 km south of Altay somon in Khobdosk ajmaq, Aug. 21, 1984—Buyan-Orshikh [UBA].

General distribution: endemic.

31. **A. luteoflorus** Ulzij. in Novit. syst. pl. vasc. 30 (1996) 112.

Described from Qinghai (Nanshan). Type in St.-Petersburg (LE). Map 1.

On sand in riverine valley.

IIIA. Qinghai: ***Nanshan*** (valley of Shara-gol'dzhina river, Paidza-tologoi area, 11,000 ft absolute height, on sand, No. 310a, July 11, 1894, Rob.—typus !).

General distribution: endemic.

32. **A. valerii** Ulzij. in Novit. syst. pl. vasc. 30 (1996) 111.

Described from Tibet (Weitzan). Type in St.-Petersburg (LE).

In meadows, slopes, river bed sand and pebble beds of montane rivers in alpine belt. Map 2.

IC. Qaidam: ***Hilly*** (Ritter mountain range, alpine meadow, 12,000 ft (3658 m), June 23, 1894; Eastern Qaidam, Saryk-ula mountains, Elistyn-Kuku-bulak spring, 11,000 ft (3353 m), on sand, May 11, 1895—Rob.).

IIIB. Tibet: ***Weitzan*** (Yangtze river basin, Dy-chyu river, 13,000 ft (3962 m), June 14 [26], 1884—Przew.; Amnen-kor mountain range, nor. slope, toward Alyk-norin-gol, 12,500 ft (3810 m), rocky bed of brook and washouts, No. 88, June 4, 1900—Lad., typus !; Yangtze river basin, Makh-mukh-chyu river, 13,500 ft (4115 m), on pebble bed, May 21; Burkhan-Budda mountain range, south. Slope, on arid conglomerate cliffs, 13,000–14,000 ft (3962–4267 m), June 9, 1901—Lad.).

General distribution: endemic.

33. **A. subscaposus** M. Pop. ex Boriss. in Tr. Tadzhik. bazy AN SSSR, 2 (1936) 164; Boriss. in Fl. Tadzhik. 5 (1937) 278; idem in Fl. SSSR, 12 (1946) 57; Fl. Uzbek. 3 (1955) 492; Fl. Kirgiz. 7 (1957) 299; Fl. Kazakhst. 5 (1961) 103; Ikonn. Opred. rast. Pam. [Key to Plants of Pamir] (1963) 164; Bait. Astrag. Tyan'-Shanya (1977) 38; Podlech et Anders. in Mitt. Bot. staatssamml. München, 13 (1977) 442; Fl. Tadzhik. 6 (1981) 64.—*A. densiflorus* auct. non Kar. et Kir.: Y.C. Yang, Claves pl. Xinjiang, 3 (1985) 126, pro pl. e Tian-Schan.

—**Ic.:** Fl. Uzbek. 4, Plate 58, fig. 28, Fl. Tadzhik. 6, Plate 5, fig. 18–23.

Described from Mid. Asia (Pamiro-Alay). Type in St.-Petersburg (LE).

In meadows, steppes, melkozem-rubbly and rocky-rubbly slopes as well as around springs, in middle and upper mountain belts, 2800–4500 m.

IIA. Junggar: ***Tien Shan*** (Bagrashkul lake region, Luitsigen in Khomote on southern slope, 3140 m, No. 7192, July 10; along road to Kashgar from Urumchi on slope, 2980 m, No. 5984, July 21—1958, A.R. Lee (1958)).

IIIC. Pamir (Kunlun, Kara-Dzhilga river, alpine pasture at 4000–4500 m alt., July 22, 1942—Serp.).

General distribution: Cen. Tien Shan, East. Pamir; Mid. Asia (Pamiro-Alay).

*__A. fetissovii__ B. Fedtsch. in Acta Horti Petrop. 24 (1905) 202; Fedtsch. Konsp. fl. Turk. 2 (1909) 198; Boriss. in Fl. SSSR, 12 (1946) 59; Fl. Kirgiz. 7 (1957) 230; Bait. Astrag. Tyan'-Shanya (1977) 39; Opred. rast. Sr. Azii [Key to Plants of Mid. Asia] 6 (1981) 108.—*A. densiflorus* auct. non Kar. et Kir.: Lipsky in Acta Horti Petrop. 26 (1907) 140, quoad syn. *A. fetissovii* et pl. e Tian-Schan.

Described from Kirghiz (Cen. Tien Shan). Type in St.-Petersburg (LE).

On rock screes in alpine belt.

Reports possible from Kokshaal-tau mountain range in Nor. Kashgar within Cen. Asia.

General distribution: Cen. Tien Shan.

34. **A. jagnobicus** Lipsky in Acta Horti Petrop. 26 (1907) 138, 223; O. et B. Fedtsch. Konsp. fl. Turk. (1909) 198; Boriss. in fl. Tadzhik. 5 (1937) 280; idem in Fl. SSSR, 12 (1946) 58; Kitamura, Fl. Afghan. (1960) 201; Opred. rast. Sr. Azii [Key to Plants of Mid. Asia] 6 (1981) 107; Fl. Tadzhik. 6 (1981) 66.

—**Ic.:** Fl. SSSR, 12, Plate 4, fig. 3; Fl. Tadzhik. 6, Plate 6, fig. 13–18.

Described from Mid. Asia (Pamiro-Alay). Type in St.-Petersburg (LE).

In meadows, scrub vegetation, more rarely in pebble beds and outcrops of red sandstones in middle and upper mountain belts.

IIIC. Pamir (Ulug-Tuz gorge in Charlym river basin, alongside bushes around brook, June 28, 1909—Divn.).

General distribution: East. Pamir; Mid. Asia (Pamiro-Alay), Afghanistan.

*__A. schugnanicus__ B. Fedtsch. Trav. Mus. Bot. Ac. Petersb. 1 (1902) 124; Lipsky in Acta Horti Petrop. 26 (1907) 136; O. et B. Fedtsch. Konsp. fl. Turk. 2 (1909) 198; Boriss. in Fl. Tadzhik. 5 (1937) 276; idem in Fl. SSSR, 12 (1946) 57; Fl. Kirgiz. 7 (1957) 226; Fl. Kazakhst. 5 (1961) 102; Bait. Astrag. Tyan'-Shanya (1947) 38; Opred. rast. Sr. Azii [Key to Plants of Mid. Asia] 6 (1981) 107; Fl. Tadzhik. 6 (1981) 63.

—**Ic.:** Fl. SSSR, 12, Plate 4, fig. 3; Fl. Tadzhik. 6 (1981), Plate 6, fig. 7–12.

Described from Mid. Asia (Pamiro-Alay). Type in St.-Petersburg (LE).

In sedge, sedge-*Cobresia* and short-grass meadows, in grasslands along banks of brooks and rivulets, alpine rock-melkozem slopes.

Reports possible from Tashkurgan adjoining Takhta-korum pass and Mats regions of Chin. Pamir.

General distribution: East. Pamir, Cen. Tien Shan; Mid. Asia (Pamiro-Alay).

35. **A. tulinovii** B. Fedtsch. in Acta Horti Petrop. 21 (1903) 315; O. et B. Fedtsch. Konsp. fl. Turk. 2 (1909) 198; Fedtsch. Rast. Turk. [Vegetation of Turkestan] (1915) 518; Boriss. in Fl. Tadzhik. 5 (1937) 278; idem in Fl. SSSR, 12 (1946) 60; Ikonn. in Opred. rast. Pam. [Key to Plants of Pamir] (1963) 165; Fl. Tadzhik. 6 (1981) 68; Opred. rast. Sr. Azii [Key to Plants of Mid. Asia] 6 (1981) 108; Y.C. Yang in Claves pl. Xinjiang, 3 (1985) 129.—*A. densiflorus* auct. non Kar. et Kir.: Lipsky in Acta Horti Petrop. 26 (1907) 140, quoad syn. *A. tulinovii* et pl. e Pamir; O. et B. Fedtsch., Konsp. fl. Turk. 2 (1909) 198, quoad pl. e Pamir.

—**Ic.:** Fl. Tadzhik. 6 (1981) Plate 6, fig. 19–23.

Described from Pamir. Type in St.-Petersburg (LE).

Along banks of rivers and in alpine grasslands.

IA. Mongolia: ***Mong. Alt.*** (Adzhi-Bogdo mountain range, centre of Burgastain-data pass, montane steppe, No. 12758, Aug. 5, 1977—Yun.).

IIA. Junggar: ***Tien Shan.***

IIIB. Tibet: ***Chang Tang*** (Keri mountain range, alpine zone, July 8; same locality, 3810 m, July 11; same locality, 3360–3620 m, July 16, 1885, Przew.); "Kunlun"—C.Y. Yang l.c.).

IIIC. Pamir (Kunlun, Issyk-su river, 3000–3100 m, June 21; same locality, Kashka-su river sources, 4200–5500 m, July 5; Tasnestlyk area, 4000–5000 m, July 25; Goo-dzhiro river, 4500–5500 m, July 27; Shor-luk river gorge, 4000–4500 m, July 28, 1942, Serp.; "Tash-kurgan"—C.Y. Yang 1.c.).

General distribution: East. Pamir.

Note. Plants belonging to new variety *A. tulinovii* var. *keriensis* Ulzij. var. nova have been asterisked.

Stems with finely hispid with white hairs. Leaflets up to 13 mm long, white-hairy beneath. Flowers pale-yellow. Standard up to 9 mm long.

Typus: jugum Keriense, alpina 3360–3620 m, No. 290, July 6, 1879—Przewalsky. In Herb. Inst. Bot. Ac. Sci. Ross. (St.-Petersb.), conservatur.

36. **A. imetensis** Boriss. in Not. Syst. (Leningrad) 10 (1977) 43; Boriss. in Fl. SSSR, 12 (1946) 60, descr. ross.; Fl. Kirgiz. 7 (1957) 230; Bait. Astrag. Tyan'-Shanya (1947) 39; Opred. rast. Sr. Azii [Key to Plants of Mid. Asia] 6 (1981) 108.

Described from Kirghiz (Cen. Tien Shan). Type in St.-Petersburg (LE). Plate 2, fig. 1.

On sand banks of rivers in alpine belt.

IIA. Junggar: ***Tien Shan*** (south. road up to Nanshan-kou picket on south. foot of Tien Shan, July 16, 1879—Przew.; Dzhagastai-gol, 2740 m, July 5, 1879—A. Reg.).

General distribution: Cen. Tien Shan.

Note. In east. Tien Shan, we detected new variety *A. imetensis* var. *zagastaicus* Ulzij. var. nov. Standard 9.5 mm long, obovate. Leaflets 6–9 pairs, oblong-elliptical.

Typus: Junggar, Dzhagastai-gol, 2740 m, July 5, 1879—A. Regel. In Herb. Inst. Bot. Ac. Sci. Ross. (St.-Petersb.), conservatur.

Section 10 (11). **Melilotopsis** Gontsch.

37. **A. satoi** Kitag. in Bot. Mag. Tokyo 48 (1934) 99; id. Lin. fl. Mansh. (1939) 281; id. in J. Jap. Bot. 42 (1967) 101; Fl. pl. herb. Chinae bor.-or. 5 (1976) 92; H.C. Fu in Fl. Intramong. 3 (1977) 97 and 2 ed., 3 (1989) 263; Y.C. Ho in Bull. Bot. Lab. North-East. Forest. Inst. 8 (1980) 73.—*A. austriacus* auct. non L.: Kitag. in J. Jap. Bot. 27 (1952) 204.

—**Ic.:** Kitag. 1934, l.c. fig. 12; Fl. pl. herb. Chinae bor.-or. 5, tab. 40, fig. 8; H.C. Fu l.c. 1977, tab. 97, fig. 8 and 1989, fig. 101, fig. 8.

Described from East. Mongolia (Manchuria town). Type in Tokyo (TI).

In meadowy and sandy steppes.

IA. Mongolia: ***East. Mong.*** (Ulantsab, on mountain slopes, No. 256, July 24, 1974, Ma Yu-chuan' [HIMC]; "Khulunbuir-norsk ajmaq, Manchuria town"— Y.C. Ho l.c.; H.C. Fu l.c.).

General distribution: China (Dunbei, nor.-nor. part).

38. **A. capilipes** Fisch. ex Bunge Gen. Astrag. Sp. Geront. 2 (1869) 21; Franch. in Nouv. Arch. Mus. Paris, 5 (1883) 237; Forb. et Hemsl. in J. Linn. Soc. Bot. 23 (1887) 165; Nakai et al. in Rep. First Sci. Exped. Manch., sect. 4, 4 (1935) 26; Peter-Stib. in Acta Horti Gotoburg, 12 (1937–38) 30; Kitag. Lin. Fl. Mansh. (1939) 280 (sphalm. ut *A. capillaris* Fisch.); Gontsch. in Fl. SSSR, 12 (1946) 89 (in nota); Wang and Tang in Ill. treatm. princip. pl. China, Legum. (1955) 395; Ic. cormoph. Sin. 2 (1972) 421; Fl. pl. herb. Chinae bor.-or. 5 (1976) 92; H.C. Fu in Fl. Intramong. 3 (1977) 191 and ed. 2, 3 (1989) 260; Y.C. Ho in Bull. Bot. Lab. North-East. Forest Inst. 8, 8 (1980) 73; Liou fil. in Fl. desert. Sin. 2 (1987) 251.

—**Ic.:** Wang and Tang, l.c. fig. 385; Fl. pl. herb. Chinae bor.-or. tab. 40, fig. 7; Fu l.c. (1977), tab. 97, fig. 7 and ed. 2 (1989) tab. 101, fig. 1.

Described from Nor. China. Type in St.-Petersburg (LE).

In sandy steppes, along slopes of mountains and hillocks.

IA. Mongolia: ***East. Mong.*** ("Ulankhada-khoto, Huhehot"—H.C. Fu l.c.), ***East. Gobi*** (Mongolia chinensis in itium. ad Chinam, 1840—Fisch.), ***Alash. Gobi*** ("Bayan-nur; Denkou")—H.C. Fu l.c.; Liou fil. l.c.), ***Ordos*** (Huang He river, in Denkoushan' region, July 13, 1957, Chin. collector [LZDI]; "Ike-Chzhao"—H.C. Fu l.c.).

General distribution: China (North, North-West).

39. **A. melilotoides** Pall. Reise, 3, app. (1776) 748; ej. Sp. Astrag. (1800) 51; DC. Prodr. 2 (1825) 284; Ledeb. Fl. Alt. 3 (1831) 298; id. Fl. Ross. 1 (1842) 617; Turcz. Fl. baic.-dahur. in Bull. Soc. Natur. Moscou 15, 1 (1842) 768; Bunge Gen. Astrag. Sp. Geront. 2 (1869) 89; Kom. in Fl. Man'chzh. 2 (1904) 589; Simps. in Not. Bot. Gard. Edinb. 8 (1915) 256; Pavl. in Byull. Mosk. obshch. ispyt. prir., biol. 38, 1–2 (1929) 90; Kryl. Fl. Zap. Sib. 7 (1933) 1643; Peter-Stib. in Acta Horti Gotob. 12 (1937–38) 30; Kitag. Lin. Fl. Mansh. (1939) 280; Gontsch. and Boriss. in Fl. SSSR, 12 (1946) 89; Boriss. in Fl. Zabaik. 6 (1954) 578; Grub. Konsp. fl. MNR (1955) 185; Wang and Tang in Ill. treatm. princip. pl. China, Legum. (1955) 395; M. Pop. in Fl. Sr. Sib. 1 (1957) 332; F1. Krasnoyarsk. Kr. 6 (1960) 33; Ulzij. Opred. rast. okrestn. Ulan-Batora [Key to Plants in the Vicinity of Ulan Bator] (1972) 172; Fl. Tsentr. Sib. 2 (1979) 602; Ic. cormoph. Sin. 2 (1972) 421; Fl. Pl. herb. Chinae bor.-or. 5 (1976) 94; H.C. Fu in Fl. Intramong. 3 (1977) 194 and ed. 2, 3 (1989) 261; Y.C. Ho in Bull. Bot. Lab. North-East. Forest Inst. 8 (1980) 74; Sanczir in Grub. Opred. rast. Mong. [Key to Plants of Mongolia] (1982) 158; Ulzij. in Tr. Inst. bot. AN MNR, 8 (1982) 18; Opred. rast. Tuv. ASSR [Key to Plants of Tuva Autonomous Soviet Socialist Republic] (1984) 146; Ulzij. and Gub. in Byull. Mosk. Obshch. ispyt. prir., biol. 92, 5 (1987) 116; Pl. vasc. Helanshan (1986) 154; Liou fil. in Fl. Desert. Sin. 2 (1987) 251.—*Indigofera melilotoides* Hance in J. Bot. 7 (1969) 163.

—**Ic.:** Pall. 1800, l.c., tab. 41; Fl. SSSR, 12, Plate 6, fig. 2; Fl. Zabaik., Plate 6, fig. 296; Wang and Tang l.c. fig. 384; H.C. Fu l.c. 1977, tab. 97, fig. 1–6 and ed. 2, 1989, tab. 101, fig. 2–7.

Described from East. Siberia. Type in London (LINN). Plate 2, fig. 5.

In steppes and steppe meadows, steppe valleys of rivers and forest borders, rocky and rubbly slopes, sandy steppes and as weed on fallow lands and along irrigation ditches.

IA. Mongolia: ***Cen. Khalkha*** (Zorgol-Khairkhan-ula, nor. slope, 1770 m, July 5, 1974 —Golubkova, Tsogt, Tsetsegma), ***East. Mong.*** (Muni-ula mountains, July 6 1871—Przew.; Guikhua-chen [Khukh-khoto] town, Si-ustu-chizhao monastery, July 15, 1884—Pot.; steppe south of Buir-nor lake, June 20, 1899—Pot. and Sold.; midcourse of Kerulen river, gorge in Mergenkhamar mountains, 1899—Pal.; 20–25 km nor.-west of Beitszy-fu on way to Syaokhe-tszy station, Esty-tukhum, July 20, 1903—Rudnev; Outer Mongolia, No. 578, 1925—Chaney; Dariganga, vicinity of Ikhe-bulak, Aug. 20, 1927—Zam.; Kerulen river, 150 km before Tsetsenkhan, arid slopes, Aug. 12, 1928—Tug.; Ongon-els sand, near Khada-khuduk well, on road to Baishintu-Dariganga, slopes of sand ridges, Aug. 7, 1970 —Grub., Ulzij. et al.; Sukhe-Batorsk ajmaq, Asgatyn-tsagan-toogoi mountain 35 km south of Dariganga on trail of nor. slope, July 6, 1971—Dashnyam, Karam. et al.; "Shilin gol, Ulashan'"—H.C. Fu l.c.), ***Depr. Lakes*** (foothill of Dzhargalant-ula mountain range, 40 km nor.-east of Mankhan settlement, Aug. 24, 1984—Gub. [MW]), ***Val. Lakes*** (in arid bed in hills along right bank of Tatsyn-gol river, Sep. 16, 1924—Pavl.), ***Gobi Alt.*** (Shine-Dzhinst-ula mountains 5 km south of Shine-Dzhinst settlement, July 14, 1979—Gub. [MW]; Artsa Bogdo, No. 375, 1925—Chaney), ***East. Gobi*** (Baga-Ude, Urguni-ulan, July 15, 1926—Gus.; Baga-Ude, gully in Khara-ula mountain, Aug. 16, 1926—Lis.; Alkha-Khoshuny Gobi,

Aug. 13, 1927—Zam.; Argali mountain range and vicinity of Khodata-khuduk, Sep. 5, 1928—Shastin; Kalgansk route, road from Dolo-chelut ridges to Ude well, subdesert, Aug. 24, 1931—Pot.; Erdene somon, western extremity of Borokha-Tal area, desert steppe on loamy sand, June 17, 1941—Yun.; Tsagan-Obo knolls on Bayan-Munkh-khid plain, along floor of gorge, Aug. 6, 1970—Grub., Ulzij. et al.; mountains nor.-west. of Bayan-Obo somon, Aug. 9, 1971—Kerzhner; Galbyn Gobi, 55 km south-south-east of Khan-Bogdo somon, June 25, 1972—Rachk. and Guricheva; 50 km nor.-east of Khatan-Bulak somon along road to Khubsugul somon, granitic montane area, in gorge, July 27, 1974—Rachk., Isach.; 200 km south of Sain-Shanda town, foothill of Khutag-ula mountain range, July 10, 1982—Gub. [MW], "Ulan-tsab"—Y.C. Fu l.c.), ***Alash. Gobi*** (Alashan mountain range near Dyn-yuan'-in town, July 26, 1873; Alashan, Tengeri sand, July 27, 1880—Przew.; Tengeri sand, Shargin-dolon area, June 10, 1908—Czet.; in Ulan-tsab region around Shilut mountain, Bogdo-ulyn-kholai area, July 29, 1970—Grub., Ulzij. et al.; 90 km south of Nomgon settlement, 14 km nor. of Shuulin post, July 2, 1981—Gub. [MW]; 115 km south-south-east of Nomgon settlement, July 4, 1981—Gub. [MW]), ***Ordos*** (right bank of Huang He river before Khekhkou, on meadows in sand dunes—Pot.; Dzhasygen-Qaidam area, Aug. 30, 1884—Pot.; Khanginchi, outcrops of red sandstone on top of ridge 70 km south of town, Aug. 5; same locality, Ushinchi town, semiovergrown sand 15 km west of town, July 26; same locality, Khanginchi, sandy-pebbly plain on fringe of ridge 35 km south-east of town, Aug. 7; same locality Dzhasakachi town, sand 24 km nor. of town, Aug. 15, 1957, Petr.), ***Khesi*** (Inter Kansu et Tianschan et hinc ad fines rossicos, July 17, 1875—Piassezki).

General distribution: East. Sib. (Daur. seleng.), Nor. Mong. Hent. south., Hang., Mong.-Daur.), China (Dunbei, North, North-West: Shen'si; South-West: Sichuan nor.).

Note. Plants with transitional form closer to this species have been asterisked.

40. **A. tenuis** Turcz. in Bull. Soc. Natur. Moscou 15 (1842) 768; Pavl. in Byull. Mosk. Obshch. ispyt. prir., biol. 38, 1–2 (1929) 90; Gontsch. and Boriss. in Fl. SSSR, 12 (1946) 90; Boriss. in Fl. Zabaik. 6 (1954) 580; Grub. Konsp. fl. MNR (1955) 187; M. Pop. in Fl. Sr. Sib. 1 (1957) 332; Ulzij. in Opred. rast. okrestn. Ulan-Batora [Key to Plants in the Vicinity of Ulan Bator] (1972) 172; Fl. Tsentr. Sib. 2 (1979) 605; Sanczir in Grub. Opred. rast. Mong. [Key to Plants of Mongolia] (1982) 158 p.p.; Ulzij. in Tr. Inst. bot. AN MNR, 8 (1982) 18.—*A. melilotoides* var. *tenuis* Ledeb. Fl. Ross. 1 (1842) 618; Nakai et al., Rep. First. Sci. Exped. Manch. sect. 4, 4 (1935) 26; Kitag. Lin. Fl. Mansh. (1939) 280; Fl. pl. herb. Chinae bor.-or. 5 (1976) 94; H.C. Fu in Fl. Intramong. 3 (1977) 195 and ed. 2, 3 (1989) 261; Y.C. Ho in Bull. Bot. Lab. North-East. Forest Inst. 8, 8 (1980) 84.

—**Ic.:** Fl. pl. herb. Chinae bor.-or. 5 (1976) tab. 40, fig. 9; H.C. Fu l.c. 1977, tab. 97, fig. 9; Grub. Opred. rast. Mong. [Key to Plants of Mongolia] Plate 84, fig. 387.

Described from East. Siberia (Transbaikal). Type in St.-Petersburg (LE).

On steppe rubbly and rocky slopes, talus, coastal pebble beds and in sandy steppes.

IA. Mongolia: ***Cen. Khalkha*** (numerous localities), ***East. Mong.*** (numerous localities).

General distribution: East. Sib., Nor. Mong. (except Fore Hubs.), China (Dunbei).

Section 11 (12). **Polycladus** Y.C. Ho (=*Kuschakewiczia* R. Kam.)

41. **A. polycladus** Bur. et Franch. in J. de Bot. 5 (1891) 23; Forbes et Hemsl. in J. Linn. Soc. bot. 36 (1904) 459; Simps. in Not. Bot. Gard. Edinb. 8 (1915) 254; Peter-Stib. in Acta Horti Gotoburg, 12 (1937–38) 33; Wang and Tang in Ill. treatm. princip. pl. China, Legum. (1955) 403; Y.C. Ho in Bull. Bot. Research, 1, 3 (1981) 110. *A. polycladus*—var. *nigrescens* (Franch.) Peter-Stib. in Acta Horti Gotoburg, 12 (1937–38) 34.—*A. nigrescens* Franch. Pl. Delav. (1890) 162; Pall. 1800, nec Nutt. 1847, nec A. Gray 1863.—*A. decumbens* Kom. in Feddes Repert. 13 (1915) 230.—*A. tataricus* auct. non Franch.: Simps. in Not. Bot. Gard. Edinb. 8 (1915) 255.—*A. yunnanensis* Tsai et Yu in Bull. Fan Mem. Inst. Biol. Peiping, Bot. ser. 9 (1940) 267.

—**Ic.:** Wang and Tang l.c. fig. 396.

Described from South-West China (Sichuan). Type in Paris (P).

On slopes, in mountain valleys.

IA. Mongolia: ***Khesi*** ? (Gansu: No. 2184, 2245; Potanin 1885, sine num. (LE); Przewalsky 1872, sine num.—LE).

IIIA. Qinghai: ***Nanshan*** (Kukunor, Fenzel, No. 2305, 2352; Hao, No. 1210; Ba valley; Rock, No. 14233—Peter-Stib. l.c.; Y.C. Ho l.c.).

General distribution: China (North-West, South-West).

42. **A. zacharensis** Bunge, Gen. Astrag. Sp. Geront. 1 (1868) 23 and 2 (1869) 27.—*A. tataricus* Franch. Pl. David. 1 in Nouv. Arch. Mus. Paris, Ser. 2, 5 (1883) 239; Forbes et Hemsl. in J. Linn. Soc. Bot. 23 (1887) 167; Nakai et al. in Rep. First Sci. Exped. Manch. Sect. 4, 4 (1935) 27; Peter-Stib. in Acta Horti Gotoburg, 12 (1937–38); Kitag. Lin. Fl. Mansh. (1939) 281; Wang and Tang in Ill. treatm. princip. pl. China, Legum. (1955) 403; Fl. Pl. herb. Chinae bor.-or. 5 (1976) 91; H.C. Fu in Fl. Intramong. 3 (1977) 198 and ed. 2, 3 (1989) 265; Y.C. Ho in Bull. Bot. Research 1, 3 (1981) 109; Pl. vasc. Helanshan (1986) 154.—*A. brachycarpa* Turcz. in Bull. Soc. Natur. Moscou, 5 (1832) 185, non M. Bieb.—*A. hulunensis* P.Y. Fu et Y.A. Chen in Fl. Pl. pl. herb. Chinae bor.-or. 5 (1976) 175, 89.—*A. skvorzovii* Bar. et Chu in Liou f. et al. Claves pl. Chinae bor.-or. (1959) 178 (nom seminud.).—*A. alpinus* auct. non L.: Sanczir in Grub. Opred. rast. Mong. [Key to Plants of Mongolia] 159, p. min. p.; Ulzij. Opred. korm. rast. MNR [Key to Forage Plants of Mongolian People's Republic] 310, p. min. p.

—**Ic.:** Wang and Tang l.c. fig. 395; H.C. Fu l.c., 1977, tab. 100, fig. 1–8 and 1989, tab. 102, fig. 6–10; P.Y. Fu et Y.A. Chen l.c. 1976, tab. 39, fig. 1–8 (sub nom. *A. hulunensis*).

Described from China (East. Mong.). Type in St.-Petersburg (LE). Map 6.

On rocky and rubbly slopes of mountains and hillocks.

IA. Mongolia: ***East. Mong.*** (In locus subarenosis Mongoliae chinensis, pr. Zagan-Balgasu, 1831—Kusnezow, typus !—*A. brachycarpa* Turcz. non M. Bieb.; Mongolia chin. 1842—Kirilow; nor. of Shopin-fu, July 13, 1884—Pot.; Shilin-khoto town, true steppe, 1959—Ivanov, Dariganga somon, Shiliin-Bogdo mountain, nor. slope, mountain steppe, Aug. 11, 1970—Grub., Ulzij. et al.; same locality, No. 9808, 9808a, July 12, 1985—Gub. [MW]; "Shilingol, Datsin-shan'"]—H.C. Fu l.c.), ***Alash. Gobi*** (Alashan mountain range, Dartym-to area, south. slope, May 23, 1908, Czet.; nor. part of Gansu province, Govya-vonu-tan valley, in grasslands, July 17; same locality, along rocky arid river bed, July 17–1908, Czet.; on road to Dzin-dzin from Choëmpor village, April 22, 1909—Dimidenko).

IIIA. Qinghai: ***Nanshan*** (Mon'yuan', Tatungkhe river valley, near stud farm, 2800 m, nor.-east. slope of knoll, steppe, Aug. 20, 1958—Dolgushin; 33 km west of Xining, rocky slopes of knolls, montane steppe, 2450 m, Aug. 5, 1959—Petr.).

General distribution: China (North: Hebei, Shansi).

43. **A. mongutensis** Lipsky in Acta Horti Petrop. 26 (1910) 143; Boriss. in Fl. SSSR, 12 (1946) 45; Opred. rast. Sr. Azii [Key to Plants of Mid. Asia] 6 (1981) 95; Y.C. Ho in Bull. Bot. Research 1, 3 (1981) 114; C.Y. Yang in Claves pl. Xinjiang 3 (1981) 129.

Described from Sinkiang (Tien Shan). Type in St.-Petersburg (LE).

In shrubs, gorges and along montane slopes, on rocks and grasslands in high mountains.

IIA. Junggar: ***Tien Shan*** (Kul'dzha, Mëngëto, 3050–3350 m, July 4, 1879—A. Reg., typus !; "Mëngëto"—Y.C. Ho l.c.; "south. foothills of Tien Shan"—C.Y. Yang l.c.).

General distribution: Cen. Tien Shan.

Note. The closest occurrence of this species has been reported from Kukurtuk valley (Tien Shan) in Kirghiz, its distribution being highly localised.

44. **A. kuschakewiczii** B. Fedtsch. ex O. Fedtsch. in Acta Horti Petrop. 21, 3 (1903) 310, Fl. Pamir (1903) 78; Lipsky in Acta Horti Petrop. 26 (1907) 227; O. et B. Fedtsch. Konsp. fl. Turk. 2 (1909) 199; Rast. Turk. [Vegetation of Turkestan] (1915) 518; Boriss. in Fl. Tadzhik. 5 (1937) 283; idem in Fl. SSSR 12 (1946) 46; Fl. Kirgiz. 7 (1957) 225; Fl. Kazakhst. 5 (1961) 101; Ikonn. Opred. rast. Pam. [Key to Plants of Pamir] (1963) 167; Podlech et Anders. in Mitt. Bot. Staatssamml. München, 13 (1977) 440; Bait. Astrag. Tyan'-Shanya (1977) 37; Opred. rast. Sr. Azii [Key to Plants of Mid. Asia] 6 (1981) 95; Fl. Tadzhik. 6 (1981) 58; Y.C. Yang in Claves pl. Xinjiang, 3 (1985) 127.—*A. eugenia* B. Fedtsch. in Not. syst. (Leningrad) 8, 10–12 (1940) 166.—*A. pulvinalis* P.C. Li et Ni in Acta Phytotax. Sin. 17 (1979) 110; id. in Fl. Xizang, 2 (1985) 838.

—**Ic.:** Fl. SSSR, 12, Plate 4, fig. 1; Fl. Kazakhst. 5, Plate 12, fig. 3; Fl. Tadzhik. 6 (1981) Plate 5, fig. 7–11; Fl. Xizang, 2, tab. 275, fig. 1–7.

Described from Pamir. Type in St.-Petersburg (LE).

On rocky slopes, along sandy river banks, pebble beds, moraines, sedge meadows and more rarely on sandy-pebbly detritus in middle and upper mountain belts.

IB. Kashgar: ***East.*** (in Machangou, Turfan, on shaded slope of rocky mountain, 2100 m, No. 5628, June 15; along road from Sansanko to Shipaotszy, Turfan, on shaded slope, steppe, 2400 m, No. 5661, June 16; Kalangou, on summit, 2650 m, No. 5836, June 24—1958, A.R. Lee (1958)).

IIA. Junggar: ***Tien Shan*** (Sudliches Kuikonik Tal, beim Lager under Tschon-Yailak Pass, June 15, 1908—Merzb.; upper Hanga river, 7–8 km before Kotyl' pass on road to Yuldus from Karashar, 2900 m, Aug. 1; Kotyl' pass on road to Yuldus basin from Karashar, 3100 m, Aug. 15, 1958, Yun. and I-f. Yuan'; Malyi Yuldus, Ulastai, 2500 m, No. 6318, Aug. 2, 1958—A.R. Lee (1958), "West. Part of Chinese Tien Shan"—C.Y. Yang l.c.).

IIIA. Qinghai: ***Nanshan*** (24 km from Aksai settlement along road to Qaidam, pass through Altyntag mountain range 3460 m, Aug. 2, 1958—Petr.).

IIIB. Tibet: ***Chang Tang*** (nor. slope of Russky mountain range, upper Aksu river, 3658 m, on pebble bed on brooks, July 1; Przewalsky mountain range, nor. slope, 4267–4572 m, on rocks and meadows, Aug. 24, 1890, Rob. ("Ban'ge"—P.C. Li et Ni l.c.), ***South.*** ("Lankatsza; Pulan'"—P.C. Li et Ni l.c.).

IIIC. Pamir (Kun'-Lun', Tynnen-davan pass, 4000–4200 m, June 26; same locality, upper Lanet river, on maraine, July 20; same locality, Goo-dzhiro river, 4500–5500 m, July 27; Pakhtu river gorge, 2700 m, Aug. 2, 1942, Serp.; upper Tiznaf river 15 km beyond Kyude settlement on Tibetan highway to Seryk-daban, short-grass meadow, June 1; upper course of Raskem- [Yarkend]-Darya, 20 km beyond Mazar along road to Kyrgyz daban, on pebble beds, 3950 m, June 1, 1959, Yun. and I-f. Yuan'—C.Y. Yang l.c.).

General distribution: Nor. and Cen. Tien Shan, East. Pamir; China (South-West), Himalayas, Afghanistan.

Note. Transitional forms closer to *A. mongutensis* Lipsky are seen among East. Tien Shan plants.

45. **A. confertus** Benth. ex Bunge Gen. Astrage. Sp. Geront. 1 (1868) 23 and 2 (1869) 27; Baker in Hook. f. Fl. Brit. Ind. 2 (1876) 123; Peter-Stib. in Acta Horti Gotoburg, 12 (1937–38) 33; Wang and Tang in Ill. treatm. princip. pl. China, Legum. (1955) 379; Ali in Nasir. Fl. West. Pakistan, No. 100 (Papilionac.) (1977) 160; Y.C. Ho in Bull. Bot. Research, 1, 3 (1981) 109; P.C. Li et Ni in Fl. Xizang, 2 (1985) 838; Ulzij. and Gub. in Byull. Mosk. obshch. ispyt. prir., otd. biol. 92, 5 (1987) 112.

—**Ic.:** Fl. Xizang, 2, tab. 277, fig. 8–15.

Described from Himalayas. Type in Paris (P).

On rubbly-rocky slopes of mountains and alpine meadows, along gorges and river banks.

IA. Mongolia: ***Mong. Alt.*** (beyond Tashenta pass on mountain slope, around Dandzhur-nor lake, July 1, 1898—Klem.; 60 km south of Tonkhil settlement near Tamchi daba pass, July 9, 1984—Gub.), ***Alash. Gobi*** (Alashan mountain range, No. 177, June 20–July 10, 1873, Przew.).

IIIA. Qinghai: ***Nanshan*** (Tangut, 1872; Nanshan, alpine meadow, June 15–30, 1879; Yusun-Khatyma river, 2743–3048 m, July 23, 1880—Przew.), ***Amdo*** (upper Huange He river, 2440–2745 m, May 31; same locality, Kha-Gomi area, farm, June 9, 1880, Przew.; "Shalakutu, Kukunor, Hao, No. 871"—Peter-Stib. l.c.).

IIIB. Tibet: ***Chang Tang*** ("West Tibet"—Peter-Stib. l.c.); ***Weitzan*** (descent from waterdivide between Huang He river and Murusu, June 11; camp on left bank of Dy-chyu river or Mur-usu in Goluboi river basin, 3962 m, June 23, 1884, Przew.; Burkhan-Budda mountain range, nor. slope, Khatu gorge, 3200 m, June 15, 1901—Lad.), ***South.*** (Karo-La pass, 16,500 ft (5029 m), July 1904, H.J. Walton; Kariakde, 4021 m, Aug. 12, 1892—Deutreil de Rhins; Pulan', 3900 m, No. 8407, July 12, 1976, Chin. collector [PE].

General distribution: Himalayas.

Note. A more critical identification of specimens collected in Mong. Altay based on sufficient material is required.

46. **A. saxorum** N.D. Simps. in Not. Bot. Gard. Edinb. 8 (1915) 245; Peter-Stib. in Acta Horti Gotoburg, 12 (1937–38) 36; Y.C. Ho in Bull. Bot. Research, 1, 3 (1981) 114; P.C. Li et Ni in Fl. Xizang, 2 (1985) 838. —**Ic.:** Fl. Xizang, 2, tab. 276, fig. 8–14.

Described from South-West China (Sichuan). Type in Edinburgh (E).

In alpine bows and moraines, along gorges, at 2500–3700 m.

IIIA. Qinghai: *Nanshan* (Nanshan mountain range, alpine region, 3353 m, July 11; same locality, camp on Kuku-usu river, 3353 m, July 16; same locality, camp on Machan-ula mountains, July 26; same locality, No. 360, July 30, 1879, Przew.).

IIIB. Tibet: *Chang Tang* (nor. slope of Russky mountain range, Aksu river, on meadows along gorges, 3350–3658 m, June 2, 1890, Rob.; Keri mountain range, up along Kurab river, 5 versts (1 verst = 1.067 km) and along Araldyk river, 6 versts, 3048 m, July 6; same locality, alpine region, up to Kyuk-egil' river, 6 versts, July 11, 1885, Przew.).

General distribution: China (South-West: Sichuan, Yunnan).

Section 12 (13). **Komaroviella** Gontsch.

47. **A. changaicus** Sancz. ex Ulzij. in Fl. Changai (1989) 121; Sanczir, 1982, in Grub. Opred. rast. Mong. [Key to Plants of Mongolia] (1982) 159, nom subnud., descr. ross. in Clave; Grub. in Novosti sist. vyssh. rast 21 (1984) 206.

Described from Nor. Mongolia (Hangay). Type in Ulan Bator (UBA).

In sedge-*Cobrersia* meadows in alpine belt and borders of larch forests.

IA. Mongolia: *Mong. Alt.* (valley of Nariin-gol river, upper and watershed levels, July 14, 1984—Kam. and Dariima [UBA, LE].

General distribution: Nor. Mong. (Hang.).

48. **A. alpinus** L. Sp. pl. 2 (1753) 760; Turcz. in Bull. Soc. Natur. Moscou, 15 (1842) 761; Ledeb. Fl. Ross. 1 (1843) 601; Bunge Gen. Astrag. Sp. Geront. 1 (1868) 39 and 2 (1869) 26; ej. Astrag. Turk. (1880) 216; id. in Acta Horti Petrop. 7 (1880) 369; Baker in Hook. f. Fl. Brit. Ind. 2 (1876) 123; Lipsky in Acta Horti Petrop. 26 (1907) 217; O. et B. Fedtsch. Konsp. fl. Turk. 2 (1909) 200; Miura, Fl. Manch. and East. Mong. 2 (1926) 131; Kryl. Fl. Zap. Sib. 7 (1933) 1653; Boriss. in Fl. Tadzhik. 5 (1937) 288; Gontsch. and Boriss. in Fl. SSSR, 12 (1946) 43; Grub. Konsp. fl. MNR (1955) 182; Fl. Kirgiz. 7 (1957) 222; Fl. Kazakhst. 5 (1961) 100; Fl. pl. herb. Chinae bor.-or. 5 (1976) 91; Fl. Intramong. 3 (1977) and ed. 2, 3 (1989) 268; Y.C. Ho in Bull. Bot. Research, 1, 3 (1981) 116; Fl.

Tadzhik. 6 (1981) 56; Opred. rast. Sr. Azii [Key to Plants of Mid. Asia] (1981) 94; C.Y. Yang in Claves pl. Xinjiang, 3 (1985) 127.—*A. alpinus* var. *altaicus* Ledeb. Fl. Ross. 1, 3 (1843) 601.—*A. alpinus* var. *glacialis* Bunge in Bull. Soc. Natur. Moscou, 39, 2 (1868) 18.—*A. ferganicus* Freyn in Bull. Herb. Boiss. 2, ser. 4 (1904) 453.—*A. olginensis* Freyn l.c. 454.—*A. danicus* auct. non Retz.: Liou et al., Claves Pl. bor.-or. (1959) 180.—*Phaca astragalina* DC. Astrag. (1802) 64.

—**Ic.:** Fl. SSSR, 12, Plate 3, fig. 1; Fl. Kazakhst. 5, Plate 12, fig. 2; Fl. Tadzhik. 6 (1981), Plate 5, fig. 1–6; Fl. pl. herb. Chinae bor.-or. 5 (1976), tab. 39, fig. 9–17; Fl. Intramong. 3 (1989), tab. 103, fig. 1–6.

Described from Switzerland. Type in London (LINN).

In alpine and subalpine meadows, montane tundra, pine forests and along their borders, along banks of rivers in middle and upper mountain belts.

IIA. Junggar: *Cis-Alt.* ("Altay"—C.Y. Yang l.c.), ***Tarb.*** (33 km north-east of Khobsair, on montane slope, 1750–1800 m, No. 10485, June 23, 1959—A.R. Lee), ***Tien Shan*** (nor. slope of East. Tien shan, Tumyrtyin-gol, Aug. 24, 1895—Rob.; in Savan area, Datszymyao, on meadow, No. 1283, July 8; Tesitai town, Magolyan village, in steppe, No. 4436, Sep. 22, 1957, Kuan; left bank of Manas basin, valley of Ulan-usu river, 1 km before confluence of Koi-su, spruce forest, July 17, 1957—Yun., I-f. Yuan'; "Tien Shan"—C.Y. Yang l.c.).

General distribution: Jung.-Tarb., Cen. and Nor. Tien Shan, East. Pamir; Arct. (Asian: Anad.), Europe (West., Cen.), Caucasus, Mid. Asia (Pamiro-Alay), West, Sib. (Altay), East. Sib. (Sayans, Daur.), Far east (Kamch., Okhot.), Nor. Mong. (Fore Hubs.), Nor. Amer.

49. **A. abramovii** Gontsch. in Not. Syst. (Leningrad) 9, 4–12 (1946) 113; Gontsch. in Fl. SSSR, 12 (1946) 869; Opred. rast. Sr. Azii [Key to Plants of Mid. Asia] 6 (1981) 94; Bait. Astrag. Tyan'-Shanya (1977) 41; Fl. Tadzhik. 6 (1981) 59.—*A. pseudobrachytropis* Gontsch. in Not. Syst. (Leningrad) 10 (1947) 31; Gontsch. in Fl. SSSR, 12 (1946) 49, Fl. Kirgiz. 7 (1957) 225; Fl. Kazakhst. 5 (1961) 102; Ikonn. Opred. rast. Pam. [Key to Plants of Pamir] (1963) 168; Podlech et Anders. in Mitt. Bot. Staatssamml. München, 13 (1977) 442; C.Y. Yang in Claves pl. Xinjiang, 3 (1985) 126.—*A. brachytropis* auct. non C.A. Mey.: Bunge Gen. Astrag. Sp. Geront. 2 (1869) 26, quoad pl. e Fl. Asia Med.; O. et B. Fedtsch. Konsp. fl. Turk. 2 (1909) 206; Boriss. in Fl. Tadzhik. 5 (1937) 288.—*A. densiflorus* auct. non Kar. et Kir.: P.C. Li et Ni in Fl. Xizang, 2 (1985) 825, p.p.

—**Ic.:** Fl. Kazakhst. 5, Plate 12, fig. 4; Fl. Tadzhik. 6 (1981), Plate 5, fig. 12–17.

Described from Kirgizia (Kirgiz Ala Tau, Tien Shan). Type in St.-Petersburg (LE).

On rocky slopes, alpine meadows, moraines, river banks and pebble beds in middle and upper mountain belts.

IA. Mongolia: ***Khobd.*** (Ulan-daban, in forest, shaded portion of gorge, June 23, 1879— Pot.).

IB. Kashgar: *Nor.* (declivitas australis jugi montium Tianschan, Kum-Aryk, hinten am Steilufer des Flüsses, No. 408, mitte June; Mittleres Dschanart Tal, June 14–17, 1903, Merzb.), *West.* (Sarykol' mountain range, Bostan-Terek locality, July 10, 1929—Pop.).

IIA. Junggar: *Jung. Ala Tau* (Borotala, 2591 m, Aug. 1878—A. Reg.), *Tien Shan* (Urtak-sary, south of Borotal, July 20, 1878—Fet.; Dumbedan-Kemdaban, 2743 m, May 28; Kumdaban in Irenkhabyrga hills, May 29; Junggar-daban nor. of Borborogussun, June 13, 1878; Kumbel', 3048 m, June 3; Bagadusling-Bainamun, tributary of Dzhin river, 2100–2700 m, June 4—1879, A. Reg.; Koshetyn-daban pass through Tien Shan, June 5, 1879— Przew.; south. slope of Tien Shan, Ui-tal river gorge, montane slope, 2743 m, May 31, 1889; Sary-shora pass, Konsai river, 2438 m, in meadow, June 22, 1893—Rob.; Passe zwischen ken-su und Kurdai, July 3; Plateau eines Bergesim oberen Koksu Gebiet, ca 3400 m, July 8–10; Musstamass Tal, imsudlichen, Seitental Aksai, Mitte July—1907, Merzb.; 7–8 km south of Danu, 3950 m, No. 490, July 22, 1957—Shen-Tyan'), Ulastai, Malyi Yuldus, in floodplain of valley, 2500 m, No. 6321, Aug. 2, 1958—A.R. Lee.

IIIA. Qinghai: *Nanshan* (pass through saddle in Sininskoi river basin and road to Ara-Khaldzyn river, July 19; up to Yusun-Khatyma river, 2743–3048 m, July 23; around pass through South Tetung mountain range, July 31—1880, Przew.; Xining Alps, Lyanzha-syan' pass, June 20 and 23—1890, Gr.-Grzh.), *Amdo* (Mudzhik mountain, 2896–3353 m, June 18; downward along Mudzhik-khe river, return to Guidui, 3353 m, June 28 —1880, Przew.).

IIIB. Tibet: *Chang Tang* ("Kunlun"—C.Y. Yang l.c.), *Weitzan* (downward along Chyum-ch-uma river, alp., July 4; downward along By-dzhun and upward along Talachyu rivers, July 6—1884, Przew.; Russkoe and Ekspeditsii lakes, among willow thickets, in a fault of mountain vent separating Russkoe and Ekspeditsii lakes, 4115 m, June 28—1900, Lad.).

IIIC. Pamir (under Ucha pass, on meadow and slopes, June 18; Ulug-tuz gorge, on right side, Charlym river, around juniper bushes, June 27—1909, Divn.; Kunlun, Karadzhilga river, alp. pasture, 4000–4500 m, July 22, 1942—Serp.).

General distribution: Nor. and Cen. Tien Shan, East. Pamir; Mid. Asia (Pamiro-Alay), Afghanistan.

Note. The plant from Ulug-tuz gorge (Charlym river) differs distinctly from type specimens in long teeth of calyx.

Section 13 (14). **Orobella** Gontsch.

50. **A. luxurians** Bunge Gen. Astrag. Sp. Geront. 1 (1868) 23 and 2 (1869) 25; Kryl. Fl. Alt. (1903) 297; idem, Fl. Zap. Sib. 7 (1933) 1651; Gontsch. and Boriss. in Fl. SSSR, 12 (1946) 51; Grub. in Bot. zh. 61, 12 (1976) 1753; Sanczir in Grub. Opred. rast. Mong. [Key to Plants of Mongolia] (1982) 159; Ulzij. in Tr. inst. bot. AN MNR 8 (1982) 23.

Described from Altay (Chuya river). Type in Paris (P).

In larch forests, along banks of hill rivers.

IA. Mongolia: *Mong. Alt.* (left tributary of Ulyastain-gol river, June 28, 1973—Golubkova and Tsogt; Ulyastain-gol river gorge in Bulgan-gol river basin, left bank tributary in upper courses, July 10, 1984, Kam. and Dariima*).

General distribution: West. Sib. (Alt. east: Chuya river).

Note. Plant belonging to new variety *A. luxurians* var. *uliastaicus* Ulzij. var. nov. has been asterisked.

51. **A. politovii** Kryl. in Animadv. Syst. ex Herb. Univ. Tomsk. 3 (1932) 3; Kryl. Fl. Zap. Sib. 7 (1933) 1652; Gontsch. and Boriss. in Fl. SSSR, 12 (1946) 50.

—**Ic.:** Kryl. l.c., p. 7.

Described from Altay (Tabyn-Bogdo-ula mountain range). Type in Tomsk (TK).

On gently-inclined southern rocky slopes of upper part of mountains and in sparse larch forests.

IA. Mongolia: ***Mong. Alt.*** (upper Buyantu river, Chigirtei-gol river 12 km beyond lake, nor. slope of Chigirtei-ul hill, 2600–2800 m, larch forest along creek valley with neve basin brook, July 4; upper Kobdo river, Dayan-nur lake, south. extremity of settlement, nor. slope of Yamatyn-ul town, 2350–2500 m, larch forest, July 9–1971, Grub., Ulzij. and Dariima).

General distribution: West. Sib. (Altay south-east).

Section 14 (15). **Chrysopteris** Y.C. Ho

52. **A. chrysopteris** Bunge in Mel. Biol. 10 (1877) 51; Forbes et Hemsl. in J. Linn. Soc. 23 (1887) 165; Simps. in Not. Bot. Gard. Edinb. 8 (1915) 255; Peter-Stib. in Acta Horti Gotoburg, 12 (1937–38) 39; Wang and Tang in Ill. treatm. princip. pl. China, Legum. (1955) 399; Y.C. Ho in Bull. Bot. Lab. North-East. Forest Inst. 8 (1955) 56.—*A. chrysopteris* Bunge var. *wutaicum* Hand.-Mazz. in Osterr. Bot. Zeitschr. 82 (1933) 248.

—**Ic.:** Wang and Tang l.c., fig. 390.

Described from Qinghai. Type in St.-Petersburg (LE). Plate III, fig. 2. Map 7.

IIIA. Qinghai: ***Nanshan*** (Tangut, 1872; same locality, No. 164, June 1–15, 1873; 70 km south-east of Chzhan'e town, Matisy temple, Tsilyanshan' mountains, spruce forest with undergrowth on nor. slope of mountain range, 2000 m, July 12, 1958—Petr.), ***Amdo*** (downward along Mudzhik-khe river, return to Guidui, in forest, 2743 m, No. 396, June 28, 1880—Przew.).

General distribution: China (North-West: Gansu nor.).

Section 15 (16). **Hemiphragmium** Koch

53. **A. vaginatus** Pall. Astrag. (1800) 46; Bunge Gen. Astrag. Sp. Geront. 1 (1868) 22 and 2 (1869) 23; Kryl. Fl. Zap. Sib. 7 (1933) 1648; Gontsch. in Fl. SSSR, 12 (1946) 65; Boriss. in Fl. Zabaikal. 6 (1954) 582 p.p.; M. Pop., Fl. Sr. Sib. 7 (1957) 330; Fl. Kazakhst. 5 (1961) 104; Opred rast. Tuv. ASSR [Key to Plants of Tuva Autonomous Soviet Socialist Republic] (1984) 147.—*A. semibilocularis* DC. Astrag. (1802) 136.—*A. phacoformis* Bunge Enum. Alt. (1835) 69.—*A. australis* auct. non L. C.Y. Yang in Claves pl. Xinjiang, 3 (1985) 127.—*Phaca australis* Ledeb. Fl. Alt. 3 (1831) 270.—*P. australis* L. α *altaica* Fisch. in DC. Prodr. 2 (1825) 274.

Described from East. Sib. (Yenisei basin). Type in London (BM).

In hill meadows.

IIA. Junggar: ***Cis-Alt.*** ("Altay"—C.Y. Yang l.c.), ***Tarb.*** (Saur mountain range, southern slope, Karagaitu river valley, Bain-Tsagan creek valley, subalpine meadow, June 23, 1957—Yun. and I-f. Yuan').

General distribution: West. Sib. (Altay, south).

*__A. sarchanensis__ Gontsch. in Not. Syst. (Leningrad) 10 (1947) 31; idem in Fl. SSSR, 12 (1946) 70, descr. ross.; Fl. Kazakhst. 5 (1961) 107; Bait. Astrag. Tyan'-Shanya (1977) 39; Opred. rast. Sr. Azii [Key to Plants of Mid. Asia] 6 (1981) 92.

—**Ic.:** Fl. Kazakhst. 5, Plate 13, fig. 2.

Described from East. Kazakhstan (Jung. Ala Tau). Type in St.-Petersburg (LE).

On rocks and rocky slopes of alpine and subalpine belts.

Reports possible from Sinkiang part of Jung. Ala Tau.

General distribution: Jung.-Tarb. (Jung. Ala Tau).

54. **A. beketovii** (Krassn.) B. Fedtsch. in Bull. Herb. Boiss. 2 ser., 5, 4 (1905) 316; Lipsky in Acta Horti Petrop. 26 (1907) 225; O. et B. Fedtsch. Konsp. fl. Turk. 2 (1909) 201; Boriss. in Fl. Tadzhik. 5 (1937) 289; Gontsch. and Boriss. in Fl. SSSR, 12 (1946) 72; Fl. Kirgiz. 7 (1957) 277; Fl. Kazakhst. 5 (1961) 108; Ikonn. Opred. rast. Pam. [Key to Plants of Pamir] (1963) 168; Y.C. Ho in Bull. Bot. Lab. North-East. Forest. Inst. 8 (1980) 56; Fl. Tadzhik. 6 (1981) 70; Opred. rast. Sr. Azii [Key to Plants of Mid. Asia] 6 (1981) 92; C.Y. Yang in Claves pl. Xinjiang, 3 (1985) 127. —*A. polychromis* Freyn, Bull. Herb. Boiss. 2, ser. 4, 5 (1904) 454.—*Oxytropis beketovii* Krassm. Spisok rast. Vost. Tyan'-Shanya [List of Plants of East. Tien Shan] (1887) 42; Script. Horti Univ. Petrop. 1 (1889) 15.

—**Ic.:** Fl. Kazakhst. 5, Plate 13, fig. 3; Fl. Tadzhik. 6 (1981), Plate 8, fig. 1–7.

Described from Kirghiz (Cen. Tien Shan). Type in St.-Petersburg (LE).

On rocky and rubbly slopes, pebble beds, talus and grasslands, along gorges, in alpine belt.

IA. Mongolia: ***Khobd.*** (Ulan-daban pass, nor. slope, gorge floor, June 23; same locality, in forest on shaded side of gorge, June 23–1879, Pot.).

IB. Kashgar: ***Nor.*** (Uchturfan, Karagailik gorge, June 18, 1908—Divn.), ***West.*** ?

IIA. Junggar: ***Tien Shan*** (between Danyu and Daban, No. 1988, July 19, 1957—Kuan; for 6–7 km south from Danyu, on east. slope, No. 476, July 22, 1957—Shen-Tyan;"Tien Shan"—C.Y. Yang l.c.).

IIIC. Pamir ("Kunlun"—C.Y. Yang l.c.).

General distribution: Cen. Tien Shan, East. Pamir.

55. **A. tschuensis** Bunge Gen. Astrag. Sp. Geront. 1 (1868) 22 and 2 (1869) 24; Kryl. Fl. Alt. (1909) 295 ("tschujensis"); Pavl. in Byull. Moskyu obshch. ispyt. prir., otd. biol. 38, 1–2 (1929) 90; Kryl. Fl. Zap. Sib. 7 (1933) 1651; Gontsch. in Fl. SSSR, 12 (1946) 71; Grub. Konsp. fl. MNR (1955) 187; Opred. rast. Sr. Azii [Key to Plants of Mid. Asia] 6 (1981) 92; Sanczir in Grub. Opred. rast. Mong. [Key to Plants of Mongolia] (1982) 158; Ulzij. in Tr. Inst. bot. AN MNR, 8 (1982) 19; Grub. in Novosti sist. vyssh. rast. 21 (1984) 214.

Described from Altay (Chuya belki—snow-covered, flattened mountain summits in Siberia). Type in St.-Petersburg (LE).

On arid rubbly and meadow slopes of hills.

IA. Mongolia: ***Mong. Alt.*** (Uirtyn-Khuren-ula mountains 20 km nor.-east of Bugat somon and 5 km from pass, 2543 m, July 7, 1984—Kam., Dariima; "Oiguryn-gol"— Grub. 1955, l.c.).

General distribution: West. Sib. (Altay, south).

Section 16 (17). **Hemiphaca** Bunge

56. **A. laceratus** Lipsky in Acta Horti Petrop. 26 (1910) 144; Gontsch. in Fl. SSSR, 12 (1946) 85; Fl. Kirgiz. 7 (1957) 236; Fl. Kazakhst. 5 (1961) 113; Bait. Astrag. Tyan'-Shanya (1977) 42; Opred. rast. Sr. Azii [Key to Plants of Mid. Asia] 6 (1981) 94; Y.C. Ho in Bull. Bot. Lab. North-East. Forest Inst. 8 (1980) 71; C.Y. Yang in Claves pl. Xinjiang, 3 (1985) 128.

—**Ic.:** Fl. Kazakhst. 5, Plate 14, fig. 3.

Described from Sinkiang (East. Tien Shan). Type in St.-Petersburg (LE).

On meadow slopes, in spruce forests and juniper groves, on rocky slopes and pebble beds, in midbelt of mountains.

IIA. Junggar: ***Tien Shan*** (Karagol am Passe ad Nilki 10,000 ft, July 5; Mengute, 9000 ft, June 20–1879, A. Reg. typus !; "Inin"—C.Y. Yang l.c.).

General distribution: Nor. and Cen. Tien Shan.

***A. hemiphaca** Kar. et Kir. in Bull. Soc. Natur Moscou, 15 (1842) 328; Bunge Gen. Astrag. Sp. Geront. 1 (1868) 21 and 2 (1869) 23; id. in Izv. Obshch. lyub. estestv., antr. i etnogr. 26, 2 (1880) 215; O. et B. Fedtsch. Konsp. fl. Turk. 2 (1909) 200; Boriss. and Gontsch. in Fl. SSSR, 12 (1946) 84; Fl. Kirgiz. 7 (1957) 235; Fl. Kazakhst. 5 (1961) 112; Bait. Astrag. Tyan'-Shanya (1977) 41; Opred. rast. Sr. Azii [Key to Plants of Mid. Asia] 6 (1981) 93.—*A. tauczilikensis* Golosk. in Fl. SSSR, 12 (1946) 882, 869, Fl. Kirgiz. 7 (1957) 236; Fl. Kazakhst. 5 (1961) 112.

—**Ic.:** Fl. SSSR, 12 (1946), Plate 6, fig. 1; Fl. Kazakhst. 5, Plate 12, fig. 2.

Described from East. Kazakhstan (Jung. Ala Tau). Type in Moscow (MW). Isotype in St.-Petersburg (LE).

In meadows, forest borders, among shrubs, in middle and upper belts of mountains.

Jung. Ala Tau, Tien Shan—common in these territories outside People's Republic of China.

General distribution: endemic.

57. **A. alaschanus** Bunge ex Maxim. in Mel. Biol. 10 (1877) 50; id. in Bull. Ac. Sci. St.-Petersb. 24 (1878) 31; Peter-Stib. in Acta Horti Gotoburg, 12 (1937–38) 32; Wang and Tang in Ill. treatm. princip. pl. China. Legum. (1955) 379; Y.C. Ho in Bull. Bot. Lab. North-East. Forest Inst. 8 (1980) 70; Pl. vasc. Helanshan (1986) 152; Fl. desert. Sin. 2 (1987) 253.—*A. chingianus* Peter-Stib. in Acta Horti Gotoburg, 12 (1937–38) 36; Wang and Tang in Ill. treatm. princip. pl. China, Legum. (1955) 377; Fl. Intramong. 3 (1977) 191 and 3 (1989) 260.

—**Ic.:** Pl. vasc. Helanshan (1986), tab. 26, fig. 1–8; Fl. desert Sin. 2 (1987), tab. 88, fig. 16–19; Fl. Intramong. 3 (1989), tab. 99, fig. 8–12.

Described from Inner Mongolia (Alashan mountain range). Type in St.-Petersburg (LE). Map 8.

On steppe rocky and rubbly slopes of mountains.

IA. Mongolia: ***Gobi Alt.*** (Dundu-Saikhan mountains, upper belt, south. slope, July 6, 1909—Czet.; same locality, on rubbly slopes of hills in upper zone, Aug. 19, 1931—Ik.-Gal.), ***Alash. Gobi*** (Alashan mountain range, No. 135, June 20–July 10, 1873—Przew. typus !; Alashan, 5570 ft, July 20, 1892—Deutreil de Rhins; Alashan mountain range, Yamata gorge, nor.-east. slope, midbelt, in forest, June 13, 1908—Czet.; "No. 1048—Ching"—Peter-Stib. l.c.); Ordos ("Ordos, No. 5476—Licent, non vidi"—Peter-Stib. l.c.).

IIIA. Qinghai: ***Nanshan*** ("Kukunor, No. 2338 p. min. p., No. 2357—Fenzel"—Peter-Stib. l.c.).

General distribution: endemic.

***A. aurantiacus** Hand.-Mazz. Symb. Sin. 7 (1933) 557; Peter-Stib. in Acta Horti Gotoburg, 12 (1937–38) 31; Wang and Tang in Ill. treatm. princip. pl. China, Legum. (1955) 376 (in Clave).—*A. dependens* Bunge var. *aurantiacus* (Hand.-Mazz.) Y.C. Ho in Bull. Bot. Lab. North-East. Forest Inst. 8 (1980) 71.

Described from South-West China. Type in Vienna (W).

IA. Mongolia: ? ***Khesi*** ("Licent No. 4111, 4254"—Peter-Stib. l.c.).

General distribution: China (South-West: Sichuan).

58. **A. dependens** Bunge in Bull. Ac. Sci. St.-Petersb. 26 (1880) 471; id. in Mel. Biol. 10 (1880) 640; Forbes and Hemsl. in J. Linn. Soc. Bot. 23 (Index Fl. Sin. 1) (1887) 165; Simps. in Not. Bot. Gard. Edinb. 8 (1915) 262; Peter-Stib. in Acta Horti Gotoburg, 12 (1937–38) 31; Wang and Tang in Ill. treatm. princip. pl. China, Legum. (1955) 378 (in clave); Y.C. Ho in Bull. Bot. Lab. North-East. Forest Inst. 8 (1980) 70.

Described from North-West China (West. Gansu). Type in St.-Petersburg (LE).

IIIA. Qinghai: ? *Nanshan* or *Khesi* (Nor. Gansu) Kansu; 2250 m, No. 5596, Aug. 4, 1959, Chin. collector [PE]; "Kansu bor.—Licent, 3911, 5898"—Peter-Stib. l.c. ("Kokonor" —Y.C. Ho l.c.).

General distribution: endemic.

Section 17 (18). **Paraphaca** R. Kam.

59. **A. rytidocarpus** Ledeb. Fl. Alt. 3 (1831) 315; id. Fl. Ross. 1 (1842) 118; Bunge Gen. Astrag. Sp. Geront. 1 (1868) 21 and 2 (1869) 22; Pavl. in Byul. Mosk. obshch. ispyt. prir., otd. biol. 38, 1–2 (1929) 90; Kryl. Fl. Zap. Sib. 7 (1933) 1644; Boriss. and Gontsch. in Fl. SSSR, 12 (1946) 83; Grub. Konsp. fl. MNR (1955) 186; Fl. Krasnoyarsk. kr. 6 (1960) 33; Ulzij. Opred. rast. okrest. Ulan-Batora [Key to Plants in the Vicinity of Ulan Bator] (1972) 172, p.p.; idem in Fl. Hang. (1989) 124; Sanczir in Grub. Opred. rast. Mong. [Key to Plants of Mongolia] (1982) 158, p.p.; Ulzij. and Gub. in Byul. Mosk. Obshch. ispyt. prir., otd. biol. 92, 5 (1987) 118. —**Ic.:** Ledeb. Ic. pl. fl. Ross. 3 (1842) tab. 291.

Described from Altay. Type in St.-Petersburg (LE).

On steppe rocky and rubbly slopes of moutains, in desert-steppe valleys of montane rivers, more rarely in solonetzic sections in steppes.

IA. Mongolia: ***Mong.-Alt.*** (nor.: Kak-kul' lake (Khar-nur) between Tsagan-gol and Kobdo, arid rubbly ravines, June 22, 1906—Sap.), ***Khesi*** (Aksai 5 km toward south, high nor. foothills of Altyntag mountain range, near foothills, Aug. 2, 1958—Petr.).

General distribution: West. Sib. (Altay, south), East. Sib. (Sayans), Nor. Mong. (Hent., Hang.).

60. **A. macropteris** DC. Prodr. 2 (1825) 283; Bunge Gen. Astrag. Sp. Geront. 1 (1869) 22; Baker in Hook. f. Fl. Brit. Ind. 2 (1879) 128; Kryl. Fl. Zap. Sib. 7 (1933) 1646; Boriss. in Fl. Tadzhik. 5 (1937) 284; Gontsch. and Boriss. in Fl. SSSR, 12 (1946) 82; Fl. Kirgiz. 7 (1957) 234; Fl. Krasnoyarsk. kr. 6 (1960) 33; Fl. Kazakhst. 5 (1961) 110; Ikonn. Opred. rast. Pam. [Key to Plants of Pamir] (1963) 166; Podlech et Anders. in Mitt. Bot. Staatssamml. München, 13 (1977) 441; Ali in Nasir, Fl. West. Pakistan, No. 100, Papilionac. (1977) 158; Bait. Astrag. Tyan'-Shanya (1977) 41; Y.C. Ho in Bull. Bot. Lab. North-East. Forest. Inst. 8 (1980) 73; Fl. Tadzhik. (1981) 71; Ulzij. in Tr. Inst. bot. AN MNR, 8 (1982) 20; Sanczir in Grub. Opred. rast. Mong. [Key to Plants of Mongolia] (1982) 158; C.Y. Yang in Claves pl. Xinjiang, 3 (1985) 129.—*A. vicioides* Ledeb. Fl. Alt. 3 (1831) 301; id. Fl. Ross. 1 (1842) 618.—*A. pseudomacropteris* Orazova in HFR 108 (1975) No. 5377; Bait. Astrag. Tyan'-Shanya (1977) 41. —**Ic.:** Fl. Tadzh. 5 (1937) Plate 28.

Described from Siberia. Type in Geneva (G).

On rocky slopes of mountains, forb-cereal grass plains and montane steppes, juniper groves, on sandy-pebbly shoals and talus.

IIA. Junggar: ***Cis-Alt.*** ("Altay"—C.Y. Yang l.c.), ***Tarb.*** (?), ***Jung. Ala Tau*** (?), ***Tien Shan*** ("In'lin"—C.Y. Yang l.c.), ***Zaisan*** (?).

IIIC. Pamir: ***East*** ("Kunlun"—C.Y. Yang l.c.).

General distribution: Fore Balkh., Jung.-Tarb. and Cen. Tien Shan; Pamiro-Alay; West. Sib. (Altay, south), East. Sib. (Sayans), Nor. Mong. (Fore Hubs. West.), Himalayas (west. Kashmir), Afghanistan, Pakistan.

61. **A. longipes** Kar. et Kir. in Bull. Soc. Natur. Moscou, 15 (1842) 405; Ledeb. Fl. Alt. 1, 3 (1843) 618; Fl. Kazakhst. 5 (1961) 109; Bait. Astrag. Tyan'-Shanya (1977) 40 p.p.; C.Y. Yang in Claves pl. Xinjiang, 3 (1985) 128.—*A. macropteris* auct. non DC.: Boriss. and Gontsch. in Fl. SSSR, 12 (1946) 82, min. p.—*A. vicioides* var. *longipes* Trautv. in Bull. Soc. Natur. Moscou, 33, 2 (1860) 499.

Described from Altay. Type in Moscow (MW). Isotype in St.-Petersburg (LE).

IIA. Junggar: ***Cis-Alt.*** ("Altay")—C.Y. Yang l.c.), ***Tarb.*** ("Dachen"—C.Y. Yang l.c.), ***Tien Shan*** ("south. and nor. Slopes of Tien Shan"—C.Y. Yang l.c.).

General distribution: West. Sib. (Altay, south).

62. **A. versicolor** Pall. Astrag., (1800) 45; DC. Astrag. (1802) 139 excl. var. β; Bunge Gen. Astrag. Sp. Geront. 1 (1869) 21 and 2 (1869) 22; Boriss. and Gontsch. in Fl. SSSR, 12 (1946) 77; Boriss. in Fl. Zabaik. 6 (1954) 584, p.p.; Grub. Konsp. fl. MNR (1955) 187 p.p.; M. Pop. Fl. Sr. Sib. 1 (1957) 331; Fl. Krasnoyar. kr. 6 (1960) 31; Opred. rast. Tuv. ASSR [Key to Plants of Tuva Autonomous Soviet Socialist Republic] (1984) 148; Fl. Tsentr. Sib. 2 (1979) 606; Ulzij. Opred. rast. okrestn. Ulan-Batora [Key to Plants in the Vicinity of Ulan Bator] (1972) 172; idem in Tr. Inst. bot. AN MNR, 8 (1982) 21; idem in Fl. Khang. (1989) 125; Sanczir in Grub. Opred. rast. Mong. [Key to Plants of Mongolia] (1982) 158.

—**Ic.:** Pall. Astrag.: tab. 35.

Described from East. Siberia. Type in London (BM). Plate II, fig. 4.

On steppe rocky slopes of mountains and on coastal pebble beds in sparse larch and pine groves, along sandy-pebbly beds of gullies.

IA. Mongolia: ***Khobd.*** (mountains north-east of Uryuk-nur lake, June 22, 1879—Pot.), ***Mong. Alt.*** (Adzhi-Bogdo mountain range, nor. Slope, Urgen-gol, July 30, 1877—Pot.; Tugrik-gola [Khukh-khabchil] gorge, around estuary, left bank, on steppe slope, June 27, 1971—Grub., Ulzij., Dariima), ***Cen. Khalkha*** (15 km west of Tsenkher Mandal settlement, steppe, June 18, 1987—Kam., Gub. et al.), ***East. Mong.*** (Monogolia australis, Suma-hada, 1871—Przew.).

General distribution: East. Sib. (Sayans, Daur.), Nor. Mong. (Fore Hubs. west., Hent. south., Hang., Mong.-Daur.).

63. **A. pavlovii** B. Fedtsch. et N. Basil. in Bull. Soc. Natur. Moscou, ser. biol. 38, 1–2 (1929) 90; Grub. Konsp. fl. MNR (1955) 186; Sanczir in Grub. Opred. rast. Mong. [Key to Plants of Mongolia] (1982) 158; Ulzij. in Tr. Inst. bot. AN MNR, 8 (1982) 22; Grub. in Novosti sist. vyssh rast. 21 (1984) 207; Ulzij. in Gub. in Byull. Mosk. Obshch. ispyt. prir., otd.

biol. 92, 5 (1987) 117.—*A. lioui* Tsai et Yu in Bull. Fan. Mem. Inst. Biol. (Bot.) 7, 1 (1936) 21; Peter-Stib. in Acta Horti Gotoburg, 12 (1937) 62; Wang and Tang in Ill. treatm. princip. pl. China, Legum. (1955) 384; Fl. Intramong. 3 (1977) 195 and ed. 2, 3 (1989) 269; S.B. Ho in Bull. Bot. Research, 3, 1 (1983) 41; Liouil. in Fl. desert. Sin. 2 (1987) 279.—*A. discolor* auct. non Bunge: Grub. Konsp. fl. MNR (1955) 184, p. min. p.—*A. multicaulis* auct. non Ledeb.: Sanczir in Grub. Opred. rast. Mong. [Key to Plants of Mongolia] (1982) 158, p. min. p.

—**Ic.:** Byull. Mosk. obshch. ispyt. prir., otd. biol. 38, 1–2 (1929) fig. 4; Tsai et Yu (1936) l.c. fig. 22; Fl. Intramong. 3 (1977), tab. 99.

Described from Mongolia (Alash Gobi). Type in Moscow (MW), isotype in St.-Petersburg (LE). Plate II, fig. 3, Map 6.

In desert steppes and deserts, solonetzic meadows, steppe slopes of knolls and foothills.

IA. Mongolia: ***Gobi-Alt.*** (50 miles south of Gurban-Saichan, Outer Mongolia, sandy places, No. 403, 1925—Chaney; Vain-Tsagan hills, on rubbly trail, Aug. 3, Tszolin hills, on rubbly trail, Aug. 8; Bain-Tukhum area, on rubbly trail of Bain-Tsagan mountain Aug. 31—1931, Ik.-Gal.; Bain-Tukhum area, rocky trail of Bain-Tsagan mountain range, along gorge, Aug. 31, 1938—Luk'yanov; Khurmein somon, Gurvan-Saikhan mountain range, rocky slopes of hills and valley floor, June 3, 1939—Donoi Surmazhab; 55 km west-south-west of Bayan-Dalai somon, lower part of trail of Dzolingiin-nuru, biurgun desert, Aug. 4, 1976—Rachk. and Damba), ***East. Gobi*** (on way to Urgu from Alashan, Khara-Teg area, June 25, 1909—Czet.), ***West. Gobi*** (Bayan-Undur somon, nor. slope of Khukh-Tumurtu mountain range near Boomyn-Khuduk well, rubbly-rocky desert, Aug. 6; Tseel somon, 40–50 km south of Maikhan-bulak, saxaul rubbly-rocky desert, Aug. 16–1943, Yun.; Noyan somon, border road to south of Tsagan-Suburga-khural (31 km from Obotu-khural toward west), saltwort desert, Aug. 13; same locality, Khukh-tologoin-bulak 21 km west of Obotu-khurel along border road, toirim, Aug. 13—1948, Grub.; 15 km east-nor.-east of Talyn-Bilgikh-bulak spring, in gorges, July 18; 50 km west-nor.-west of Tsagan-bulak post. gorge floor, July 21–1973; 10 km south-east of Bayan-bulak spring, desert, June 28–1974, Rachk. and Isach.; 21 km south-east of Dzamyn-Shanda spring, along border road, hillocky area, desert, Aug. 25; south-west. hillocky ridge 6 km south-east of Engeriin-us spring, rocky trail, rubbly desert, Aug. 26; hillocky area nor. of Bulgan-Khoshuny-nuru mountain range 22 km south-west of Dzamyn-Bilgekh-bulak spring along border road, sandy plain, Aug. 27—1979, Grub. et al.; foothills of Adzhi-Bogdo mountain range, 35 km east of Altay settlement, Aug. 28; south of Atas-Bogdo-ul mountain, July 30; 40 km south-west of Shar-Khulsny-bulak spring near Dzamyn-Bilgekh post, Aug. 4—1978; between Ederengiin-nuru and Atas-Bogda mountain ranges, near Maikhan-bulak, July 16, 1984—Gub.; Shine-Zhinst somon, 148 km nor. of Ekhiin-gol spring, gorge floor, Sep. 7, 1979—Sanczir), ***Alash. Gobi*** (steppe south of Tostu mountain range, Nariin-bulak, Aug. 16, 1886—Pot.; Khodes well, granite, Sep. 3, 1924—Pakhomov, typus !; Shil'bisyn-gol basin, Shil'bis-khuduk, in trough, on dry river bed, on sand, Sep. 16, 1925; Dugan-gol river, near Dugan-sume, dry river bed, Aug. 3, 1926—Glag.; Noyan somon, 20 km east of Obotu-khural, desert, June 10, 1949—Yun.; 25 km south-west of Tsagan-Deris border post, July 6, 1981—Gub.), ***Khesi*** ("Su-chow, 2315 Liou"—Peter–Stib.).

IC. Qaidam: ***Plain*** (in deserto montuoso boreali in limosis glareosis fragum, No. 377, Aug. 13 [25], 1879—Przew.).

IIA. Junggar: ***Jung. Gobi*** (Altay et Baityg, inter praice, in limosis, May 5 [17], 1879—Przew.; road to Urumchi from Altay 20 km from Datsa-khu well, along road to Guchen, desert, July 16, 1959, Yun. and I-f. Yuan'); ***Bulun-Tokhoi***, No. 139, Sep. 18, 1982—Chzhu Tsyuan'-yu [HIMC].

IIIA. Qinghai: ***Nanshan*** (Humboldt mountain range nor. slope, valley of Sharagol'dzhin river, pebble bed steppe, 11,000 ft abs. height (3353 m) June 15–1894, Rob.).

General distribution: endemic.

Note. Until 1989, many reports had erroneously placed this species in section **Craccina** subgenus *Cercidothrix*.

64. **A. qingheensis** Liou f. in Fl. desert. Sin 2 (1987) 44, 277.

—**Ic.:** Liou f. l.c. tab. 98, fig. 1–5.

Described from Sinkiang (Junggar: Chingil' river). Type in Lanzhou (LZDI)).

On sand.

IIA. Junggar: ***Cis-Alt.*** (Qinghe, in arenosis, No. 720630, June 15, 1972, C.Y. Yang—typus ! (LZDI).

General distribution: endemic.

Note. The author of this species Liou fil. placed it in subgenus *Cercidothrix* Bunge Based on description, this species is related to *A. lioui* Tsai et Yu (we identified this species as *A. pavlovii* B. Fedtsch. et N. Basil.). Therefore, *A. qingheensis* Liou f. should be placed in subgenus *Phaca*.

65. **A. puberulus** Ledeb. Fl. Alt. 3 (1831) 299; id. Fl. Ross. 1 (1842) 618; Bunge Gen. Astrag. Sp. Geront. 1 (1868) 21 and 2 (1869) 22; Kryl. Fl. Alt. (1909) 292; idem, Fl. Zap. Sib. 7 (1933) 1645; Gontsch. and Boriss. in Fl. SSSR, 12 (1946) 78; Grub. Konsp. fl. MNR (1955), 186, p.p.; Fl. Krasnoyar. kr. 6 (1960) 32; Fl. Kazakhst. 5 (1961) 108; Sanczir in Grub. Opred. rast. Mong. [Key to Plants of Mongolia] (1982) 158; Ulzij. in Tr. Inst. bot. AN MNR, 8 (1982) 22; idem in Fl. Khang (1989) 124; Opred. rast. Tuv. ASSR [Key to Plants of Tuva Autonomous Soviet Socialist Republic] (1984) 147; C.Y. Yang in Claves pl. Xinjiang, 3 (1985) 128.

—**Ic.:** Ledeb. Ic. pl. Fl. Ross. 3, tab. 291; Fl. SSSR, 12, Plate 6, fig. 3; Fl. Kazakhst. 5, Plate 13, fig. 4.

Described from South-East. Altay. Type in St.-Petersburg (LE). Plate II, fig. 2.

On rubbly and stony steppe sloppes, on rocks and in sandy steppes.

IA. Mongolia: ***Mong. Alt.*** (on Altyn-Khadasu cliff between Shara-bulak spring and Koshety brook, July 13, on cliffs of mountain ranges running between Taishir-Ol and Burkhan-Ol, July 18–1894, Klem.; Tumun somon, 8–10 km nor.-east of Khabchigiin-daba pass [west. extremity of Khan-Taishiri mountain range], steppe, July 12; west. bank of Tonkhil-nur lake, trails of knolls, July 16—1947, Yun.; east. slope of Khatsavchiin-Zara-ul 20 km south-east of Bayan-Undur somon off road, Aug. 26; east. extremity of Gichinine-nuru mountain range 3 km south-west of Amani-bulak spring, Aug. 27—1948, Grub.; 30 km west-south-west of Bugat somon, hillocky area, Aug. 1, 1977—Volk. and Rachk. Shadzgain-nuru mountain range, south. slope of Khoit-Dzhargalant-gol river basin, Bayan-sala gorge, July 27, 1984—Kam. and Dariima), ***Depr. Lakes*** ([Kuisin-Gobi], sandy steppe between Kurginein-khuduk and Dolon-turu—Klem.; east. extremity of Guilin-tala area, 10 km west of Bayan-Khongor formation, among knolls, Aug. 27, 1943—Yun.), ***Val. Lakes*** ([Beger] around Tsakhir-bulak spring, on cliffs, July 19, 1894—Klem.), ***Gobi-Alt.*** (60 km east of Bayan-Tsagan somon along road to Ikhe-Bogdo-ul, low-mountain massif, Aug. 2; 10 km nor. of Shine-Dzhinst. Somon, Adagin-Khabtsagaityn-nuru mountain range, Aug. 6—1973, Isach. and Rachk.).

IIA. Junggar: ***Cis-Alt.*** ("Altay"—C.Y. Yang l.c.), ***Tarb.*** ("Dachen"—C.Y. Yang l.c.), ***Jung. Gobi*** (Ikhe-Khabtag-ul mountain range, nor. macro slope, 2300 m, montane steppe, Aug. 12, 1977—Volk. and Rachk.; Ikhe-Alag-ula mountains along road to former Khairkhan somon—Altay somon [Bayan-Obo], 43–47 km from the former toward south-east and 12–16 km from gorge beginning, along bottom of large gorge, Aug. 20, 1979—Grub. et al.).

General distribution: Jung. Tarb.; West. Sib. (Altay, south).

66. **A. multicaulis** Ledeb. Fl. Alt. 3 (1831) 295; Bunge Gen. Astrag. Sp. Geront. 1 (1868) 21 and 2 (1869) 22; Pavl. in Byull. Mosk. Obshch. ispyt. prir., otd. biol. 38, 1–2 (1929) 90; Kryl. Fl. Zap. Sib. 7 (1933) 1644; Gontsch. and Boriss. in Fl. SSSR, 12 (1946) 81; Boriss. in Fl. Zabaik. 6 (1954) 585; Grub. Konsp. fl. MNR (1955) 186; M. Pop. Fl. Sr. Sib. 1 (1957) 331; Fl. Krasnoyar. kr. 6 (1960) 32; Fl. Kazakhst. 5 (1961) 109; Sanczir in Grub. Opred. rast. Mong. [Key to Plants of Mongolia] (1982) 158; Ulzij. in Tr. Inst. bot. AN MNR, 8 (1982) 22; idem in Fl. Khang. (1989) 124; Opred. rast. Tuv. ASSR [Key to Plants of Tuva Autonomous Soviet Socialist Republic] (1984) 148; C.Y. Yang in Claves pl. Xinjiang, 3 (1985) 128.—*A. multicaulis* α *viridis* Ledeb. Fl. Ross. 1 (1842) 606; Bunge Gen. Astrag. Sp. Geront. 2 (1869) 25.—*A. multicaulis* var. *albiflorus* M. Pop. l.c. (1957) 331.—*A. confertus* auct. non Benth. ex Bunge: Grub. l.c. (1955) 183.

—**Ic.:** Ledeb. Ic. pl. Fl. Ross. 4 (1842) tab. 316.

Described from Altay. Type in St.-Petersburg (LE).

On rocky and rubbly slopes and around rocks in montane steppe belt.

IA. Mongolia: ***Khobd.*** (Borealis altaica, ad muniment, finitii Bugusun-daba, June 24, 1869—Malevskyi; 12 km west of Ulan-daba pass, nor. slope, larch forest, July 14; same locality, steppe, July 16–1977, Sanczir et al.), ***Mong. Alt.*** (Altai australis, cacumine Dolon-nor daban, in rupilus graniticus, July 8, 1877—Pot.; between Dayan-gol and Ak"-korum lakes, June 29; same locality, Bor-Burgasun river, July 2; Tiekty or Terekty river, July 6—1903, Gr.-Grzh.; Oigur river valley, Tsagan-gol river, July 16, 1909—Can.; Tsakhir-khalgany-nur mountain range, nor. macro slope, in rock crevices, Aug. 12, 1973—Isach. and Rachk.; Modon-Khushe pass, 2700 m, alpine steppe, July 28, 1977—Karam. et al.), ***Gobi-Alt.*** (Baga-Bogdo, Outer Mongolia, steep slopes, canyon bottoms and terraces 6000–8500 ft (1829—2591 m), No. 212, 1925—Chaney; Bain-Tsagan mountains, on rocks, Aug. 9, 1931—Ik.-Gal.; Gurvan-Saikhan mountain range, pass between Dzun- and Dundu-Saikhan, summit of eastern margin of Dundu-Saikhan mountain, on rocks, July 22, 1943; Dzun-Saikhan mountain range, middle and lower belts, June 19, 1945—Yun.).

IIA. Junggar: ***Cis-Alt.*** ("Altay"—C.Y. Yang l.c.), ***Tarb.*** ("Dachen"—C.Y. Yang l.c.).

General distribution: West. Sib. (Alt.), East. Sib. (West. Sayan), Nor. Mong. (Hang. cent.).

Subgenus 3. **Pogonophaca** Bunge (*Trichostylus* Baker)

1. Style glabrous, stigma densely covered with long hairs .... 2.
\+ Style and stigma covered with long hairs (section 4 (22). **Trichostylus** (Baker) Taub.) .... 11.
2. Pods unilocular. Racemes axillary, elongated, few-flowered. Bracts absent or small (section 1 (19). **Phyllolobium** (Fisch.) Bunge) .... 3.
\+ Pods bilocular, subbilocular or semibilocular, sometimes unilocular. Racemes axillary, subumbellate, few-flowered, dense. Bracts small or conspicuous .... 6.
3. Stems elongated, 50–100 cm tall. Racemes with 3–9 flowers. Corolla yellow or white, tip of keel violet, standard 9–12 mm long; calyx about 6 mm long, teeth nearly as long as tube. Ovary rather densely pilose, stigma with tuft of hairs. Pods cylindrical, 25–30 (40) mm long, leaflets 5–15 pairs, 3–7 mm broad, oval or oblong-ovate, obtuse .... 67. **A. complanatus** R.Br.
\+ Stems shortened, creeping. Racemes with few (1–4) flowers. Standard shorter than keel. Ovary glabrous or slightly pubescent, stigma with tuft of long hairs. Calyx teeth pubescent within and outside. Leaflets pubescent beneath .... 4.
4. Pedicel longer than calyx tube. Ovary on long stalk. Standard about 16 mm long. Leaflets 6–7 pairs, obovate, 5–8 mm long, 2–3 mm broad, with emarginate or truncate tip .... ***A. tingriensis** Ni et P.C. Li
\+ Pedicel shorter than calyx tube. Ovary on short stalk. Blade of standard suborbicular. Leaflets oval, subacute or obtuse, 7–15 mm long, 3–7 mm broad .... 5.
5. Leaflets 6–11 pairs, standard 9–10 mm long, white spot at base of blade. Pods 12–15 mm long, 5–6 mm broad. .... 68. **A. tribulifolius** Benth. ex Bunge.
\+ Leaflets 4–7 (9) pairs. Standard 12–14 (17) mm long, without spot. Pods 20–25 mm long, 5–6 mm broad .... 69. **A. pastorius** Tsai et Yu
6. Stipules large, herbaceous, leaflike. Leaflets emarginate at tip. Stems glabrous (section 2 (20). **Sesbanella** Bunge) .... 7.
\+ Stipules small, not leaflike. Leaflets round or truncate at tip, even acuminate (section 3 (21). **Bibracteolati** Simps.) .... 8.
7. Plant with erect stems. Leaflets 12–19 pairs, 3–7 mm long, 2–6 mm broad, obovate, broadly emarginate at tip. Corolla yellow;

standard about 8 mm long, obovate, as long as wings, pods inflated, about 15 mm long, 4 mm broad, on long stalk, semibilocular, with wall about 1 mm broad .... 70. **A. tsataencis** Ni et P.C. Li

\+ Plant with long procumbent stems. Leaflets (7) 8–10 pairs, 8–10 mm long, 3–4 mm broad. Corolla purple-violet, standard 9–12 mm long, wings 10–13 mm broad. Pods falcate, unilocular, 20–25 mm long, 5–6 mm broad, on 5–8 mm long stalks .... 71. **A. falconeri** Bunge.

8. Ovary invariably glabrous. Leaflets 6–8 pairs, 10–25 mm long, 2–3 mm broad, lanceolate or lanceolate-oblong, acuminate toward base and tip. Racemes with 1–4 flowers. Corolla violet, standard 10–13 mm long; calyx 5–6 mm long. Plant 6–10 cm tall .... 72. **A. camptodontoides** Simps.

\+ Ovary pubescent. Leaflets pubescent on both surfaces. Standard longer than keel or as long. Calyx teeth pubescent inside .... 9.

9. Bracts up to 2 mm long, ovate-lanceolate. Leaflets linear or linear-lanceolate, 5–11 mm long, of unequal size. Standard 8 mm long, reniform or suborbicular, emarginate .... 73. **A. prodigiosus** K.T. Fu

\+ Bracts longer than 5 mm. Leaflets of equal size .... 10.

10. Bracts 8–10 mm long, longer than calyx tube or as long. Leaflets 5–10 pairs, 5–10 mm long, 2–5 mm broad, elliptical or oblong, acuminate, covered with long, white, silky, soft hairs on both surfaces. Standard about 13 mm long, orbicular-obcordate, cuneately narrowed toward base into short claw .... 74. **A. lhasaensis** Ni et P.C. Li

\+ Bracts 5 mm long, shorter than calyx tube. Leaflets 7–10 pairs, 7–10 mm long, 3–4 mm broad, oblong-obovate, with broad notch at tip, covered with short, white, soft hairs on both surfaces. Standard 9 mm long, suborbicular with very short claw .... 75. **A. tanguticus** Batal.

11. Leaflets densely covered on both surfaces with long, soft, white hairs. Standard longer than wings and keel, with short keel; wings slighly broader than keel .... 76. **A. hendersonii** Baker

\+ Leaflets pubscent only beneath, initially sparsely hairy above, glabrate later. Wings and keel of same breadth but claw 1/3 as long as petals .... 77. **A. heydei** Baker

Section 1 (19). **Phyllolobium** (Fisch.) Bunge

67. **A. complanatus** R. Br. ex Bunge Gen. Astrag. Sp. Geront. 1 (1868) 4 and 2 (1869) 1; Franch. Pl. David. in Nouv. Arch. Mus. Paris, n.s. 5 (1882) 236; Simps. in Not. Bot. Gard. Edinb. 8 (1915) 252; Peter-Stib. in Acta Horti. Gotoburg, 12 (1937–38) 57; Wang and Tang, Ill. treatm. princip. pl. China, Legum. (1955) 389; Ic. cormoph. Sin. 2 (1972) 419; Fl. pl. herb. Chinae bor.-or. 5 (1976) 106; K.T. Fu in Bull. Bot. Research, 2, 1 (1982) 119; Fl. desert. Sin. 2 (1987) 251; Fl. Intramong. 2 ed., 3 (1989) 266.—*A. complanatus* var. *eutrichus* Hand.-Mazz. in Osterr. Bot. Zeitschr. 82 (1933) 248.—*A. pratensis* Ulbr. in Repert. Nov. Sp. Beih. 12 (1922) 417.

—**Ic.:** Wang and Tang l.c. fig. 376; Fl. Intramong. 3 (1989), tab. 103, fig. 7–13.

Described from North China. Type in London (BM).

In arid steppes, along gorges and river banks, roadsides, 1000–1700 m., sometimes up to 2400 m.

IA. Mongolia: ***Ordos*** (Ike-Chzhao, in Khatan river basin, No. 7799, Aug. 13, 1956, Chinese collector (LZDI)).

General distribution: China (North, North-West, East, South-West: nor. Sichuan).

***A. tingriensis** Ni et P.C. Li in Acta Phytotax. Sin. 18, 3 (1980) 367; id. in Fl. Xizang 2, (1985) 817.

Described from Tibet. Type in Beijing (PE). Map 6.

In sandy sites in montane valleys at 4500 m.

IIIB. Tibet: ***South*** (Tengri, alt. 4500 m, in crevice on sand in valley, May 29, 1959, Mt. Qomolungma Fang Exp., No. 85, typus !—beyond south. boundary of the region).

General distribution: endemic.

68. **A. tribulifolius** Benth. ex Bunge Gen. Astrag. Sp. Geront. 1 (1868) 4 and 2 (1869) 2; K.T. Fu in Bull. Bot. Research, 2, 1 (1982) 120; Ni et P.C. Li in Fl. Xizang, 2 (1985) 813.—*A. tribulifolius* var. *pauciflorus* Marq. et Shaw in J. Linn. Soc. Bot. 41 (1929) 171.

—**Ic.:** Fl. Xizang, 2, tab. 263, fig. 1–9.

Described from West. Tibet. Type in London (K).

On sandy-rocky slopes and in alpine grasslands, 3700–4800 m.

IIIA. Qinghai: ***Nanshan*** (ad fl. Yussun-Chatyma, 9000-10,000 ft (2743–3048 m), July 24, 1880—Przew.).

IIIB. Tibet: ***South*** (Lhasa, among rocks on slopes, 3100 m, No. 3648, July 14, 1974. Exp. Compl. Qinghai-Xizang [PE]; ("Lhasa, Naidun, Nan'mulin, Pulan', Chzhunba, Tszilun" —Fl. Xizang l.c.).

General distribution: China (North-West, South-West), Himalayas.

69. **A. pastorius** Tsai et Yu in Bull. Fan. Mem. Inst. Biol. Peiping, bot. ser. 9 (1940) 264; K.T. Fu in Bull. Bot. Research, 2, 1 (1982) 128; Li et Ni

in Fl. Xizang, 2 (1985) 815 (incl. var. *linearibracteatus* K.T. Fu.).—*A. pastorius* var. *linearibracteatus* K.T. Fu in Bull. Bot. Research, 2, 1 (1982) 129.

Described from Tibet. Type in Beijing (PE). Plate III, fig. 3.

In alpine meadows, 3100-4300 m alt.

IIIB. Tibet: *South* ("Tszyanda, Tszyacha"—Fl. Xizang l.c.).

General distribution: China (North-West).

Section 2 (20). **Sesbanella** Bunge

70. **A. tsataensis** Ni et P.C. Li in Acta Phytotax. Sin. 17, 2 (1979) 106; id. in Fl. Xizang, 2 (1985) 811.

—**Ic.:** Ni et Li (1979) l.c. fig. 5; Fl. Xizang, 2, tab. 262, fig. 1–9.

Described from South. Tibet (Chzhada). Type in Beijing (PE).

In river floodplains, meadows and sandy-rubbly montane slopes, 3000–3500 m.

IIIB. Tibet: *South* ("Chzhada"—F. Xizang l.c.).

General distribution: endemic.

71. **A. falconeri** Bunge Gen. Astrag. Sp. Geront. 1 (1868) 4 and 2 (1869) 2; K.T. Fu in Bull. Bot. Research, 2, 1 (1982) 131 (incl. var. *paucistrigosus* K.T. Fu); Ni et P.C. Li in Fl. Xizang, 2 (1985) 812.

Described from Himalayas. Type in London (K).

On rocky and rubbly montane slopes, 3750 m.

IIIB. Tibet: *South* ("Pulan'"—Fl. Xizang l.c.).

General distribution: Himalayas.

Section 3 (21). **Bibracteolati** Simps.

72. **A. camptodontoides** Simps. in Not. Bot. Gard. Edinb. 8 (1915) 240; Peter-Stib. in Acta Horti Gotoburg, 12, (1937–38) 58; K.T. Fu in Bull. Bot. Research 2, 1 (1982) 126; Ni et P.C. Li in Fl. Xizang, 2 (1985) 813.

Described from China (Yunnan). Type in Edinburgh (E).

On rocky slopes of mountains.

IIIB. Tibet: *South* ("Lhasa"—Fl. Xizang l.c.).

General distribution: China (South-West: Yunnan).

73. **A. prodigiosus** K.T. Fu in Bull. Bot. Research, 2, 1 (1982) 121.

—**Ic.:** K.T. Fu l.c. tab. 2, fig. 1–8.

Described from Tibet. Type in Wugung (NWBI).

Along margins of scrubs.

IIIB. Tibet: ***South*** (Suburbium occidentale in Lasa Shi [Lhasa], in margine fruticeti flabelli alluvii, 3800 m, No. 0011, May, 21, 1973, Tib. Exp.—typus !).

General distribution: endemic.

74. **A. lhasaensis** Ni et P.C. Li in Acta Phytotax. Sin. 17, 2 (1979) 107; id. in Fl. Xizang, 2 (1985) 815.

—**Ic.:** Ni et P.C. Li (1979) l.c. fig. 6.

Described from South. Tibet. Type in Beijing (PE).

Along rubbly slopes and in alpine meadows, 4500–4600 m.

IIIB. Tibet: ***South*** ("Lhasa"—Fl. Xizang l.c.).

General distribution: endemic.

75. **A. tanguticus** Batal. in Acta Horti Petrop. (1891) 485; Peter-Stib. in Acta Horti Gotoburg, 12 (1937–38) 59; K.T. Fu in Bull. Bot. Research, 2, 1 (1982) 125; Ni et P.C. Li in Fl. Xizang, 2 (1985) 186.—*A. milingensis* Ni et Li in Acta Phytotax. Sin. 17, 2 (1979) 107; id. in F1. Xizang, 2 (1985) 817.

—**Ic.:** Fl. Xizang, 2, tab. 263, fig. 10–18 and tab. 265, fig. 1–7, sub nom. *A. milingensis* Ni et P.C. Li.

Described from Qinghai. Type in St.- Petersburg (LE). Plate III, fig. 1.

In alpine meadows, along rocky banks of rivers, among shrubs, 3300–3950 m.

IIIA. Qinghai: ***Nanshan*** (Xining mountains, Myn'-dan'-sha river, May 29, 1890—Gr.-Grzh. typus !), ***Amdo*** (Balekun area, 3048 m, May 25 [June 6], 1880—Przew.; Huang He river, Guide, (?) June 13; along Mudzhik river, 2700–2850 m, June 18 [30]; South Kukunor mountain range, desert along nor. foothills, 3048 m, June 23–1880, Przew.).

IIIB. Tibet: ***Weitzan*** (Yangtze river basin, Dy-chyu river, 3962 m, on rocks, June 14, 1884—Przew.; Yan'tszy-tszyana river basin (Goluboi), along valley of I-Chyu river, 3810 m, July 28, 1900; Alyk-Norin-gol river valley, 1901—Lad.; Radjaa Yellow River gorges, grassy slopes, alt. 11,000 ft (3358 m), No. 14182, June 1926—Rock; "Leinyaotszy, Sosyan' [Sok-Gompa]"—Fl. Xizang l.c.).

General distribution: China (South-West: Sichuan).

Section 4 (22). **Trichostylus** (Baker) Taub.

76. **A. hendersonii** Baker in Hook. f. Fl. Brit. Ind. 2 (1876) 111; K.T. Fu in Bull. Bot. Research, 2, 1 (1982) 119; Ni et P.C. Li in Fl. Xizang, 2 (1985) 809.

—**Ic.:** Fl. Xizang, 2, tab. 261, fig. 10–15.

Described from Himalayas (Kashmir). Type in London (K).

In sandy-rubbly steppes, on debris cones, along banks of rivers and lakes, 4300–5300 m.

IIIA. Qinghai: ***Nanshan*** (on sandy banks of Kukunor lake, 3100 m, June 27 [July 9] 1880—Przew.; valley of Sharagoldzhin river, Paidza-Tologoi area, 3353 m in sandy-pebbly steppe, No. 309, June 11, 1894—Rob.).

IIIB. Tibet: ***Chang Tang*** (Przewalsky mountain range, nor. slope, 4267–4572 m, foremontane sandy steppe, Aug. 21—1890, Rob.), ***Weitzan*** (Valle ft. Allaknor-gol, caespites in arenosis format, July 30 [Aug. 11] 1884—Przew.; "Shuankhu, Bizhu"—Fl. Xizang l.c.), South. ("Dintsze; Pulano, Chzhada"—Fl. Xizang l.c.).

General distribution: Himalayas.

77. **A. heydei** Baker in Hook. f. Fl. Brit. Ind. 2 (1876) 118; K.T. Fu in Bull. Bot. Research, 2, 1 (1982) 118; Ni et P.C. Li in Fl. Xizang, 2 (1985) 811.

—**Ic.:** Fl. Xizang, 2, tab. 261, fig. 1–9.

Described from Himalayas. Type in London (K).

In sandy-rubbly sites, along banks of glacial lakes and brooks, alpine meadows.

IIIA. Qinghai: *Nanshan* (Sharagoldzhin river valley, Paidza-Tologoi area, 3353 m, in sandy-pebbly steppe, June 11, 1894—Rob.).

IIIB. Tibet: ***Chang Tang*** ("Zhitu"—Fl. Xizang l.c.), ***South.*** ("Pulan', Chzhada, Tszilun"—Fl. Xizang l.c.).

General distribution: Himalayas (west., Kashmir).

Subgenus 4. **Hypoglottis** Bunge

1. Calyx shortly-campanulate .... 2.

\+ Calyx tubular, tubular-campanulate or tubular-funnel-shaped but then calyx teeth elongated. Peduncles axillary. Stipules not adnate with petiole. Plant with stems (section 1 (23). **Hypoglottis** Bunge) .... 3.

2. Plant with stems. Pods unilocular, bivalved. Stipules connate (section 2 (24). **Poliothrix** Bunge) .... 7.

\+ Plant nearly acauline. Pods bilocular. Stipules not connate (section 3 (25). **Tapinodes** Bunge) .... 10.

3. Calyx villous with patent long; white hairs with minor mixture of short black hairs; calyx teeth as long as tube or barely shorter; corolla pale-violet or albescent, 15–18 mm long. Pods sessile, ovate. Leaflets 6–13 pairs, oblong-ovate or oblong, 5–20 mm long, obtuse or emarginate at tip .... 78. **A. dasyglottis** Fisch. ex DC.

\+ Calyx with appressed black hairs, sometimes mixed with white hairs; calyx teeth 1/3–1/2 (2/3) of tube length; corolla violet or purple-violet or bluish-violet. Pods on 1–4 mm long stalks .... 4.

4. Bracts oblong-ovate. Racemes dense, capitate, ovate or oblong-ovate, 2–3 cm long; corolla purple-violet, 15–18 mm long, blade of standard ovate; calyx teeth nearly 1/2 as long as tube.

Pods highly inflated, compressed from back to front, ovate, 7–8 mm long, on about 1 mm long stalk, coriaceous, sulcate on back, round-keeled in front .... 79. **A. danicus** Retz.

\+ Bracts lanceolate or linear-subulate. Racemes capitate, with 5–15 flowers, dense; corolla bluish-violet, 16–22 mm long, blade of standard oblong-obovate; calyx teeth subulate, 1/3 of tube length. Pods oblong or linear-oblong, erect, slightly curved, 13–17 mm long, acute, on 2–4 mm long stalk, carinate in front, sulcate, leptodermatous on back .... 5.

5\. Plants 10–35 cm tall. Leaflets pilose beneath, glabrous or with extremely diffuse hairs above .... 6.

\+ Plant 4–10 cm tall, mostly with dense patent hairs. Leaflets pubescent on both surfaces .... 80. **A. chadjanensis** Franch.

6\. Plant with diffuse or dense, often patently pubescent with mixed (white and black) hairs. Pods with dense or sparse black pubescence, on well-developed stalk .... 81. **A. tibetanus** Benth. ex Bunge.

\+ Plant with appressed pubescence or white hairs predominate in pubescence. Pods with white pubescence or white and black pubescence; if diffuse, glabrescent soon, sessile .... 82. **A. laxmanni** Jacq.

7\. Corolla 9–10 mm long, violet; calyx teeth almost as long as tube .... 8.

\+ Corolla up to 8 mm long, yellow, white or bluish; calyx teeth 1/2–2/3 of tube length .... 9.

8\. Calyx teeth narrowly-deltoid. Corolla yellow or white. Standard 8 mm long, wings 7 mm long, keel 6 mm long. Leaflets 11–13 pairs, pilose. Pods densely covered with short white hairs .... 83. **A. leucocephalus** Grah.

\+ Calyx teeth subulate. Corolla bluish. Standard 7 mm long, wings 6 mm long, keel 5 mm long. Leaflets 10–11 pairs. Pods totally glabrous .... 84. **A. rigidulus** Benth. ex Bunge.

9\. Leaflets 8–16 pairs, 5–14 mm long, 3–6 mm broad. Calyx 6–7 mm long .... 85. **A. strictus** Grah.

\+ Leaflets 6–8 pairs, 3–4 mm long, 2 mm broad. Calyx 4–5 mm long .... 86. **A. nanjiangianus** K.T. Fu

10\. Corolla 10–11 mm long; standard oval, somewhat emarginate at tip; wings 8.5–9 mm long, keel 6 mm long. Leaflets 6–9 pairs, oval or elliptical, barely emarginate at tip, 2–4 mm long, 1.5–2.5 mm broad. Ovary glabrous. Plant 4–8 cm tall .... *__A. dingjiensis__ Ni et P.C. Li

+ Corolla 5–8 mm long. Racemes extremely dense, many-flowered .... 11.

11. Ovary and pod covered with dense hairs .... 12.

+ Ovary and pod glabrous. Leaflets (4) 5–7 pairs, 2.5–4 mm long, about 1.5 mm broad. Calyx about 4 mm long; standard about 6 mm long .... 87. **A. malcolmii** Hemsl. et Pearson

12. Peduncle weak, slender, long, sometimes up to 10 cm tall. Stipules herbaceous, light-green with lilac band and gland; initially covered with short, soft, white hairs. Petiole slender, 3–7 cm long; leaflets oblong or narrowly-oblong, 5–8 mm long, densely covered beneath with erect, short, soft, white hairs. Wings twice broader than keel .... ***A. longiscapus** Ni et P.C. Li

+ Peduncle stiff, short, 2–4 cm long. Stipules thick, membranous, light-yellow, without glands, without pubescence. Leaf petiole short, 1–2 cm long; leaflets suborbicular, thick, longitudinally folded, 2.5–6 mm long, 2.5 mm broad, covered beneath with sparse, soft, short hairs. Wings and keel nearly equally broad .... 88. **A. orbicularifolius** P.C. Li et Ni

Section 1 (23). **Hypoglottis** Bunge

78. **A. dasyglottis** Fisch. in DC. Prodr. 2 (1825) 282; Bunge Gen. Astrag. Sp. Geront. 1 (1868) 52 and 2 (1869) 84; idem in Izv. Obshch. lyub. estestv., antr. i etnogr. 26, 2 (1880) 242; O. et B. Fedtsch. Konsp. fl. Turk. 2 (1909) 211; Kryl. Fl. Zap. Sib. 7 (1933) 1666; Gontsch. and Boriss. in Fl. SSSR, 12 (1946) 257; Fl. Kazakhst. 5 (1961) 148; Opred. rast. Sr. Azii [Key to Plants of Mid. Asia] 6 (1981) 109; C.Y. Yang in Claves pl. Xinjiang, 3 (1985) 139.—*A. hypoglottis* var. *dasyglottis* Ledeb. Fl. Alt. 3 (1831) 293; id. Fl. Ross. 1, 3 (1843) 603.—*A. tibetanus* auct. non Benth. Jager in Flora, 177 (1985) 69.

Described from Altay. Type in Geneva (G).

In meadows, steppes, common in solonetzic and sandy soils, riverine pebble beds.

IA. Mongolia: ? ***Khobd.*** (Mongolie-Von Ulussutaja bis Kosch-Agatsch, June 15–July 15, 1880—Pevts.), ***Mong. Alt.*** (floodplain of Bulgan-gol river near confluence of Ulyastai-gol river with it, July 20, 1947—Yun.; Uljastain-gol-Tal, Unterlauf des Flusses, in Lasiagrostis-Bestanden, No. 3556, 1964—Danert et al. [UBA, GAT]; Uliastai-gol river, at its emergence into Bulgan-gol river valley, in pebble bed, Aug. 16, 1979—Grub. et al.), ***Depr. Lakes*** (Ulangom, in arid sections of meadows, along brooks, July 3, 1879—Pot.; around irrigation ditches 10 versts (1 verst = 1.067 km) from lake Ubsa-nur—Kryl.).

IB. Kashgar: ***West.*** (80 km from Kashgar, on road to Kensu and Ulugchat, along irrigation ditch, June 17, 1959—Yun. and I-f. Yuan').

IIA. Junggar: ***Cis-Alt.*** ("Altay"—C.Y. Yang l.c.), ***Jung. Gobi*** (Kuitun region, No. 251, June 29, 1957—Shen-Tyan'; same locality, in desert lands, No. 1097, June 27, 1957—Kuan).

General distribution: Fore Balkh., Jung.-Tarb.; West. Sib. (Alt., Irt.), East. Sib. (except Yenisei), China (Alt.), Nor. Amer. (Pacific Ocean section).

79. **A. danicus** Retz. Observ. Bot. 3 (1781) 41; Kryl. Fl. Zap. Sib. 7 (1933) 1665; Kitag. Lin. Fl. Mansh. (1939) 280; Gontsch. and Boriss. in Fl. SSSR, 12 (1946) 256; P.Y. Fu et Y.A. Chen, Fl. Pl. herb. Chin. bor.-or. 5 (1976) 95; Opred. rast. Sr. Azii [Key to Plants of Mid. Asia] 6 (1981) 109; Fl. Kazakhst. 5 (1961) 148; K.T. Fu in Bull. Bot. Research, 2, 4 (1982) 72; C.Y. Yang in Claves pl. Xinjiang, 3 (1985) 139.—*A. arenarius* auct. non L.: DC. Prodr. 2 (1825) 281; Bunge Gen. Astrag. Sp. Geront. 1 (1868) 52 and 2 (1869) 83, p.p.

—**Ic.:** Fl. SSSR, Plate 34, fig. 1.

Described from Denmark. Type in London (LINN).

In meadows, forest glades, thin forests, along steppes.

IIA. Junggar: ***Cis-Alt.*** (25–30 km north of Koktogai, right bank of Kairta river, valley of Kuityn river, nor. slope, spruce-larch forest, July 15, 1959—Yun.; "Altay"—C.Y. Yang l.c.), ***Tarb.*** ("Dachen"—Y.C. Yang l.c.), ***Tien Shan*** (20 km south-west of Urumchi, along gorges, July 19, 1956—Ching; alongside Urumchi-Karashar highway, near water, 2300 m, No. 6109, July 22; mountain road from Bartu to timber plant in Khomote, 1825 m, No. 6962, Aug. 3, same locality on foothills, 2300 m, No. 7007, Aug. 3—1958, A.R. Lee (1958)).

General distribution: ***Jung.-Tarb.***; Europe, Mediterr., Caucasus, West. Sib., East. Sib., Nor. Mong. (Fore Hubs. west.), China (Dunbei).

80. **A. chadjanensis** Franch. in Bull. Mus. Hist. Natur. Paris, 2, 7 (1896) 344; Fl. Tadzhik. 5 (1937) 401; Ikonn. Opred. rast. Pam. [Key to Plants of Pamir] (1963) 168; Fl. Tadzhik. 7 (1981) 199.—*A. olufsenii* Freyn in Bull. Herb. Boiss. ser. 2, 45 (1904) 450.—*A. tibetanus* auct. non Benth.: Gontsch. and Boriss., in Fl. SSSR, 12 (1946) 258, p. min. p.

Described from East. Pamir (valley of Shadzhan river). Type in Paris (P).

In sedge-*Cobresia* sasas (solonchaks on lateral seepages), sedge-grass and grass-forb associations, on sandy and rocky slopes in alpine desert belt and cryophilic steppes.

IB. Kashgar: ***Nor.*** (Uch-Turfan, Uital bay desert near Karol', June 27, 1908—Divn.; 30 km south-east of border post. Turugart on road to Kashgar, 3100 m, montane steppe belt, on floor of arid ravine, June 20, 1959—Yun. and I-f. Yuan'), ***West.*** (?), ***South.*** (Russky mountain range, 2280–2600 m, June 2; Keri mountain range, 2300 m, Atshan', on moist sand, June 22—1885, Przew.; Kunlun, nor. foothill, on floor of gorge, July 16, 1889; Russky mountain range, Aksu river, 3658 m, along river bed, June 16; same locality, Kara-Sai village, 3048 m, along irrigation ditches, July 6; same locality, Saiganchi, 2134–2743 m, in meadows, July 23—1890, Rob.; Polour, 2582 m, July 17, 1892—Deutreil de Rhins).

IIIC. Pamir (Charlym river, along bank, June 21; valley of Subashi river, on stones, July 23—1909, Divn.; Tashkurgan, on rocky terrace, July 25, 1913—Knor.; in Arpalyk-Dar'ya river gorge 10 km from Kyzyl-Daban, about 3000 m, July 6, 1941; in midcourse of Kanlyk river, 2500–3200 m, July 12, 1942—Serp.; Tashkurgan Valley, 2–3 km west of Tashkurgan town, debris cone, June 13, 1959—Yun. and I-f. Yuan').

General distribution: endemic.

81. **A. tibetanus** Benth. ex Bunge Gen. Astrag. Sp. Geront. 1 (1868) 52 and 2 (1869) 85; id. Astrag. Turk. (1880) 242 p.p.; Baker in Hook. f. Fl. Brit. Ind. 2 (1876) 124; O. et B. Fedtsch. Konsp. fl. Turk. 2 (1909) 212; Gontsch. and Boriss. in Fl. SSSR, 12 (1946) 258; Grub. Konsp. Fl. MNR, (1955) 187; Wang and Tang in Ill. treatm. princip. pl. China, Legum. (1955) 411; Fl. Kirgiz. 7 (1957) 267; Kitam. Fl. Afghan. (1960) 193; Fl. Kazakhst. 5 (1961) 149; Ali in Nasir et Ali, Fl. West Pakist. No. 100 (1977) 180; Bait. Astrag. Tyan'-Shanya (1977) 56; Ni et Li in Fl. Xizang, 2 (1985) 843; Opred. rast. Sr. Azii [Key to Plants of Mid. Asia] 6 (1981) 109, p.p.; K.T. Fu in Bull. Bot. Research 2, 4 (1982) 73; Grub. in Byul. Mosk. obshch. ispyt. prir., otd. biol. 87, 1 (1981) 127; Sanczir in Grub. Opred. rast. Mong. [Key to Plants of Mongolia] (1982) 157, p.p.; Ulzij. in Tr. Inst. bot. AN MNR, 8 (1982) 16 p.p.; Opred. rast. Tuv. ASSR [Key to Plants of Tuva Autonomous Soviet Socialist Republic] (1984) 148; C.Y. Yang in Claves pl. Xinjiang, 3 (1985) 138; Gub. et al. in Byul. Mosk. obshch. ispyt. prir., otd. biol. 92, 1 (1987) 120.—*A. laxmannii* auct. non Jacq.: Bunge Astrag. Turk. (1880) 241 p. pl; id. in Acta Horti Petrop. (1880) 7.

—**Ic.:** Ill. Treatm. princip. pl. China, Legum. fig. 406; Grub. Opred. rast. Mong. [Key to Plants of Mongolia] Plate 85, fig. 392.

Described from Tibet. Type in London (K).

In solonetzic coastal meadows and fallow lands, on steppefied mountain slopes.

IA. Mongolia: ***Mong.-Alt.*** (Adzhi-Bogdo mountain range, Dzusylyn gorge, alpine meadow, June 29; on Saksa river, July 7; on Tsitsiryn-gol river, July 9; same locality, alps south of Tsitsiryn-gol, July 9; same locality, on pebble bed July 10—1877, Pot.; on bank of Tsakhir-bulak spring, July 18, 1894—Klem.; Khara-Azkarga mountain range, Shutyn-gol valley, rocky gorge, July 27, 1930—Pob.; Bayan somon, Dzun-bulak area 22 km south-west of ajmaq centre on road to Sharkain-Gobi, among barley plantations, July 15, 1947—Yun.; Gichgeniin-nuru mountain range, 17 km south-west of Tsogt settlement, Aug. 15, 1977—Gub. [MW]; Ulyastain-gol river area 10 km south-west of Bugat somon, on pebble beds, July 5; Bulgan-gol river basin, upper Ulyastain-gol, gorge, July 9; Nariin-gol river valley, middle and lower courses, July 16—1984, Kam. and Dariima; 35 km south-west of Khalyun settlement, Aug. 14, 1984—Gub. [MW], ***Depr. Lakes*** (nor. bank of Khirgis-nur lake, near Chatsyrganyn-bulak spring, on disused fallow land, Aug. 21, 1944—Yun.), ***Val. Lakes*** (40 km east of Beger settlement, July 12, 1984—Gub. [MW]), ***West. Gobi*** (Atas-Bogda-ula, south. macro slope, on gorge terrace, 2450 m, Aug. 24, 1973—Isach. and Rachk.), ***Alash. Gobi*** (Kobden-usu area, Aug. 13, 1886—Pot.).

IB. Kashgar: ***West.*** (Turkestania orientalis, May 25, 1990—Grombch; upper Kyzil-su river, above Kashgar, near Egin mountain, in lucerne plantations, July 1, 1929—Pop.), ***South.*** (Keriisk mountain range, 3139 m, Nura river valley, July 23, 1885—Przew.).

IIA. Junggar: ***Tien Shan*** (nor. slope, Tumirtu-gol river, Aug. 24, 1895—Rob.; valley of Muzart river 7–8 km beyond its emergence from gorge near Kurgan settlement, in floodplain, among boulders, Sep. 7; same locality, in upper course of Muzart river, Sazlik area, along shoals, Sep. 9—1958, Yun. and I-f.Yuan'), ***Jung. Gobi*** (Kenderlik river, meadow, Aug. 3; valley of Ul'kon-Ulasty river on Tumandy, Aug. 7—1876; Adak, July 16, 1877—Pot.; Tsyn'-tsyuan' lake, No. 1222, July 7, 1957—Kuan; Baitag-Bogdo mountain range, July 27 and 28, 1979—Gub. [MW]).

IIIB. Tibet: ***Chang Tang*** ("West. Tibet"—Fl. Xizang l.c.).

General distribution: Jung.-Tarb.; Mid. Asia (Pam.-Alay, West. Tien Shan), Iran, West. Sib. (Altay, Irt.).

82. **A. laxmannii** Jacq. in Hort. Bot. Vindobon. (1776) 22; Pall. Astrag. (1800) 38; Bunge Gen. Astrag. Sp. Geront. 1 (1868) 52 and 2 (1869) 84; O. et B. Fedtsch. Konsp. fl. Turk. 2 (1909) 212, p.p.; Opred. rast. Sr. Azii [Key to Plants of Mid. Asia] 6 (1981) 110.—*A. adsurgens* Ledeb. Fl. Ross. (1842) 603 p. pl., non Pall.; Turcz. Fl. baic.-dahur. (1842) 335 p.p.—*A. adsurgens* Ledeb. var. *laxmanni* Trautv. in Bull. Soc. Natur. Moscou, 33, 1 (1860) 461.—*A. wulumuqianus* Wang et Tang ex K.T. Fu in Bull. Bot. Research, 2, 4 (1982) 71, tab. 4–19—*A. tibetanus* auct. non Benth. ex Bunge: Sanczir in Grub. Opred. rast. Mong. [Key to Plants of Mongolia] (1982) 157, p. max. p.

—**Ic.:** Jacq. 1776 l.c. tab. 37.

Described from Altay. Type in Paris (P).

In meadows, rocky and rubbly slopes, montane steppes.

IA. Mongolia: ***Mong.-Alt.*** (Iter ad Chobdo, No. 199, July 12, 1870—Kalning; valley of Bulgan river, Sep. 18, 1930—Bar.; Bombotu-Khairkhan mountains, plateau between El' and Khabchik rivers, Oct. 10, 1930—Pob.), ***Depr. Lakes*** (Ulangom, Sep. 6, 1876—Pot.).

IB. Kashgar: ***Nor.*** (Uch-Turfan, Kukurtuk gorge, June 1908—Divn.), ***West.*** (Yangi-Gissar region, Yagiz'-yar' village, along banks of irrigation ditch, May 30, 1909—Divn.; Sarykol mountain range, Bostan-Terek, July 10, 1929—Pop.; 80 km from Kashgar on road to Kensu and Ulugchat, along irrigation canal, June 17, 1959—Yun. and I-f. Yuan'), ***South.*** (Posarbat area, 2500–3000 m, Aug.–Sep. 1941—Serp.).

IIA Junggar: ***Tarb.*** (Tarbagatai mountain range, ascent to Kuzgon' pass, in ravine, Aug. 2, 1908—Fedtsch.; Saur mountain range, valley of Karagaitu river, Bayan-Tsagan creek valley, subalpine meadow, June 23, 1957—Yun. and I-f. Yuan'), ***Jung. Ala Tau*** (Dzhair mountain range, 1–1.5 km nor. of Otu settlement, along road to Chugkchak, montane steppe, July 4, 1957—Yun. and I-f. Yuan'), ***Tien Shan*** (Talki gorge nor.-west of Kul'dzha, July 25; Sairam lake, July—1977; Kuiankus, 914 m, May 31; Khanakhai brook south of Kul'dzha, 1219–1524 m, June 15, 1878; Kash river, 1372 m; Dzhirumtai, May 2; Taldy midcourse, 1524 m, May 22; central valley of Dzhin river, Tsagan-Tunge tributary, 1219–1829 m, June 7; Dzhin river, 975 m, June 8, 1879—Reg.; Nanshan-kou gorge, on rocks, June 10, 1877—Pot.; Ili-Dzhagastai, in Ili river floodplain, No. 3049, July 5, 1957—Kuan; along road to Karashar from Urumchi, on valley terrace, 1900 m, No. 5939, July 21; Khetszin district, Lotogou village, 2550 m, No. 6280, Aug 1; A. R. Lee; vicinity of Tyan'chi lake, No. 4250, Sep. 19, 1957, Kuan, around nor. Nom, No. 2469, Aug. 4, 1957—Kuan), ***Jung. Gobi*** (in Nyutsyuan'tsza region, desert, No. 1381, July 16, 1957—Kuan).

General distribution: Fore Balkh., Jung.-Tarb., Nor. and Cen. Tien Shan.

Section 2 (24). **Poliothrix** Bunge

83. **A. leucocephalus** Grah. in Wall. Cat. No. 5923 and 5926, nom., ex Benth. in Royle Ill. 32, 2 (1839–1840) 198; Bunge Gen. Astrag. Sp. Geront. 1 (1868) 48 and 2 (1869) 76; Baker in Hook. f. Fl. Brit. Ind. 2 (1876) 128; id. in J. Linn. Soc. Bot. 18 (1881) 45; Rech. in K. Danske. Vid. Selsk. Biol. Skrift. 9, 3 (1958) 37; Ali in Nasir et Ali, Fl. West Pakistan, No. 100 (1977) 147; K.T. Fu in Bull. Bot. Research, 2, 1 (1982) 66; Li et Ni in Fl. Xizang, 2 (1985) 841.

—**Ic.:** Rech. l.c. fig. 28.

Described from Himalayas. Type in London (K).

In ravines, meadow-covered mountain slopes, 3000–3800 m.

IIIB. Tibet: ***South.*** (Gyantse, No. 108, July–Sep. 1904—Walton; "Lhasa"—Fl. Xizang l.c.).

General distribution: Himalayas.

84. **A. rigidulus** Benth. ex Bunge Gen. Astrag. Sp. Geront. 1 (1868) 23 and 2 (1869) 25; Baker in Hook. f. Fl. Brit. Ind. 2 (1876) 123; K.T. Fu in Bull. Bot. Research, 2, 1 (1982) 66; P.C. Li et Ni in Fl. Xizang, 2 (1985) 844.

—**Ic.:** Fl. Xizang, 2, tab. 278, fig. 9–15.

Described from Himalayas (Sikkim). Type in London (K).

In alpine meadows and moraines, 3800–5000 m alt.

IIIB. Tibet: ***South.*** ("Lhasa, Chzhada, Tszyanga"—Fl. Xizang l.c.).

General distribution: Himalayas.

85. **A. strictus** Grah. ex Benth. in Royle Ill. (1839–1840) 198; Bunge Gen. Astrag. Sp. Geront. 1 (1868) 23 and 2 (1869) 27; Baker in Hook. f. Fl. Brit. Ind. 2 (1876) 124; Ulbr. in Repert. Nov. Sp. Beib. 12 (1922) 418; Ali in Nasir. et Ali, Fl. West Pakistan, No. 100 (1977) 160; K.T. Fu in Bull. Bot. Research, 2, 4 (1982) 66; P.C. Li et Ni in Fl. Xizang, 2 (1985) 841.

—**Ic.:** Fl. Xizang, 2, tab. 278, fig. 1–8.

Described from Himalayas. Type in London (K).

On river banks, moist sites on steppified mountain slopes, 2900–4600 m.

IIIB. Tibet ("common"—Fl. Xizang l.c.).

General distribution: Himalayas (nor., Kashmir).

86. **A. nanjiangianus** K.T. Fu in Bull. Bot. Research, 2, 4 (1982) 69.

—**Ic.:** K.T. Fu l.c. tab. 1, fig. 8–13.

Described from Sinkiang. Type in Shaanxi, Wugung (NWBI).

In small wet ravines in dried-up meadows and along brooks.

IIA. Junggar: ***Tien Shan*** ("Xinjiang: Yu-tian, ad locos humidos sulci in prato siccis, 2500 m, No. 120, July 5, 1970 Ai Zhilin—typus ! [NWBI]; Ho-tian Xian pascium Fungguang commun., prope rivum, 3200 m, No. 750510 and 750593, July 20, 1975—Yang Chang-you"—K.T. Fu l.c.).

IIIB. Tibet: ? *Chang Tang.*

General distribution: endemic.

Section 3 (25). **Tapinodes** Bunge

***A. dingjiensis** Ni et P.C. Li in Acta Phytotax. Sin. 17, 2 (1979) 109; id. in Fl. Xizang, 2 (1985) 820; K.T. Fu in Bull. Bot. Research, 2, 4 (1982) 74.

—**Ic.:** Acta Phytotax. Sin. (1979) tab. 8, fig. 11–20; Fl. Xizang, 2, tab. 266, fig. 11–20.

Described from Tibet, Type in Beijing (PE).

On rocky hill slopes, 4800 m.

IIIB. Tibet: ***South.*** ("Dintsze"—Fl. Xizang l.c., outside Cen. Asia).

General distribution: endemic.

87. **A. malcolmi** Hemsl. et Pears. in J. Linn. Soc. Bot. 35 (1903) 172; P.C. Li et Ni in Enum. Vasc. Pl. Xizang (Tibet) (1980) 181; id. in Fl. Xizang, 2 (1985) 844; K.T. Fu in Bull. Bot. Research, 2, 4 (1982) 74.

Described from Tibet. Type in London (LINN).

In apline belt at 5400 m.

IIIB. Tibet: *Chang Tang* ("Shuankhu"—Fl. Xizang l.c.).

General distribution: endemic.

***A. longiscapus** P.C. Li et Ni in Acta Phytotax. Sin. 17, 2 (1979) 108; id. Enum. Vasc. Pl. Xizang (Tibet) (1980) 181; id. in Fl. Xizang, 2 (1985) 818; K.T. Fu in Bull. Bot. Research, 2, 4 (1982) 74.

—**Ic.:** P.C. Li et Ni (1979) l.c. tab. 8, fig. 1–10; id. (1985) l.c. tab. 266, fig. 1–10.

Described from Tibet. Type in Beijing (PE).

In alpine meadows and rock talus, 4050-4100 m.

IIIB. Tibet: ***South.*** ("Nelamu, Tsona"—Fl. Xizang l.c., outside Cen. Asia).

General distribution: endemic.

88. **A. orbicularifolius** P.C. Li et Ni in Acta Phytotax. Sin. 17, 2 (1979) 112; id. Enum. Vasc. Pl. Xizang (Tibet) (1980) 187; id. in Fl. Xizang, 2 (1985) 819; K.T. Fu in Bull. Bot. Research, 2, 4 (1982) 74.

—**Ic.:** P.C. Li et Ni (1979) l.c. tab. 11, fig. 8–16.

Described from Tibet. Type in Beijing (PE).

On hill slopes, among rocks, 4900–5500 m.

IIIB. Tibet: *Chang Tang* ("Shuankhu"), ***South.*** ("Pulan'Chzhada"—Fl. Xizang l.c.).

General distribution: endemic.

Subgenus 5. **Astragalus** (*Caprinus* Bunge)

1. Spiny shrubs, subshrubs or dwarf shrubs with woody (and well-developed) stems (caudex) and sharp, stiff, persistent petioles and inflorescence axis. Spines usually persisting on stem for more than one vegetative season. Inflorescence sessile or subsessile or on short peduncles .... 2.

\+ Perennial with shortened or tall stems and nonspiny shedding petioles .... 11.

2. Flowers sessile, 2–5 each in axils of leaves approximated in upper part of shoots. Inflorescence globose. Pods bilocular or almost so (section 1 (26). **Astenolobium** (Nevski) Gontsch.) ..... 3.

\+ Flowers on short pedicels, 1–3 (7) each in axils of leaves, distant. Inflorescence lax. Pods almost unilocular or semibilocular (section 2 (27). **Aegacantha** Bunge) .... 4.

3. Ovary glabrous, calyx narrowly-tubular, 15–17 mm long, teeth narrowly-lanceolate, 1/2 of tube. Standard 20–24 mm long, subpandurate, gradually narrowed toward base into claw. Pods glabrous, 15–20 (25) mm long, 5–6 mm broad. Leaflets (13) 17–23 pairs, obovate or oval-oblong, 5–10 mm long, (1) 3–7 mm broad .... 89. **A. webbianus** Grah. ex Benth.

\+ Ovary pubescent. Calyx narrowly-tubular, 12–15 mm long, teeth 1/3 as long as tube. Standard 24–30 mm long, oblong, gradually narrowed into claw. Pods with short white pubescence or glabrate, 17–26 cm long, 6–7 mm broad, ventral side convex, keeled, dorsal sulcate. Leaflets (6) 9–13 pairs, elliptical, 8–12 mm long, 5–8 mm broad, puberulent or subglabrous .... 90. **A. royleanus** Bunge

4. Inflorescence with (2) 3–7 flowers. Peduncle short, 5–6 mm long. Calyx about 12 mm long, teeth subulate, 1/4–1/3 as long as tube. Standard about 23 mm long, oblong or obovate. Pods up to 13 mm long, 5 mm broad, oblong or obovate, glabrous above, glabrous or diffusely pilose below .... ***A. polyacanthus** Royle ex Benth.

\+ Flowers very large. Characteristics different .... 5.

5. Limb of standard glabrous outside .... 7.

\+ Limb of standard with dense, white, silky pubescence outside. Leaflets 6–11 pairs, obovate, oblong-lanceolate or lanceolate, (2) 3–8 (10) mm long .... 6.

6. Peduncle 8–30 (40) mm long. Corolla yolk-yellow, standard 22–26 mm long, calyx 13–16 mm long, teeth linear-subulate, 1/6–1/3 as long as tube. Year-old shoots longer than 5 cm, with

mostly long internodes. Pods 10–11 mm long, oblong-lanceolate, subbilocular …………… *A. **roschanicus** B. Fedtsch.

\+ Peduncle very short, up to 5 mm long. Corolla greenish-yellow, standard 19–25 mm long. Calyx 12–16 mm long, teeth linear-lanceolate, 1/3–1/2 as long as tube. Year-old shoots less than 5 cm long, with very short internodes. Pods 14–17 mm long, semioval, semibilocular .... 91. **A. lasiosemius** Boiss.

7. Old shoots elongated, procumbent, young shoots suberect. Inflorescence on distinct, 2–6 cm long peduncle. Calyx 17–19 mm long, brownish, bristly; standard 25–28 mm long, limb oblong-obovate. Pods 15–20 mm long, 5–7 mm broad, narrowly-ovate, with strong long beak. Stipules membranous, bristly. Leaflets 13–16 pairs, 5–10 mm long, 3–7 mm broad, elliptical, obtuse or acuminate, bristly above, covered beneath along midrib and along margin with sparse long hairs .... 92. **A. rhizanthus** Royle ex Benth.

\+ Old branches short and compact .... 8.

8. Calyx somewhat inflated. Pods pubescent, as long as calyx. Leaflets 4–6 pairs, obovate, obtuse, with dense silky pubescence on both surfaces. Stipules membranous. Peduncle with (1) 2–7 flowers. Blade of standard narrowed toward base .... ***A. multiceps** (Royle) Wall.

\+ Calyx not inflated .... 9.

9. Calyx wholly pubescent with white hairs. Corolla albescent, later flavescent. Limb of standard oblong, angular at base, 4–5 times longer than claw, blade of wings 1.5–2 times longer than claw .... 93. **A. leiosemius** (Lipsky) M. Pop.

\+ Calyx pubescent with white and black hairs, sometimes with extremely dense black hairs, about 15 mm long; teeth lanceolate, 1/3 as long as tube .... 10.

10. Leaflets 15–21 pairs, elliptical or oblong-lanceolate, acuminate, 5–9 mm long, 3–4 mm broad, glabrous on both surfaces or younger ones covered with sparse long hairs. Inflorescence with 2–5 flowers. Standard 24–26 mm long, oblong-obovate. Petiole of year-old leaves hardened, turning into yellow spine. Pods up to 20 mm long, 6–7 mm broad, oblong .... 94. **A. oplites** Benth. ex Parker

\+ Leaflets 5–10 (15) pairs, oval or obovate, somewhat emarginate at tip, 5–10 mm long, 2–4 mm broad, glabrous above, pubescent with sparse hairs beneath along margin. Inflorescence with 2–4 flowers. Strandard 20 mm long, oblong-obovate. Petiole of year-old leaves hardened but not into spine .... 95. **A. bicuspis** Fisch.

11 (2). Petals of corolla, all or at least standard, pilose outside ...... 12.

+ Corolla glabrous .... 17.

12. Leaves lanate-arachnoid or lanate-villous above. Pods unilocular or semibilocular. Flowers pale-yellow or white, sometimes erubescent (section 3 (28). **Mucidifolia** R. Kam.) .... 13.

+ Leaves totally glabrous or pubescent on top but not lanate-arachnoid. Pods bilocular or semibilocular, more rarely unilocular but then, apart from a different type of pubescence of leaves, racemes radical and corolla bright-yellow (section 4 (29). **Erionotus** Bunge) .... 15.

13. Limb of keel (measured without auricles, from notch to tip) (7) 8–10 (12) mm long, oblong, only slightly recurved at tip. Calyx tube (10) 12–14 (16) mm long. Standard (20) 25–30 (35) mm long, 4–5 (7) mm longer than keel; latter 14–24 (28) mm long. Pods (14) 16–21 mm long (without beak), concave-sulcate on back, semibilocular for 2/3, with uniform compact wall .... 96. **A. lanuginosus** Kar. et Kir.

+ Limb of keel (3) 4–6 mm long, oblong, helmet-shaped or almost rectangularly recurved at tip. If limb of keel up to 7 mm long (*A. mucidus*, occasionally), entire keel not longer than 15 mm and standard not more than 18 mm long, only 2–3 mm longer than keel .... 14.

14. Leaflets 18–25 (30) pairs, oval-oblong or oblong-elliptical, rarely lanceolate or ovate. Standard (18) 19–23 mm long, (4) 5–6 mm longer than keel. Calyx tube 7–14 mm long, (3.5) 4–4.5 mm broad. Pods (11) 12–17 mm long, oblong-ovate, largely sulcate-concave on back, semibilocular for 1/3 with uniform wall. Hairs on leaf rachis and calyx horizontally divergent or obliquely erect .... 97. **A. floccosifolius** Sumn.

+ Leaflets 14–26 pairs, ovate or oblong-ovate. Standard 13–16 (18) mm long, only 2 (3) mm longer than keel. Calyx tube (6) 6.5–7.5 (8) mm long, about 2.5 mm broad. Pods 8–11 mm long, oblong or oblong-ovate, somewhat sulcate on back, semibilocular for 1/3, with oblique wall; pod nearly solid at base. Hairs on calyx and rachis not obliquely erect .... ***A. mucidus** Bunge.

15. Stipules green, herbaceous, lanceolate or ovate-lanceolate, up to 10 mm long, 2–3 mm broad. Leaflets (5) 7–10 (18) mm long, pubescent with long hairs above and beneath along entire

surface. Racemes lax, with 4–7 flowers; flowers greenish-albescent; calyx 9–11 mm long, teeth nearly as long as or slightly shorter than tube; standard 14–19 mm long, glabrous inside, wings sericeous outside, keel glabrous. Pods oblong-lanceolate, (10) 14–17 mm long, 5–6 mm broad, bilocular .... 98. **A. orbiculatus** Ledeb.

\+ Stipules white-membranous, oblong, oblong-ovate or lanceolate-oblong. Flowers yellow .... 16.

16\. Leaflets (7) 9–12 (15) pairs, oblong-ovate, (10) 16–28 (40) mm long, subglabrous above, villous beneath. Stipules lanceolate-oblong, or oblong-ovate, 10–15 mm long. Racemes dense with (6) 8–12 flowers; calyx campanulate, 12–15 (18) mm long, teeth 2–3 times longer than tube; standard 14–20 mm long, wings silky outside, keel pilose at tip. Pods ovate or elliptical, 12–15 (18) mm long, not completely bilocular .... 99. **A. lasiopetalus** Bunge

\+ Leaflets 15–22 (29) pairs, ovate or elliptical, (5) 8–18 (24) mm long, albescent-sericeous on both surfaces. Lower stipules ovate or oblong, upper lanceolate, (6) 10–16 (35) mm long. Racemes lax, with 2–7 (12) flowers; calyx tubular, 13–18 (22) mm long, teeth 2/3 as long as tube or more rarely as long; standard (20) 23–28 (32) mm long; all petals sericeous outside. Pods oblong-ovate, 15–17 mm long, nearly entirely bilocular .... 100. **A. nicolai** Boriss.

17\. Plant usually robust or tall, invariably with well-developed stems. Stipules free, cauline, distant. Peduncles axillary ...... 18.

\+ Plant stemless or almost so, with strongly shortened year-old stems, usually not longer than 5 cm. Stipules largely adnate to petiole for much of their length. Flowers in radical racemes or on highly shortened branches. Calyx 10–15 mm long. Corolla bright-yellow or green-yellow, usually erubescent or viridescent toward end of anthers .... 20.

18\. Bracts caducous. Raceme one-sided, dense, flowers compact. Standard 10–14 mm long, oblong-orbicular, base cuneate with long claw. Leaflets 9–12 pairs, oblong, 15–25 mm long, 6–8 mm broad, densely covered beneath with appressed soft, long white hairs. Pods bilocular, oblong-ovate, 10–15 mm long, 6–7 mm broad, glabrous tip of pod extended into long beak. Erect, shrubby, large, herbaceous plant, 1–1.5 m tall (section 5 (30). **Chlorostachys** Bunge) .... ***A. tunbatsica** Marq. et Airy-Shaw

\+ Bracts persistent. Racemes not one-sided. Pods unilocular. Robust mesophilic herb .... 19.

19. Flowers yellow; calyx broadly-tubular, 14–15 mm long. Pods oblong, 12–22 mm long, with patent white hairs, subbilocular. Leaflets 15–18 pairs, lanceolate-oblong, or oblong, 15–20 mm long, 7–8 mm broad. Peduncle 5–10 cm long, 1/3–1/2 as long as leaves. Plant 12–40 (50) cm tall (section **Pendulina** Gontsch.) .... *__A. rubtzovii__ Boriss.

\+ Flowers light-yellow; calyx large, 18–22 mm long. Pods large, inflated, 20–25 mm long, 15–20 mm broad, densely lanate, entirely bilocular. Leaflets 8–12 (14) pairs, oblong-elliptical or lanceolate, 35–40 (50) mm long, glabrous above, pilose beneath. Racemes with 3–5 (rarely more) flowers, axillary, subsessile. Plant 60–150 cm tall (section 6 (31). **Lithoon** (Nevski) Gontsch.) .... 101. **A. sieversianus** Pall.

20. Leaves imparipinnate .... 21.

\+ Leaves somewhat whorled (more than 3 leaflets in a whorl). Stipules adnate to petiole in lower part (section 9 (34). **Gontscharoviella** R. Kam.) .... 47.

21. Plants acauline or almost so. Stipules free, i.e. not adnate to petiole. Racemes few- or many-flowered, invariably on peduncles 2 cm or more long. Flowers usually nutant. Bracts 2 or absent. Pods unilocular or subunilocular (section 7 (32). **Skythropos** Simps.) .... 22.

\+ Plant acauline. Stipules usually adnate to petiole for much of their length. Racemes subsessile, few-flowered. Flowers erect or horizontal. Bracts absent. Pods bilocular (section 8 (33). **Myobroma** Bunge). .... 29.

22. Leaflets (2) 4–5 pairs, glabrous on both surfaces, 10–12 mm long, 8–10 mm broad. Corolla, yellow, wings falcate, longer than standard, latter 12–14 mm long. Calyx 7–9 mm long .... 102. **A. smithianus** Peter-Stib.

\+ Leaflets 12–14 pairs, covered with long, soft, white hairs on both surfaces or only beneath. Wings not curved, nearly as long as standard .... 23.

23. Flowers yellow .... 24.

\+ Flowers violet, blue or red .... 27.

24. Keel longer than standard and wings. Calyx teeth 1/5–1/2 as long as tube .... 25.

\+ Keel as long as standard and wings or shorter. Calyx teeth nearly as long as tube .... 26.

25. Racemes dense, with 20–22 flowers. Standard 17 mm long, wing auricles short, up to 2 mm long. Leaflets 4–10 mm long,

entirely glabrous above, long-ciliate beneath along margin .... 103. **A. fenzelianus** Peter-Stib.

\+ Racemes lax, with 4–6 flowers. Standard up to 15 mm long, wing auricles elongated, up to 4 mm long. Leaflets 4–6 mm long, covered on both surfaces with long appressed white hairs .... 104. **A. datunensis** Y.C. Ho

26. Standard oblong, 15–20 mm long, limb of standard nearly as long as claw; corolla twice longer than calyx; calyx teeth nearly as long as tube. Leaflets 12–14 (18) pairs, 9–13 mm long, 6–9 mm broad, orbicular or orbicular-cordate, glabrous above, ciliate along margin .... 105. A. **yunnanensis** Franch.

\+ Standard suborbicular, claw 1/2 of limb of standard .... 106. **A. tatsienensis** Bureau et Franch.

27. Leaflets acute, ovate or oblong-ovate, 5–13 mm long, 2–8 mm broad .... 107. **A. skythropos** Bunge.

\+ Leaflets obtuse to emarginate, from oblong-ovate to orbicular .... 28.

28. Wings as long as keel. Leaflets 7–12 pairs, 4–8 (12) mm long, 3–9 mm broad .... 108. **A. licentianus** Hand.-Mazz.

\+ Wings shorter than keel. Leaflets 7–19 pairs, 6–10 mm long, 4–7 mm broad. Pods ovate-lanceolate, 15–17 mm long, base round and tip acuminate .... 109. **A. weigoldianus** Hand.-Mazz.

29. Leaflets linear-lanceolate or oblong-lanceolate, 4–12 mm long, 2–3 mm broad, 13–16 pairs. Racemes subsessile, few-flowered; peduncle hard, short, usually shorter than 5 mm. Corolla 20–30 mm long, yellow .... ***A. acaulis** Baker.

\+ Leaflets broader, orbicular or ovate, more rarely oblong ..... 30.

30. Calyx teeth as long as tube or slightly shorter (more rarely (1/2) 2/3 as long) .... 31.

\+ Calyx teeth 1/5–1/2 as long as tube .... 36.

31. Peduncle 15–60 mm long. Racemes with (5) 8–12 flowers. Corolla yellow, standard 20–26 mm long, limb obovate, slightly emarginate at tip, pubescent or glabrous outside. Pods bilocular, oblong or oblong-ovate, 15–22 mm long, with sparse, soft, white hairs. Leaflets 12–17 pairs, ovate, (10) 15–30 mm long, glabrous above, with scattered long hairs beneath and along margin .... 110. **A. schanginianus** Pall.

\+ Inflorescence radical; if with distinct peduncle, limb of standard oblong or broadly-oblong .... 32.

32. Pods unilocular, 7–11 mm long, 6–9 mm broad, with densely white villous, ovate, erect, sessile, 2-seeded. Petiole and leaf rachis with diffuse patent hairs. Leaflets 10–20 (24) pairs, 10–30 mm long, 4–16 mm broad, broadly-oblong, or elliptical, rounded or obtuse at tip, sometimes broadly emarginate. Stipules adnate to petiole almost up to half. Peduncle almost undeveloped, racemes up to 3.5 cm long, capitate, lax, subsessile, with 6–8 flowers. Pedicels 8–11 mm long, wings of corolla undivided or shallowly emarginate at tip .... *A. **lentilobus** R. Kam. et Kovalevsk.

\+ Pods subbilocular, 11–17 mm long. Petiole and leaf rachis glabrous; if pubescent, leaflets suborbicular. Leaflets usually glabrous .... 33.

33. Petiole and leaf rachis glabrous .... 34.

\+ Petiole and leaf rachis pubescent .... 35.

34. Leaflets 5–8 (10) pairs, orbicular, 10–12 (16) mm long, distant, obtuse or shallowly emarginate at tip, glabrous. Racemes with 2–4 flowers. Corolla pale-yellow; standard 25–30 mm long, limb oblong, orbicular. Pods glabrous or sparsely hairy .... 111. **A. aksaricus** N. Pavl.

\+ Leaflets 7–12 (15) pairs, ovate or orbicular-ovate, (7) 10–25 (45) mm long, glabrous or more rarely diffusely hairy along margin. Racemes sessile, radical, 4–8–(16)-flowered. Corolla yellow, standard 17–20 (32) mm long, limb ovate or broadly-oblong, rounded or barely emarginate. Pods pilose, more rarely glabrous .... 112. **A. severtzovii** Bunge.

35. Pods 12–15 mm long ...... ***A. merkensis** R. Kam. et Kovalevsk.

\+ Pods 16–18 mm long .... ***A. tianschanicus** Bunge.

36 (30). Leaflets with reddish, appressed, silky hair above (rarely beneath). Pods on 1–2 mm long stalks, elliptical or oblong, 14–18 mm long, 4–5 mm thick, 7–8 mm broad, flattened or slightly sulcate on back .... ***A. abbreviatus** Kar. et Kir.

\+ Leaflets pubescent only beneath or glabrous on both surfaces .... 37.

37. Leaflets orbicular, orbicular-oval, orbicular-ovate or orbicular-obovate, velutinous beneath, sometimes albescent due to dense pubescence or long patent hairs, or glabrous .... 38.

\+ Leaflets of different form; if, however, oval or, more rarely, orbicular-oval, pubescent differently or even with red fringe and emarginate at tip, more rarely obtuse .... 40.

38. Peduncle stout, together with inflorescence generally equalling leaves. Wings shorter than keel, very rarely longer; keel deeply laciniate at tip. Calyx narrowly-tubular, 14–18 mm long, teeth subulate-linear, 2–3 mm long. Pods ovate-oblong, inflated, (14) 16–24 mm long, on 5–8 mm long stalk, hard-skinned. Leaflets 7–12 pairs, orbicular or orbicular-ovate, (6) 8–18 (20) mm long, reddish-ciliate along margin ..... 113. **A. flexus** Fisch.

\+ Peduncle invariably shorter than leaves. Wings longer than keel, undivided at tip .... 39.

39. Peduncle 2–3 cm long. Raceme with (3) 5–6 flowers; standard up to 20 mm long. Pods elliptical or orbicular-elliptical, (18) 27–32 mm long, (9) 11–13 mm broad, bilocular, with soft white hairs. Leaflets oval or oblong-obovate, 6–15 mm long, 4–9 mm broad, with long and soft white hairs beneath and along margin, 8–11 pairs .... 114. **A. sanczirii** Ulzij.

\+ Peduncle well developed. Standard 30–35 mm long. Pods oval, 35–45 mm long, stalked, semibilocular, glabrous or diffusely pilose. Leaflets (6) 8–10 pairs, orbicular or oval, with long or short patent white hairs beneath .... ***A. austrodschungaricus** Golosk.

40. Bracteoles present. Corolla yellow and later erubescent ...... 41.

\+ Bracteoles absent. Corolla green, yellow and later viridescent, sometimes erubescent .... 42.

41. Leaflets (12) 15–17 pairs, glabrous above, with appressed or semiappressed hairs beneath. Calyx 12–16 mm long, teeth subulate, 2–5 mm long. Standard 26–27 mm long, limb oblong-spathulate or elliptical, with distinct constriction at middle. Pods oblong, 18–20 mm long, 10–11 mm broad, on 7–9 mm long stalk .... 115. **A. neo-chorgosicus** Podl.

\+ Leaflets 10–14 pairs, glabrous above, canescent beneath, short villous. Calyx 10–12 mm long, teeth deltoid-subulate, about 2 mm long. Standard about 26 mm long, limb oblong-ovate. Pods broadly-ovate, 20–25 mm long, on 5–7 mm long stalk .... ***A. pulposus** M. Pop.

42. Peduncle with dense or lax pubescence, (2) 4–11 cm long, more rarely 0.5–2 (5) cm (only in *A. buchtormensis*) .... 43.

\+ Peduncle glabrous, poorly or usually well developed .... 46.

43. Racemes with (6) 8–14 flowers. Calyx glabrous, 12–15 (17) mm long, yellowish-green. Corolla yellow, 22–26 mm long; wings with gibbous above auricle. Pods ovate-elliptical, inflated, 17–28 mm long, on (4) 5–6 mm long stalk, hard-skinned,

bilocular, glabrous. Leaflets (7) 9–14 (18) pairs, ovate or obovate, (5) 10–20 (23) mm long, glabrous or diffusely-pilose beneath along margin .... 116. **A. altaicus** Bunge.

\+ Racemes few-flowered. Calyx patently pilose throughout or only on teeth, 10–13 (14) mm long. Wings not gibbous above auricle .... 44.

44\. Plant dwarf, 4–6 cm tall. Peduncle very short, about 4 mm long, raceme with 1–2 flowers. Standard up to 20 mm long, oblong-obovate. Leaflets small, 2–6 mm long, 1–2.5 mm broad, ovate or elliptical. Hairs up to 3 mm long .... 117. **A. przewalskianus** Podl. et Ulzij.

\+ Plant 10–35 cm tall. Peduncle short, 1–8 cm tall, racemes with (2) 3–7 flowers. Standard 20–26 mm long. Leaflets more than 6 mm long. Hairs short, up to 1 mm long .... 45.

45\. Peduncle (3) 4–8 cm long. Racemes with 5–7 flowers, lax. Corolla yellow; standard 24–26 mm long with broadly-oblong limb. Pods trigonous-oblong, 20 mm long, subsessile, with 4–6 mm long beak, with chondroid skin, bilocular, glabrous. Leaflets (10) 12–20 pairs, oblong-ovate, (6) 12–28 mm long, sparsely-ciliate beneath along veins and margin .... 118. **A. trautvetteri** Bunge.

\+ Peduncle 1–4 (6) cm long. Racemes with 2–3 (4) flowers. Corolla bright-yellow; standard 20–24 mm long with orbicular-ovate limb. Pods oval or oblong-oval, inflated, (13) 15–20 mm long, on 1.5–2 mm long stalk, with 3–5 mm long beak, coriaceous, subbilocular, with sparsely white-villous. Leaflets (11) 18–28 (30) pairs, elliptical or oblong, 6–13 (16) mm long, glabrous above, pubescent beneath along entire surface .... 119. **A. buchtormensis** Pall.

46\. Peduncle generally well developed, (1) 2–3 (5) cm long. Racemes lax, with 5–6 flowers. Calyx 10–15 mm long, glabrous, pilose only on teeth, latter 2–5 mm long. Standard 25–29 mm long, wings 22–24 mm long, keel 18–22 mm long. Pods oblong or ovate, about 20 mm long, on 2–3 mm long stalk, glabrous. Leaflets 20–22 pairs, oblong-ovate, (5) 8–18 (23) mm long .... 120. **A. chlorodontus** Bunge.

\+ Peduncle nearly undeveloped. Racemes with 2 flowers. Calyx tubular, 12–14 mm long, with diffuse, patent hairs, teeth 3–4 mm long. Standard 22–24 mm long, wings 20–22 mm long, keel 17–18 mm long. Pods elliptical or ovate, 10–15 mm long, on 1–2 mm long stalk, white-villous. Leaflets 10–20 pairs, ovate or orbicular-ovate, 4–8 (10) mm long .... 121. **A. taldycensis** Franch.

47 (20). Leaflets glabrous or subglabrous above. Pods semi-bilocular, densely villous .... 48.

\+ Leaflets pubescent above .... 49.

48. Leaflets 4–8 each in 10–18 whorls, oblong or ovate-oblong, more rarely ovate, diffusely villous beneath, (2) 3–8 (15) mm long. Racemes with 3–5 flowers, short-peduncled or subradical. Calyx 10–15 mm long, subglabrous or largely densely villous. Pods broadly-oblong, 8–15 mm long .... 122. **A. alatavicus** Kar. et Kir.

\+ Leaflets 4–6 each in 8–14 (20) approximate pairs (false whorls), oval-oblong or oblong-oval, pubescent below, canescent. Racemes with 5–10 (15) flowers on long or distinctly manifest peduncle. Calyx 13–15 mm long, densely pubescent. Pods semioval-oblong, (12) 14–18 mm long .... 123. **A. pamiriensis** Franch.

49. Leaflets appressed-pilose. Calyx diffusely appressed pilose or glabrous. Leaflets oblong or ovate-elliptical, 7–20 (25) mm long, 2–3 (4) mm broad. Pods subunilocular .... ***A. adpressipilosus** Gontsch.

\+ Leaflets and calyx patently- or semipatently-puberulent. Leaflets linear, linear-oblong or lanceolate-oblong, Pods subbilocular .... 50.

50. Plant forming small elegant turfs. Leaflets (3) 4-8 mm long, 2–3 mm broad, 6–8 (12) each in 7–12 whorls. Stipules pilose outside. Calyx 12–15 mm long. Wings bilaciniate above; limb of keel broadly-obovate .... ***A. dignus** Boriss.

\+ Plant forming very large turfs. Leaflets (7) 8–18 mm long, 3–6 mm broad, (4) 5–6 each in 7–12 (20) whorls. Stipules glabrous and ciliate only along margin. Calyx 15–17 mm long. Wings undivided above; limb of keel broadly-oblong .... 124. **A. alaicus** Freyn.

Section 1 (26). **Astenolobium** (Nevski) Gontsch.

89. **A. webbianus** Grah. ex Benth. in Royle, Ill. Bot. Himal. 3 (1835) 199; Baker in Hook. f. Fl. Brit. Ind. 2 (1876) 132; Hedin, S. Tibet, 6, 3 (1922) 60; Ali in Nasir, Fl. West Pakist. No. 100, Papilionac. (1977) 156; Y.C. Ho in Bull. Bot. Research, 1, 3 (1981) 124; Li et Ni in Fl. Xizang, 2 (1985) 832; Podl. in Mitt. Bot. Staatssamml. München, 25, 1 (1988) 187. —*A. minutifoliolatus* Wendelbo, in Nytt Mag., Bot. 1 (1952) 43.—*Tragacantha webbiana* (Grah. ex Benth.) Kuntze, Rev. Gen. 1 (1891) 949.

—**Ic.:** Fl. Xizang, 2, tab. 272, fig. 1–9; Podl. l.c., fig. 21.

Described from Himalayas. Type in Liverpool (LIV) .

In montane meadows and along sandy-pebbly shoals of rivers, 4200–4600 m.

IIIB. Tibet: ***Chang Tang*** ("Nor. Tibet"—Y.C. Ho l.c.), ***South.*** ("SW Tibet, northern slopes of Himalayas, Tsangpo spring, 5015 m, July 13, 1907—Hedin (C); plains of Tibet, 4570 m, 7—Strachey and Winterbottom (K)"—Podl. l.c.; "Chzhada"—Li et Ni l.c.).

General distribution: Afghanistan (Badakhshan: Hindukush, Vakhan), Pakistan (Chitral, Gilgit), Himalayas (Kashmir).

Note. Very few specimens of this species have evidently been collected in Tibet (Chang Tang) and East. Pamir in Cen. Asia.

90. **A. royleanus** Bunge Gen. Astrag. Sp. Geront. 1 (1868) 30 and 2 (1869) 34.—*A. candolleanus* Royle ex Benth. (non Boiss.): in Royle, Ill. Bot. Himal. (1835) 199; Podl. and Anders in Mitt. Staatssamml. München, 13 (1977) 439; Li et Ni in Fl. Xizang, 2 (1985) 835.—*A. vexillilongus* Sheldon. Minnesota Bot. Stud. 1 (1894) 140, nom. illeg.—*A. rhizantha* subsp. *candolleanus* (Royle ex Benth.) Podl. in Mitt. Bot. Staatssamml. München, 25 (1985) 184.—*Tragacantha candolleana* Royle ex Benth.) Ktze. Rev. Gen. 2 (1891) 941.

—**Ic.:** Podl. l.c., fig. 20.

Described from West. Himalayas (Kunavur). Type in London (K).

In alpine and subalpine belts, 2130–3950 m.

IIIB. Tibet: ***Chang Tang*** ("West. Tibet"—Li et Ni l.c.—sub nom. *A. candolleanus* Royle ex Benth. !).

General distribution: Himalayas (west. Kashmir).

Section 2 (27). **Aegacantha** Bunge

***A. roschanicus** B. Fedtsch. in Fl. Tadzhik. 5 (1937) 673, 388; Gontsch. and Boriss. in Fl. SSSR, 12 (1946) 240; Opred. rast. Sr. Azii [Key to Plants of Mid. Asia] 6 (1981) 141; Fl. Tadzhik. 6 (1981) 192.

—**Ic.:** Fl. Tadzhik. 6, Plate 29, fig. 10–15.

Described from Mid. Asia (Darwaza). Type in St.-Petersburg (LE).

On rocky slopes, talus, pebble beds and terraces of rivers.

Reported from border regions of East. Pamir.

General distribution: East. Pamir; Mid. Asia (Pamiro-Alay), Afghanistan ?.

91. **A. lasiosemius** Boiss. Diagn. Pl. or. nov. ser. 1, 9 (1849) 96; Bunge Gen. Astrag. Sp. Geront. 1 (1868) 44 and 2 (1869) 71; id. Astrag. Turk. (1880) 239; id. in Acta Horti Petrop. 7 (1880) 371; Fl. Tadzhik. 5 (1937) 387; Gontsch. and Boriss. in Fl. SSSR, 12 (1946) 240; Fl. Kirgiz. 7 (1957) 266; Kitam. Fl. Afghan. (1960) 200; Fl. Kazakhst. 5 (1961) 147; Ikon. Opred. rast. Pam. [Key to Plants of Pamir] (1963) 162; Bait. Astrag.

Tyan'-Shanya (1977) 55; Ali in Nasir, Fl. West Pakist. No. 100, Papilionac. (1977) 182; Podl. et Deml. in Mitt. Bot. Staatssamml. München, 13 (1977) 440; Opred. rast. Sr. Azii [Key to Plants of Mid. Asia] 6 (1981) 141; Fl. Tadzhik. 6 (1981) 190; Y.C. Ho in Bull. Bot. Research, 1, 3 (1981) 125; C.Y. Yang in Claves pl. Xinjiang, 3 (1985) 132. —*A. genistoides* Boiss. Diagn. Pl. or. Nov. Iser. 9 (1849) 97.—*A. latistylus* Freyn in Bull. Herb. Boiss. 2 ser. 4, 11 (1904) 1106.—*A. aridus* Freyn l.c. 1107.

—**Ic.:** Fl. Kazakhst. 5, Plate 19, fig. 2; Fl. Tadzhik. 6, Plate 29, fig. 6–9.

Described from Afghanistan. Type in Geneva (G).

On rocky and rubbly steppe slopes and trails, talus, more rarely on outcrops of varicoloured rocks in upper belt of mountains, sometimes in middle belt in juniper groves, usually at 3000 m.

IIIC. Pamir ("Uch-Kandy"—Y.C. Ho l.c.); "southern mountain regions of Sinkiang"—C.Y. Yang l.c.).

General distribution: Cen. Tien Shan; Mid. Asia (Pamiro-Alay), Himalayas (west. Afghanistan, Pakistan).

92. **A. rhizanthus** Royle ex Benth. in Royle. Ill. Bot. Himal. (1835) 200; Bunge Gen. Astrag. Sp. Geront. 1 (1868) 35 and 2 (1869) 60; Podl. in Mitt. Bot. Staatssamml. München, 25, 1 (1988) 177.—*A. malacophyllus* Benth. ex Bunge, Gen. Astrag. Sp. Geront. 1 (1868) 36 and 2 (1869) 61.—*A. anomalus* Bunge Gen. Astrag. Sp. Geront. 1 (1868) 35 and 2 (1869) 62; Baker in Hool. f. Fl. Brit. Ind. 2 (1876) 133; Y.C. Ho in Bull. Bot. Research, 1, 3 (1981) 125; Li et Ni in Fl. Xizang, 2 (1985) 833.—*A. nuristanicus* Sirj. et Rech. f. in Biol. Skr. 9, 3 (1957) 77, excl. var. *elasoonensis* Sirj. et Rech. f.—*A. dscherantuensis* Sirj. et Rech. f. var. *viridis* Sirj. et Rech. f. in Biol. Skr. 9, 3 (1957) 71.

—**Ic.:** Li et Ni l.c., tab. 273, figs. 1–9 (sub nom. *A. anomalus* Bunge).

Described from Himalayas. Type in Liverpool [LIV].

On grassy slopes in upper mountain belt (3400–4100 m).

IB. Kashgar: ***West.*** ("Yarkand Expedition, June 20, 1870, No. 337, Henderson"—Podl. l.c. 183).

IIIB. Tibet: ? ("Tibet"—Y.C. Ho l.c.).

General distribution: Himalayas (Kashmir).

Note. Reports possible from west. parts of Chang Tang and Pamir.

93. **A. leiosemius** (Lipsky) M. Pop. in Sched. Herb. Fl. Asia Med. fasc. 16 (1928) 50 and No. 388; Fl. Tadzhik. 5 (1937) 397; Persson in Bot. Notis. (1938) 291; Gontsch. and Boriss. in Fl. SSSR 12 (1946) 239; Kitam., Fl. Afghan. (1960) 200; Opred. rast. Sr. Azii [Key to Plants of Mid. Asia] 6 (1981) 189.—*A. lasiosemius* auct. non Boiss.: Y.C. Ho in Bull. Bot. Research, 1, 3 (1981) 125, p.p. ?—*A. lasiosemius* var. *leiosemius* Lipsky in

Acta Horti Petrop. 26 (1907) 235, p.p.; O. et B. Fedtsch. Konsp. fl. Turk. 2 (1909) 211 p.p.

Described from Mid. Asia (Kugitang mountain range). Type in Tashkent (TAK).

On rocky and rubbly slopes, talus, in juniper groves, more often in upper mountain belt.

IIIC. Pamir ("Uch-Kandy"—Y.C. Ho l.c.).

General distribution: Mid. Asia (Pamiro-Alay).

Note. Reports possible from east. Pamir and west. part of Chang Tang.

94. **A. oplites** Benth. ex Parker in Kew Bull. (1921) 270; Ali in Nasir Fl. West Pakist. No. 100, Papilionac. (1977) 193; Y.C. Ho in Bull. Bot. Research, 1, 3 (1981) 125; Li et Ni in Fl. Xizang, 2 (1985) 235; C.Y. Yang in Claves pl. Xinjiang, 3 (1985) 136.—*A. cicerifolius* Royle ex Bunge Gen. Astrag. Sp. Geront. 1 (1868) 44 and 2 (1869) 70, non Royle ex Fisch. (1835); Baker in Hook. f. Fl. Brit. Ind. 2 (1876) 134.

—**Ic.:** Li et Ni l.c. tab. 274, fig. 1–9.

Described from west. Tibet. Type in London (K).

On rocky montane slopes, 3700–4400 m.

IIA. Junggar: ? ***Tien Shan*** ("Sinkiang"—Y.C. Ho l.c.).

IIIB. Tibet: ***Chang Tang*** ("Tibeta occidentali, 10,000–14,000 ft supra mare, Thomson)" —Bunge l.c.; "Nor. Tibet"—Y.C. Ho l.c.), ***South.*** ("Pulan'"—Fl. Xizang l.c.).

IIIC. Pamir ("Tashkurgan—3800 m"—C.Y. Yang l.c.).

General distribution: Himalayas (west., east., Kashmir).

95. **A. bicuspis** Fisch. in Bull. Soc. Natur. Moscou 26 (1853) 406; Bunge Gen. Astrag. Sp. Geront. 1 (1868) 43 and 2 (1869) 67; Baker in Hook. f. Fl. Brit. Ind. 2 (1876) 135; Ali in Nasir, Fl. West Pakist. No. 100, Papilionac. (1977) 192; Y.C. Ho in Bull. Bot. Research, 1, 3 (1981) 126; Li et Ni in Fl. Xizang 2 (1985) 23.

Described from West. Himalayas. Type in London (K).

On arid sandy-rubbly hill slopes, among shrubs, 4000–4400 m.

IIIB. Tibet: ***Chang Tang*** (?"Nor. Tibet"—Y.C. Ho l.c.), ***South.*** ("Pulan'"—Li et Ni l.c.).

General distribution: Himalayas (west.).

Section 3 (28). **Mucidifolia** R. Kam.

96. **A. lanuginosus** Kar. et Kir. in Bull. Soc. Natur. Moscou 14 (1841) 409; Ledeb. Fl. Ross. 1, 3 (1843) 651; Bunge Gen. Astrag. Sp. Geront. 1 (1868) 33 and 2 (1869) 41; id. Astrag. Turk. (1880) 231 p.p.; O. et B. Fedtsch. Konsp. fl. Turk. 2 (1909) 205; Gontsch. in Fl. SSSR, 12 (1946) 127; Fl. Kirgiz. 7 (1957) 246; Fl. Kazakhst. 5 (1961) 128; Y.C. Ho in Bull. Bot. Research, 1, 3 (1981) 121; Opred. rast. Sr. Azii. [Key to Plants of Mid. Asia] 6 (1981) 132; C.Y. Yang in Claves pl. Xinjiang, 3 (1985) 133;

Fl. desert. Sin. 2 (1987) 255; Podl. in Mitt. Bot. Staatssamml. München, 25, 2 (1988) 576.—*A. mucidiformis* Sumn. in Animadv. Syst. Herb. Univ. Tomsk. 9–10 (1937) 1.—*A. larvatus* Sumn. l.c. 3.—*A. anrachaicus* Golosk. in Not. Syst. Herb. Inst. Bot. Ac. Sci. URSS, 15 (1953) 13; Fl. Kirgiz. 7 (1957) 249; Fl. Kazakhst. 5 (1961) 128.—*A. pseudoanrachaicus* E. Nikit. in Fl. Kirgiz. 7 (1957) 249, descr. ross.; Bait., Astrag. Tyan'-Shanya (1977) 48.—*Tragacantha lanuginosa* (Kar. et Kir.) Kuntze. Rev. Gen. 2 (1891) 945.

—**Ic.:** Fl. Kazakhst. 5 (1961) Plate 16, fig. 5.

Described from East. Kazakhstan. Type in St.-Petersburg (LE).

On fixed and dune sand, rocky and rubbly slopes, solonetzic low lands and abandoned fields, on rocks.

IIA. Junggar: ***Dzhark.*** (Kul'dzha, May 1877; Ili river valley east of Kul'dzha, May 14; Almaaty river, vicinity of Kul'dzha, 1000 m, April 21—1878, A. Reg.; "Ili river"—Y.C. Ho l.c.; C.Y. Yang l.c.).

General distribution: Fore Balkh., Jung.-Tarb., Nor. and Cen. Tien Shan.

97. **A. floccosifolius** Sumn. in Animadv. Syst. Herb. Univ. Tomsk. 9–10 (1937) 2; Gontsch. in Fl. SSSR, 12 (1946) 129; Fl. Kirgiz. 7 (1957) 250; Bait. Astrag. Tyan'-Shanya (1977) 48; Opred. rast. Sr. Azii [Key to Plants of Mid. Asia] 6 (1981) 133; Fl. Tadzhik. 6 (1981) 106; Podl. in Mitt. Bot. Staatssamml. München, 25, 2 (1988) 583.—*A. pseudolanuginosus* Gontsch. in Fl. Tadzhik. 5 (1937) 657 and 337.—*A. korolkowii* auct. non Bunge: O. et B. Fedtsch. Konsp. fl. Turk. 2 (1909) 205, p.p. quoad pl. e Tian-Schan.—*A. mucidus* auct. non Bunge; E. Nikit. in Fl. Kirgiz. 7 (1957) 251 p.p.—*A. ephemeretorum* auct. non Gontsch.: E. Nikit. in Fl. Kirgiz. 7 (1957) 251.

Described from Mid. Asia (Fergana mountain range). Type in Tomsk [TK]. Isotype in St.-Petersburg (LE).

On rubbly slopes of mountains, on old fallow lands, in juniper groves.

IIA. Junggar: ***Dzhark.*** (Ili river west of Kul'dzha, 914 m, April 21; Ili river valley west of Kul'dzha, No. 76, May—1878, A. Reg.).

General distribution: Nor. and Cen. Tien Shan; Mid. Asia (Pamiro-Alay).

***A. mucidus** Bunge ex Boiss. Fl. Or. 2 (1872) 279; Bunge Astrag. Turk. (1880) 230 p.p.; Gontsch. in Fl. Tadzhik. 5 (1937) 339; idem in Fl. SSSR, 12 (1946) 128; Fl. Kirgiz. 7 (1957) 246 p.p.; Fl. Kazakhst. 5 (1961) 130; Bait. Astrag. Tyan'-Shanya (1977) 48; Fl. Tadzhik. 6 (1981) 104; Opred. rast. Sr. Azii. [Key to Plants of Mid. Asia] 6 (1981) 134; Podl. in Mitt. Bot. Staatssamml. München, 25, 2 (1988) 579.—*A. serafschanicus* Freyn in Bull. Herb. Boiss. 2, ser. 4 (1904) 767.—*Tragacantha mucida* (Bunge ex Boiss.) Ktze. Rev. Gen. 2 (1891) 946.

—**Ic.:** Fl. Kazakhst. 5, Plate 16, fig. 4; Fl. Tadzhik. 6, Plate 14, fig. 1–5.

Described from Mid. Asia (Mogoltau). Type in St.-Petersburg (LE).

On loessial and rubbly slopes of desert mountains, sand mounds.

Known from Kirghizia adjoining Nor. and West. Kashgar.

Reports possible from nor.-west. part of Kashgar (Kokshaal-tau mountain range).

General distribution: Cen. Tien Shan; Mid. Asia (Pamiro-Alay).

Section 4 (22). **Erionotus** Bunge

98. **A. orbiculatus** Ledeb. Fl. Alt. 3 (1831) 311; id. Ic. pl. Fl. Ross. 3 (1831) 26; id. Fl. Ross. 1, 3 (1843) 623; Bunge Gen. Astrag. Sp. Geront. 1 (1868) 33 and 2 (1869) 39; idem in Izv. obshch. lyub. estestv., antr. i etnogr. 26, 2 (1880) 266; Boiss. Fl. Or. 2 (1872) 278; O. et B. Fedtsch. Konsp. fl. Turk. 2 (1909) 204; Kryl. Fl. Zap. Sib. 7 (1933) 1659; Gontsch. in Fl. Tadzhik. 5 (1937) 341 p.p.; idem in Fl. SSSR 12 (1946) 113; Fl. Kirgiz. 7 (1957) 244; Ali in Kew. Bull. (1958); id. in Nasir, Fl. West Pakist. No. 100, Papilionac. (1977) 143; Fl. Kazakhst. 5 (1961) 222; Bait. Astrag. Tyan'-Shanya (1977) 44; Fl. Tadzhik. 6 (1981) 97; Opred. rast. Sr. Azii [Key to Plants of Mid. Asia] 6 (1981) 126; Y.C. Ho in Bull. Bot. Research, 1, 3 (1981) 121; C.Y. Yang in Claves pl. Xinjiang, 3 (1985) 133; Podl. in Mitt. Bot. Staatssamml., München, 25, 1 (1988) 456.—*Tragacantha orbiculata* (Ledeb.) Ktze. Rev. Gen. 2 (1891) 947.

—**Ic.:** Fl. Kazakhst. 5 (1961), Plate 5, fig. 3; Fl. Tadzhik. 6, Plate 13, fig. 1–6.

Described from Altay (Bukon' river). Type in St.-Petersburg (LE).

On sand, solonetzic sand and solonchaks, in tugais, marshy low and moist short-grass meadows, along riverine valleys and on debris cones.

IIA. Junggar: ***Tarb.*** ("Dachen"—C.Y. Yang l.c.; "nor. regions of Sinkiang"—Y.C. Ho l.c.), ***Tien Shan*** ("nor. regions of Sinkiang"—Y.C. Ho l.c.), ***Zaisan*** ?, ***Dzhark.*** (Ili river valley, south of Kul'dzha, May 18, 1877—A. Reg.).

General distribution: Aralo-Casp., Fore Balkh., Nor. and Cen. Tien Shan; Mid. Asia, Himalayas (west.).

Note. Reports possible from East. Pamir.

99. **A. lasiopetalus** Bunge in Delect. Sem. Horti Dorpat. (1839) 7, in adnot. ad No. 2; Ledeb. Fl. Ross. 1 (1842) 651; Bunge Gen. Astrag. Sp. Geront. 1 (1868) 33 and 2 (1869) 40; id. Astrag. Turk. (1880) 226; O. et B. Fedtsch. Konsp. fl. Turk. 2 (1909) 205; Kryl. Fl. Zap. Sib. 7 (1933) 1660; Gontsch. in Fl. SSSR, 12 (1946) 113; Grub. Konsp. fl. MNR (1955) 185; Fl. Kirgiz. 7 (1957) 244; Fl. Kazakhst. 5 (1961) 122; Bait. Astrag. Tyan'-Shanya (1977) 45; Opred. rast. Sr. Azii [Key to Plants of Mid. Asia] 6 (1981) 128; Fl. Tadzhik. 6 (1981) 100; Y.C. Ho in Bull. Bot. Research, 1, 3, (1981) 121; Sanczir in Grub. Opred. rast. Mong. [Key to Plants of Mongolia] (1982) 156; Ulzij. in Tr. Inst. bot. AN MNR 8

(1982) 23; C.Y. Yang, Claves pl. Xinjiang 3 (1985) 133; Fl. desert. Sin. 2 (1987) 254; Podl. in Mitt. Bot. Staatssamml. München 25, 1 (1988) 476.—*A. lasianthus* C.A. Mey. in Bong. et Mey. Verz. Saisang-nor Pfl. (1841) 27. —*A. ulacholensis* B. Fedtsch. in Acta Horti Petrop. 24 (1905) 208.—*Tragacantha lasiopetala* (Bunge) Kuntze, Rev. Gen. 2 (1891) 946.

—**Ic.:** Fl. SSSR, 12, Plate 10, fig. 1; Grub. Opred. rast. Mong. [Key to Plants of Mongolia] Plate 85, fig. 389.

Described from East. Kazakhstan (Zaisan basin). Type in St.-Petersburg (LE).

In meadows, solonchak banks of rivers and irrigation ditches, in arid tugais and scrubs along rivers.

IA. Mongolia: ***Mong. Alt.*** (Bulgan region, Dzhargalant river valley, Sep. 16. 1930—Bar.; Kobdo region, Buyant river, date and collector not known; Bulgan river 18 km east of Yarantai mountain, No. 3502, 1964—Danert et al. [UBA, GAT]).

IIA. Junggar: ***Tien Shan*** ("Ili river region"—Y.C. Ho l.c.), ***Jung. Gobi*** (Bodonchiin-gol river 15–20 km south of Altay somon, No. 3703, 1964—Danert et al. [UBA, GAT]; Bodonchin-gol river floodplain 15 km south-west of Altay settlement, Aug. 1, 1979—Gub.; Bodoncin-gol-Aue, unterlauf des Bodoncin-gol 7 km unterhalb, Altqai-sum 1300 m, 1982 —Jager [HAL]), ***Zaisan*** (<Burchum>—C.Y. Yang l.c.).

General distribution: Fore Balkh., Nor. Tien Shan; Mid. Asia.

100. **A. nicolai** Boriss. in Fl. URSS, 12 (1946) 119; Fl. Kazakhst. 5 (1961) 125; Bait. Astrag. Tyan'-Shanya (1977) 45; Opred. rast. Sr. Azii [Key to Plants of Mid. Asia] 6 (1981) 128; Fl. desert. Sin. 2 (1987) 255; Podl. in Mitt. Bot. Staatssamml. München, 25, 1 (1988) 488.—*A. songoricus* Gontsch. in Not. Syst. Herb. Inst. Bot. Ac. Sci. URSS, 7 (1938) 152, non Pall. (1800).—*A. xinjiangensis* Y.C. Ho in Bull. Bot. Research, 1, 3 (1981) 121.

—**Ic.:** Fl. Kazakhst. 5 (1961) Plate 16, fig. 1.

Described from East. Kazakhstan (Jung. Ala Tau). Type in St.-Petersburg (LE).

In steppified rocky and rubbly montane slopes, small grasslands along montane brooks.

IIA. Junggar: ***Cis-Alt.*** ("Altay"—Fl. desert. Sin. l.c.), ***Tien Shan*** ("Mulei"—Y.C. Ho l.c.).

General distribution: Jung.-Tarb. (Jung. Ala Tau).

Section 5 (30). **Chlorostachys** Bunge

*__A. tunbatsica__ Marq. et Airy-Shaw in J. Linn. Soc. Bot. 48 (1929) 171 ("*tumbatisica*") ; Y.C. Ho in Bull. Bot. Research, 1, 3 (1981) 104; P.C. Li et Ni in Fl. Xizang, 2 (1985) 830.—*A. bomiensis* Ni et P.C. Li in Acta Phytotax. Sin. 18, 3 (1980) 367; id in Fl. Xizang, 2 (1985) 825.

Described from Tibet. Type in London (LINN).

Along banks of rivers, gorges, ravines, kerbs and fringes of ploughed fields, steppified montane slopes, 1700–3500 m.

IIIB. Tibet: ***South.*** ("Dintsze, Nelamu, Tszilun"—P.C. Li et Ni l.c.), outside Cen. Asia.

General distribution: Himalayas (east. Chayui).

Section **Pendulina** Gontsch.

***A. rubtzovii** Boriss. in Not. Syst. (Leningrad) 13 (1950) 127; Fl. Kazakhst. 5 (1961) 121; Bait. in Bot. mat. (Alma Ata) 9 (1975) 27; idem, Astrag. Tyan'-Shanya (1977) 44; Opred. rast. Sr. Azii [Key to Plants of Mid. Asia] 6 (1981) 167; Podl. in Mitt. Bot. Staatssamml. München, 25, 1 (1988) 454.

—**Ic.:** Podl. l.c. fig. 132, 317.

Described from East. Kazakhstan (Tien Shan, Kegen valley). Type in St.-Petersburg (LE).

On dune sand.

Reported from Jarkent region adjoining Suidun (Kul'dzha district) in Kazakhstan.

General distribution: endemic.

Note. Reports of this species possible from the adjoining Kul'dzha territory (Inin) in Sinkiang.

Section 6 (31). **Lithoon** (Nevski) Gontsch.

101. **A. sieversianus** Pall. Astrag. (1800) 15; Bunge Gen. Astrag. Sp. Geront. 1 (1868) 31 and 2 (1869) 36; idem in Izv. Obshch. lyub. estestv. antr. i etnogr. 26, 2 (1880) 221; id. In Acta Horti Petrop. 7 (1880) 370; O. et B. Fedtsch. Konsp. fl. Turk. 2 (1909) 203; Gontsch. in Fl. SSSR 12 (1946) 101; Fl. Kirgiz. 7 (1957) 243; Fl. Kazakhst. 5 (1961) 120; Bait. Astrag. Tyan'-Shanya (1977) 43; Opred. rast. Sr. Azii [Key to Plants of Mid. Asia] 6 (1981) 115; Y.C. Ho in Bull. Bot. Research, 1, 3 (1981) 120; C.Y. Yang in Claves pl. Xinjiang, 3 (1985) 133.

—**Ic.:** Fl. SSSR, 12, Plate 8, fig. 1; Fl. Kazakhst. 5, Plate 15, fig. 2.

Described from Kazakhstan (Ul'dzhar river). Type in St.-Petersburg (LE).

In rocky steppes and meadow-covered slopes, fallow lands, more rarely in plantations, from foothills to middle mountain belt.

IIA. Junggar: ***Tarb.*** ("Dachen" [Chuguchak town]—Y.C. Ho l.c., C.Y. Yang l.c.).

General distribution: Fore Balkh., Jung.-Tarb., Nor. and Cen. Tien Shan; Mid. Asia (Pamiro-Alay, Kopet Dag).

Section 7 (32). **Skythropos** Simps.

102. **A. smithianus** Peter-Stib. in Acta Horti Gotoburg, 12 (1937–38) 52; Wang and Tang, Ill. treatm. princip. pl. China, Legum. (1955) 376; Y.C. Ho in Bull. Bot. Lab. North-East. Forest Inst. 8 (1980) 57; Li et Ni in Fl. Xizang, 2 (1985) 820.

—**Ic.:** Wang and Tang l.c. fig. 379.

Described from South-West China (Sichuan). Type (?).

On rocky slopes and alpine plateau, 4800–5000 m.

IIIA. Qinghai: ***Amdo*** ("Tsinkhai"—Y.C. Ho l.c.).

IIIB. Tibet: ? ***Weitzan*** (Li et Ni l.c.).

General distribution: South-West China (Sichuan).

103. **A. fenzelianus** Peter-Stib. in Acta Horti Gotoburg, 12 (1937–38) 54; Wang and Tang, Ill. treatm. princip. pl. China, Legum. (1955) 375; Y.C. Ho in Bull. Bot. Lab. North-East. Forest Inst. 8 (1980) 57.

Described from Qinghai. Type in München (M).

In alpine grasslands, along river banks in alpine belt, 3200–5300 m.

IIIA. Qinghai: ***Nanshan*** ("Yeniu-Schan ad lac. Kukunor, No. 2343, July 22–23, 1935—Fenzel—typus !; Kokonor, Chinese collector [PE])", "Gansu, Qinghai"—Y.C. Ho l.c.), ***Amdo*** (Dzhakhar hills, 3200–3350 m, alp. grassland, June 22, 1880—Przew.).

IIIB. Tibet: ***Weitzan*** (Kon-chyun-la pass, alps, 4267–4572 m, July 2; hills along Chumcha-uma river, alps, July 3; hills, upper Tala-chyu river, 5232 m, July 6—1884, Przew.; "Dzom-la, No. 14381—Rock"—Peter-Stib. l.c.).

General distribution: endemic.

104. **A. datunensis** Y.C. Ho in Bull. Bot. Lab. North-East. Forest Inst. 8 (1980) 57.

—**Ic.:** Y.C. Ho l.c., tab. 3, fig. 1–8.

Described from Qinghai (Dabanshan' mountain range). Type in Wugung [NWBI].

In hills in alpine belt.

IIIA. Qinghai: ***Nanshan*** (Qinchai, 3800 m, July 18, 1958—Chin. collector [PE]; Datong, Dabanschan, alt. 3800 m, July 19, 1963, No. 2245, C.Y. Chang, typus !—Y.C. Ho l.c.).

General distribution: endemic.

Note. The exact identity of this species requires to be accurately defined based on a representative sample. This could probably be related to *A. weigoldianus* Hand.-Mazz.

105. **A. yunnanensis** Franch. Pl. Delav. (1889) 162; id. in Not. Bot. Gard. Edinb. 7 (1912) 160; Simps. in Not. Bot. Gard. Edinb. 8 (1915) 256; Hand.-Mazz. Symb. Sin. 7 (1933) 556; Marq. et Airy Shaw in J. Linn. Soc. Bot. 48 (1929) 172; Peter-Stib. in Acta Horti Gotoburg, 12 (1937–38) 37; Wang and Tang, Ill. treatm. princip. pl. China, Legum. (1955) 392; Y.C. Ho in Bull. Bot. Lab. North-East. Forest Inst. 8 (1980) 59; Fl. Xizang, 2 (1985) 821.

—**Ic.:** Wang and Tang l.c., fig. 380; Fl. Xizang, 2, fig. 1–7 and 8–10.

Described from South-West China (Yunnan). Type in Edinburgh [E].

In alpine meadows, in scrubs, among rocks, 4000–5100 m.

IIIB. Tibet: ***South.*** ("Lhasa"—Fl. Xizang l.c.; "Tibet"—Y.C. Ho l.c.).

General distribution: China (South-West: Yunnan, nor. Sichuan), Himalayas (east.).

106. **A. tatsienensis** Bureau et Franch. in Morot. J. de Bot. 5 (1891) 23; Simps. in Not. Bot. Gard. Edinb. 8 (1915) 256; Hand.-Mazz. Simb. Sin. 7 (1933) 556; Peter-Stib. in Acta Horti Gotoburg, 12 (1937–38) 54; Wang and Tang, Ill. treatm. princip. pl. China, Legum. (1955) 393; Y.C. Ho in Bull. Bot. Lab. North-East. Forest Inst. 8 (1980) 59.—*A. yunnanensis* var. *tatsienensis* (Bur. et Franch.) Cheng f. in Fl. Xizang, 2 (1985) 821.—*A. yunnanensis* var. *kangrenbuchiensis* Ni et P.C. Li in Acta Phytotax. Sin. 17 (1979) 110; P.C. Li et Ni in Fl. Xizang, 2 (1985) 821.—*A. tatsienensis* var. *kangrenbuchiensis* (Ni et P.C. Li) Y.C. Ho in Bull. Bot. Lab. North-East. Forest Inst. 8 (1980) 59.

—**Ic.:** Fl. Xizang, tab. 267, fig. 1–7.

Described from South-West China (Sichuan). Type in Paris [P].

On meadow-covered montane slopes and along valleys of rivers in mountains, 3850–5100 m.

IIIA. Qinghai: ***Nanshan*** ("Gansu, Qinghai"—Y.C. Ho l.c.), ***Amdo*** ("Amdo"—Y.C. Ho l.c.).

IIIB. Tibet: ***Weitzan*** (Chobaku-vrun area, Yan'tszy-tszyana basin, on meadow-covered descents of mountains along valley, 4267 m, July 17; Alyk-Norin-gol river valley, No. 254; Yan'tszy-tszyan river basin around Nyamtso, 4420–4572 m alt., July 13—1900, Lad.; left bank of Dy-chyu river, river valley of lateral tributary of Yangtze river, June 20, 1984—Przew.; "Inter Radja et Jupar range, No. 14240, June 1926—Rock"—Peter-Stib. l.c.), ***South.*** ("Pulan'"—Li et Ni l.c.).

General distribution: China (South-West: nor. Sichuan, Yunnan, Nor.-West Gansu south).

107. **A. skythropos** Bunge in Bull. Ac. Sci. St.-Petersb. 21 (1887) 31; Peter-Stib. in Acta Horti Gotoburg, 12 (1937–38) 57; Wang and Tang, Ill. treatm. princip. pl. China, Legum. (1955) 376; Y.C. Ho in Bull. Bot. Lab. North-East. Forest Inst. 8 (1980) 57; incl.—*A. skythropos* var. *acaulis* Danguy in Bull. Mus. Hist. Natur. Paris, n.s., 27 (1911) 207.

—**I.c.:** Wang and Tang l.c. fig. 382.

Described from Qinghai, Type in St.-Petersburg (LE).

Among shrubs, on alpine meadow-covered slopes.

IIA. Junggar: ***Tien Shan*** (between Danyu and Daban'sa, No. 1984, July 18, 1957—Kuan).

IIIA. Qinghai: ***Nanshan*** (mid-June 1880 ?, Przew.—typus !; around pass through South-Tetung mountain range, 3048–3658 m, July 31–1880, Przew.; "Kukunor, No. 1122, Hao"—Peter-Stib. l.c.), ***Amdo*** (Dzhakhar-chyu river, in Dzhakhar-Dzhargyn mountain area, June 24, 1880—Przew.).

IIIB. Tibet: ***Weitzan*** (left bank of Dy-chyu river or Mur-usu, 3962–4663 m, June 23–29; up to By-chyu river, July 7—1884, Przew.; Burkhan-Budda mountain range, Khatu and Nomokhun gorges, about 4267 m, June 12, 1901—Lad.).

General distribution: endemic.

Note. Cited in Ho's work (Y.C. Ho l.c.) for Sinkiang without reference to the actual locality.

108. **A. licentianus** Hand.-Mazz. in Oesterr. Bot. Zeitschr. 82 (1933) 247; Peter-Stib. in Acta Horti Gotoburg, 12 (1937–38) 56; Wang and Tang, Ill. treatm. princip. pl. China, Legum. (1955) 376, Y.C. Ho in Bull. Bot. Lab. North-East. Forest Inst. 8 (1980) 57.

Described from Qinghai (Mazushan' hill ?). Type in Vienna (W). Plate III, fig. 4.

In alpine meadows.

IIIA. Qinghai: ? ***Nanshan*** ("Kansu occid., No. 4357, 4685—Licen."—Peter-Stib. l.c.), ***Amdo*** (Jupar range; alpine meadows west of Jupar valley, alt. 13,500 ft, No. 14315, June 1926—Rock; "Tibet orient. No. 14894—Rock"—Peter-Stib. l.c.).

General distribution: endemic.

Note. Species very closely related to *A. skythropos* Bunge

109. **A. weigoldianus** Hand.-Mazz. in Symb. Sin. 7 (1933) 556; Peter-Stib. in Acta Horti Gotoburg, 12 (1937–38) 55; Wang and Tang, Ill. treatm. princip. pl. China, Legum. (1955) 393; P.C. Li et Ni in Fl. Xizang, 2 (1985) 817.

Described from South-West China (Sichuan). Type in Vienna [W]. In alpine belt at 3000–4500 m.

IIIB. Tibet: ***Weitzan*** (Burkhan-Budda mountain range, 3505–3962 m, Aug. 2 [14] 1884 —Przew., Burkhan-Budda mountain range, nor. slope, Khatu gorge, 4420 m alt., July 12, 1901—Lad.).

General distribution: China (South-West: Yunnan nor.-west, Sichuan west.).

Note. The identity of this species requires to be established.

Section 8 (33). **Myobroma** Bunge

***A. acaulis** Baker in Hook. f. Fl. Brit. Ind. 2 (1876) 132; Simps. in Not. Bot. Gard. Edinb. 8 (1915) 260; Gorrest in Not. Bot. Gard. Edinb. 14 (1924) 158; Peter-Stib. in Acta Horti Gotoburg, 12 (1937–38) 56; Wang and Tang, Ill. treatm. princip. pl. China, Legum. (1955) 375; Y.C. Ho in Bull. Bot. Research, 1, 3 (1981) 124; Ni et P.C. Li in Fl. Xizang, 2 (1985) 820.—*A. litangensis* Bur. et Franch. in J. de Bot. 5 (1891) 24.—*A. pseudoxytropis* Ulbr. in Feddes. Repert. Beih. 12 (1922) 420.

Described from Sikan. Type in London (K).

On mountains at 4100–4200 m.

IIIB. Tibet: ***South.***

General distribution: China (South-West (Sikan)), Himalayas (east.).

110. **A. schanginianus** Pall. Astrag. (1800) 77; DC. Prodr. 2 (1825) 303; Ledeb. Fl. Alt. 3 (1831) 332; id. Fl. Ross. 1 (1842) 652; Bunge Gen. Astrag. Sp. Geront. 1 (1868) 39 and 2 (1869) 54; id. Astrag. Turk. (1880) 371; O. et B. Fedtsch. Konsp. fl. Turk. 2 (1909) 210; Kryl. Fl. Zap. Sib. 7 (1933) 1664; Gontsch. and Boriss. in Fl. SSSR 12 (1946) 169; Grub. Konsp. fl. MNR (1955) 187; Fl. Kirgiz. 7 (1957) 252; Fl. Kazakhst. 5 (1961) 132; Bait. Astrag. Tyan'-Shanya (1977) 49; Opred. rast. Sr. Azii [Key to Plants of Mid. Asia] 6 (1981) 151; Y.C. Ho in Bull. Bot. Research, 1, 3 (1981) 124; Sanczir in Grub. Opred. rast. Mong. [Key to Plants of Mongolia] (1981) 159; Ulzij. in Tr. Inst. bot. AN MNR, 8 (1982) 24; Opred. rast. Tuv. ASSR [Key to Plants of Tuva Autonomous Soviet Socialist Republic] (1984) 145; C.Y. Yang in Claves pl. Xinjiang, 3 (1985) 134; Podl. in Mitt. Bot. Staatssamml. München, 25 (1988) 222, p.p.—*Tragacantha schanginiana* (Pall.) Kuntze, Rev. Gen. 2 (1891) 948.

—**Ic.**: Pall. 1800 l.c. tab. 63; Fl. Kazakhst. 5, Plate 17, fig. 5.

Described from Altay (Katun river basin). Type in St. Petersburg (LE).

In forest meadows, meadow-covered, steppified montane slopes, among scrubs, on fallow land.

IA. Mongolia: ***Mong. Alt.*** (Upper Khobdo lakes, forest meadows).

IIA. Junggar: ***Cis-Alt.*** (Bugotor area between Burchum and Kran, July 11, 1903—Gr.-Grzh.; "Altay"—Y.C. Ho l.c., C.Y. Yang l.c.), ***Tarb.*** (nor.-west of Khobsair [Chagan-Obo mountain], on slope, 2000 m, No. 10509, June 22, 1959—A.R. Lee), ***Tien Shan*** (Burchan-tau, Tereithal in Thian-Schangobiet, June 5, 1878—Fetissov; "Ili"—Y.C. Ho l.c., C.Y. Yang l.c.).

General distribution: Jung.-Tarb., Nor. and Cen. Tien Shan; West. Sib. (Alt., Tuva).

***A. lentilobus** R. Kam. et Kovalevsk. in Consp. Fl. Asiae Mediae. 6 (1981) 353 and 152; Fl. Tadzhik. 6 (1981) 148; Podl. in Mitt. Bot. Staatssamml. München, 25, 1 (1988) 405.—*A. pamiroalaicus* Lipsky in Acta Horti Petrop. 26 (1907) 147, p.p.—*A. andaulgensis* auct. non B. Fedtsch.: Gontsch. in Fl. Tadzhik. 5 (1937) 367; idem in Fl. SSSR, 12 (1946) 193, p. max. p.; Fl. Kirgiz. 7 (1957) 257; Ikonn. Opred. rast. Pam. [Key to Plants of Pamir] (1963) 165.

—**Ic.**: Fl. Tadzhik. 6, Plate 20, fig. 8–14.

Described from Mid. Asia (Peter the First mountain range). Type in St.-Petersburg (LE).

On rubble slopes, talus, moraine deposits, subalpine and alpine meadows, more rarely in juniper groves.

Reported from regions adjoining East. Pamir in Tajikistan where it is common. Finds possible in **IIIC. Pamir.**

General distribution: Cen. Tien Shan; Mid. Asia (Pamiro-Alay).

111. **A. aksaricus** N. Pavl. in Vestnik AN Kaz. SSR, 1 (1949) 30, Fl. Kazakhst. 5 (1961) 134; Bait. Astrag. Tyan'-Shanya (1977) 50; Opred.

rast. Sr. Azii [Key to Plants of Mid. Asia] 6 (1981) 150; Fl. desert. Sin. 2 (1987) 257; Podl. in Mitt. Bot. Staatssamml. München, 25, 1 (1988) 231. —*A. severtzovii* var. *orbiculatus* M. Pop. in HFAM, 15 (1928) No. 366 b.

—**Ic.:** Fl. Kazakhst. 5 (1961) Plate 17, fig. 2.

Described from East. Kazakhstan (Tien Shan). Type in Alma Ata (AA).

On rock talus near melting snow, in subalpine meadows.

IIA. Junggar: ***Zaisan*** (vicinity of Kabakhe [Akchii] river—Fl. Desert. Sin. l.c.).

General distribution: West. and Nor. Tien Shan.

Note. Reports also possible from East. Tien Shan in Sinkiang.

112. **A. severtzovii** Bunge Gen. Astrag. Sp. Geront. 1 (1868) 38 and 2 (1869) 54; Boiss. Fl. Or. 2 (1972) 289; Bunge in Acta Horti Petrop. 3 (1874) 106; id. Astrag. Turk. (1880) 238; Lipsky in Acta Horti Petrop. 26 (1907) 236, incl. var. *leiophyllus* Lipsky and var. *blepharophyllus* Lipsky; O. et B. Fedtsch. Konsp. fl. Turk. 2 (1909) 209; Gontsch. in Fl. Tadzhik. 5 (1937) 357; Gontsch. and Boriss. in Fl. SSSR, 12 (1946) 170; Fl. Kirgiz. 7 (1957) 252; Fl. Kazakhst. 5 (1961) 132; Bait. Astrag. Tyan'-Shanya (1977) 49; Y.C. Ho in Bull. Bot. Research, 1, 3 (1981) 123; Opred. rast. Sr. Azii [Key to Plants of Mid. Asia] 6 (1981) 150; Fl. Tadzhik. 6 (1981) 132; C.Y. Yang in Claves pl. Xinjiang, 3 (1985) 135; Podl. in Mitt. Bot. Staatssamml. München, 25, 1 (1988) 228.—*Tragacantha sewertzovii* (Bunge) Kuntze, Rev. Gen. 2 (1891) 948.

—**I.c.:** Podl. l.c. fig. 39.

Described from Mid. Asia (Karatau mountain range). Type in St.-Petersburg (LE).

On steppified and meadow-covered slopes, among shrubs.

IIA. Junggar: ***Cis-Alt.*** ("Altay"—Y.C. Ho l.c., C.Y. Yang l.c.), ***Tien Shan*** ("Inin"— C.Y. Yang l.c.).

General distribution: Cen. Tien Shan; Mid. Asia (Pamiro-Alay).

***A. tianschanicus** Bunge in Mém. Ac. Sci. St.-Petersb. 7 ser. 14, 4 (1869) 43; id. Astrag. Turk. (1880) 237; O. et B. Fedtsch. Konsp. fl. Turk. 2 (1909) 210, excl. pl. e Tarbagatay; Opred. rast. Sr. Azii [Key to Plants of Mid. Asia] 6 (1981) 151.

Described from Kirgiz (Cen. Tien Shan). Type in St.-Petersburg (LE).

On meadow-covered slopes in upper mountain belt.

Reported from territories adjoining mountain range and its report possible in Sinkiang.

***A. abbreviatus** Kar. et Kir. in Bull. Soc. Natur. Moscou, 15 (1842) 343; Bunge Gen. Astrag. Sp. Geront. 1 (1868) 35 and 2 (1869) 59; id. Astrag. Turk. (1880) 213; O. et B. Fedtsch. Konsp. fl. Turk. 2 (1909) 206;

Gontsch. and Boriss. in Fl. SSSR, 12 (1946) 218; Fl. Kazakhst. 5 (1961) 145; Opred. rast. Sr. Azii [Key to Plants of Mid. Asia] 6 (1981) 160; Podl. in Mitt. Bot. Staatssamml. München, 25, 2 (1988) 662.—*Tragacantha abbreviata* (Kar. et Kir.) Kuntze, Rev. Gen. 2 (1891) 942.

Described from East. Kazakhstan (Jung. Ala Tau). Type in St.-Petersburg (LE).

In solonetzic and rocky sites in plains.

Distributed in the region adjoining Jung. Ala Tau in Kazakhstan. Its report possible in the Chinese portion of Jung. Ala Tau.

General distribution: Balkh. Alak., endemic.

113. **A. flexus** Fisch. in Bull. Phys.-Mat. Ac. St.-Petersb. 3 (1844) 307; in adnot.; Bunge Gen. Astrag. Sp. Geron. 1 (1868) 36 and 2 (1869) 46; Boiss. Fl. Or. 2 (1872) 283; Bunge Astrag. Turk. (1880) 235; id. in Acta Horti Petrop. 7 (1880) 371; O. et B. Fedtsch, Konsp. fl. Turk. 2 (1909) 207, Kryl. Fl. Zap. Sib. 7 (1933) 1662; Gontsch. and Boriss. in Fl. SSSR, 12 (1946) 180; Fl. Kirgiz. 7 (1957) 253; Fl. Kazakhst. 5 (1961) 137; Bait. Astrag. Tyan'-Shanya (1977) 51; Nasir et Ali, Fl. West Pakistan, No. 100, (1977) 182; Opred. rast. Sr. Azii [Key to Plants of Mid. Asia] 6 (1981) 162; Fl. Tadzhik. 6 (1981) 140; Y.C. Ho in Bull. Bot. Research, 1, 3 (1981) 123; C.Y. Yang in Claves pl. Xinjiang, 3 (1985) 135; Fl. desert. Sin. 2 (1987) 257; Podl. in Mitt. Bot. Staatssamml. München, 25, 1 (1988) 296.—*A. pentapetaloides* Bunge in Mém. Ac. Sci. St.-Petersb. sav. etrang. 7 (1851) 274.—*A. stenanthus* Freyn in Bull. Herb. Boiss. 2 ser. 4 (1904) 761, non Bunge—*A. aquae-rubrae* B. Fedtsch. in Beith. Bot. Centralbl. 22, 2 (1908) 352; O. et B. Fedtsch. Konsp. fl. Turk. 21 (1909) 209.

—**Ic.:** Fl. SSSR, 12, Plate 14, fig. 1; Fl. Kazakhst. 5, Plate 17, fig. 4.

Described from Kirghiz. Type in St. Petersburg (LE).

In hummocky and fixed sand, fringes of takyrs (clay-surfaced deserts), solonetzic steppes, on plains.

IIA. Junggar: ***Cis-Alt.*** ("Fuyun'"—Fl. Desert. Syn. l.c.; "nor. regions"—C.Y. Yang l.c.), ***Tien Shan*** ("Ili river; Mechinula hills, Savan-Shan' mountain range, Chonzhi-ula mountains"—Fl. Desert. Syn. l.c.), ***Jung. Gobi*** (right bank of Manas river 10–15 km nor. of Podai state farm, bedded sand, June 11, 1957—Yun. and I-f. Yuan'; Manas region between Paotai and Syaeda, No. 810, June 12, 1957—Kuan; "Junggar basin; Mosavan'"—Fl. desert. Syn. l.c.).

General distribution: Aralo-Casp., Fore Balkh., Jung.-Tarb.; Mid. Asia, Iran.

114. **A. sanczirii** Ulzij. in Bull. Soc. Natur. Moscou, Ser. Biol. 95, 1 (1990) 114.—*A. patentipilosus* Sancz. in Grub. Opred. rast. Mong. [Key to Plants of Mongolia] (1982) 159, descr. ross. in clave, non *A. patentipilosus* Kitam. et *A. patentivillosus* Gontsch.; Grub. in Novosti sist. vyssh. rast. 21 (1984) 207.

Described from Mongolia (Jung. Gobi). Type in Ulan Bator (UBA), isotype in St.-Petersburg (LE).

On solonchak-like sandy soils in desert steppes.

IIA. Junggar: ***Jung. Gobi*** (75 km east of Altay somon centre, on sandy soil, No. 7153, Aug. 2, 1977, Volk. and Rachk.—typus !; same locality, 40 km nor.-east of Altay somon centre, on sandy soil, No. 7162, July 2, 1977, idem).

General distribution: endemic.

115. **A. neo-chorgosicus** Podl. in Mitt. Bot. Staatssamml. München, 25, 2 (1988) 624.

—**Ic.:** Podl. l.c. fig. 198, 346.

Described from Sinkiang (Kul'dzha). Type in St.-Petersburg (LE).

IIA. Junggar: ***Dzhark.*** (Khorgos in Kul'dzha region, No. 41, April 22, 1877—typus !; between Khorgos and Almaty, April 22–1877, A. Reg.; Kul'dzha, Talki river in Suidun region, May 7, 1878—A. Reg.).

General distribution: endemic.

116. **A. altaicus** Bunge Gen. Astrag. Sp. Geront. 1 (1868) 37 and 2 (1869) 46; id. Astrag. Turk. (1880) 235; Lipsky in Acta Horti Petrop. 26 (1907) 244, p.p., excl. syn. *A. chlorodontus;* O. et B. Fedtsch. Konsp. fl. Turk. 2 (1909) 209; Kryl. Fl. Zap. Sib. 7 (1933) 1663; Gontsch. and Boriss. in Fl. SSSR, 12 (1946) 117; Fl. Kazakhst. 5 (1961) 135; Opred. rast. Sr. Azii [Key to Plants of Mid. Asia] 6 (1981) 161; Sanczir in Grub. Opred. rast. Mong. [Key to Plants of Mongolia] (1982) 159; Ulzij. in Tr. Inst. bot. AN MNR, 8 (1982) 24; Podl. in Mitt. Bot. Staatssamml. München, 25, 2 (1988) 619.—*A. burtschunensis* Saposhn. ex Sumn. Animadv. Syst. Herb. Univ. Tomsk. 1–2 (1933) 37.—*A. longiflorus* Ledeb. Fl. Alt. 3 (1831) 331, non Pall.—*A. balchaschensis* auct. non Sumn.: Grub. in Bot. zh. 61 (1976) 1753; Ulzij. in Tr. Inst. bot. AN MNR, 8 (1982) 25.—*Tragacantha altaica* (Bunge) Ktze. Rev. Gen. 2 (1891) 942.

—**Ic.:** Podl. l.c. fig. 196.

Described from Altay (Irtysh river valley). Type in Paris (P), isotype in St.-Petersburg (LE).

On steppe slopes of mountains, sand, sandy and sandy-pebbly steppes.

IA. Mongolia: ***Mong. Alt.*** (upper Bulgan river, Ulagchin-gol river valley, along road to Khudzhirtu, left bank 1 km before Khudzhirlag-gol estuary, lateral creek valley, July 3, 1971—Grub., Ulzij., Dariima; Ulyastain-gol basin, valley of left tributary in upper Bulgan-gol river, June 28, 1973—Golubkova and Tsogt; arid valley 50 km nor.-west of Altay somon centre, Aug. 19, 1989—F. Nemeth).

IIA. Junggar: ***Cis-Alt.*** ("Altay"—C.Y. Yang l.c.), ***Jung. Gobi*** (spurs of Argalant hills 4 km from Ubchu-bulak, about 1700 m, sandy floor of valley, July 2, 1973, Golubkova and Tsogt), ***Zaisan*** (Chern. Irtysh river, left bank, Mai-kann. Konurbai area, hummocky sand, July 7; Sary-dzhasyk area west of Burchum river, solonchak, June 14; same locality, before Burchum river, Sary-dzhasyk, Kiikpai well, Sary-dzhasyk area, sand, June 14; same locality, between Burchum and Kaboi rivers, Kiikpai well—Karoi area, hummocky sand,

June 15—typus !—*A. butschumensis* [LE]); same locality, between Karoi area and village on Kaba river, along bank of irrigation canal, between Kaboi river and Besh-kuduk well, sandy-rocky steppe, June 17–1914, Schischk.).

General distribution: West. Sib. (Alt. South-west, Irt.).

117. **A. przewalskianus** Podl. et Ulzij. in Mitt. Botw. Staatssamml. München, 25, 1 (1988) 366.

—**Ic.:** Podl. et Ulzij. l.c. fig. 95.

Described from Sinkiang (East. Tien Shan). Type in St.-Petersburg (LE). Plate III, fig. 6.

On montane slopes.

IB. Kashgar: Nor. (Uch-Turfan, Karagailik gorge, along gently inclined rocky slope, June 23, 1908—Divn.).

IIA. Junggar: ***Tien Shan*** (Malyi Yuldus alpine plateau, 7500–9000 ft, May 27 [June 8] 1877, Przew.—typus !).

General distribution: endemic.

118. **A. trautvetteri** Bunge Gen. Astrag. Sp. Geront. 1 (1868) 39 and 2 (1869) 54; id. Astrag. Turk. (1880) 238; O. et B. Fedtsch. Konsp. fl. Turk. 2 (1909) 210; Gontsch. and Boriss. in Fl. SSSR, 12 (1946) 169; Fl. Kazakhst. 5 (1961) 131; C.Y. Yang in Claves pl. Xinjiang, 3 (1985) 136.—*A. schanginianus* var. *gymnocarpa* Trautv. in Bull. Soc. Natur. Moscou, 33, 2 (1860) 507.—*A. schanginianus* auct. non Pall.: Podl. in Mitt. Bot. Staatssamml. München, 25, 1 (1988) 222, p. min. p.—*A. tianschanicus* auct. non Bunge O. et B. Fedtsch. Konsp. fl. Turk. 2 (1909), quoad pl. e Tarbagatai.

—**Ic.:** Fl. Kazakhst. 5. Plate 17, fig. 1.

Described from East. Kazakhstan (Tarbagatai). Type in St.-Petersburg (LE).

In subalpine meadows.

IIA. Junggar: ***Tarb.*** ("Dachen"—C.Y. Yang l.c.).

General distribution: Jung.-Tarb., endemic.

119. **A. buchtormensis** Pall. Astrag. (1800) 76; Ledeb. Fl. Ross. 1, 3 (1843) 652; Bunge Gen. Astrag. Sp. Geront. 1 (1868) 36 and 2 (1869) 45; id. Astrag. Turk. (1880) 234; id. in Acta Horti Petrop. 7 (1880) 370; O. et B. Fedtsch. Konsp. fl. Turk. 2 (1909) 107; Kryl. Fl. Zap. Sibir. 7 (1933) 1661; Gontsch. and Boriss. in Fl. SSSR, 12 (1946) 198; Fl. Kazakhst. 5 (1961) 139; Bait. Astrag. Tyan'-Shanya (1977) 50; Y.C. Ho in Bull. Bot. Research, 1, 3 (1981) 123; C.Y. Yang in Claves pl. Xinjiang, 3 (1985) 136; Podl. in Mitt. Bot. Staatssamml. München, 25, 2 (1988) 611.—*A. buchtormensis* var. *dasycarpus* Trautv. and var. *gymnocarpus* Trautv. in Bull. Soc. Natur. Moscou, 33, 2 (1860) 508.—*A. henningii* (Steven) Boriss. in Fl. SSSR, 12 (1946) 199.—*A. novoascanicus* Klok. in Ukrain. Bot. zh. (Kiev) 3 (1946) 20.

—**Ic.:** Pall. l.c. tab. 62, fig. A; Fl. Kazakhst. 5. Plate 18, fig. 2.

Described from Altay (Bukhtarma river). Type in St.-Petersburg (LE).

On steppe sandy and rocky slopes of mountains and hillocks.

IIA. Junggar: ***Cis-Alt.*** ("Altay"—C.Y. Yang l.c.); ***Tarb.*** (Tarbagatai, April 1876—Pevts.), ***Tien Shan*** (Kuiankus, April 19; Ili river valley, April 21—1877; Dzhagastai, 2438–2743 m, June 20, 1878; between Dzhargalan and Piluchi, 1829 m, April 24; around Boroburgasun river, 2743 m, June 15; Taldy, 2743–3048 m, May 20—1879, A. Reg.; "Tien Shan"—Y.C. Ho l.c.; "Inin"—C.Y. Yang l.c.), ***Zaisan*** ("Burchum"—C.Y. Yang l.c.), ***Dzhark.*** (Almaty, nor.-west of Kul'dzha, 900–1200 m, April 22; Piluchi gorge, 914–1219 m, April 22—1879, A. Reg.).

General distribution: Aralo-Casp., Jung.-Tarb.; Europe (east.), West. Sib. (Alt., Irt.).

120. **A. chlorodontus** Bunge in Bull. Soc. Natur. Moscou, 39, 2 (1866) 29; id. Gen. Astrag. Sp. Geront. 1 (1868) 37 and 2 (1869) 47; id. Astrag. Turk. (1880) 235; id. in Acta Horti Petrop. (1880) 371; O. et B. Fedtsch. Konsp. fl. Turk. 2 (1909) 209, excl. pl. transcaspicae; Gontsch. and Boriss. in Fl. SSSR, 12 (1946) 200; Fl. Kazakhst. 5 (1961) 140; Bait. Astrag. Tyan'-Shanya (1977) 52; Opred. rast. Sr. Azii [Key to Plants of Mid. Asia] 6 (1981) 159; C.Y. Yang in Claves pl. Xinjiang, 3 (1985) 136; Podl. in Mitt. Bot. Staatssamml. München, 25, 2 (1988) 622.—*Tragacanthus chlorodonta* (Bunge) Kuntze, Rev. Gen. (1891) 944.

—**Ic.:** Podl. l.c. fig. 197.

Described from East. Kazakhstan (Jung. Ala Tau). Type in St.-Petersburg (LE).

On loessial slopes.

IIA. Junggar: ***Cis-Alt.*** ("Altay"—C.Y. Yang l.c.), ***Jung. Ala Tau*** ?, ***Tien Shan*** (Mal. Yuldus alpine plateau, 2286–2743 m, Sep. 30, 1876—Przew.; Taldy, 2743–3048 m, May 20, 1879—A. Reg.; "Inin"—C.Y. Yang l.c.).

General distribution: Jung.-Tarb., Cen. Tien Shan.

121. **A. taldycensis** Franch. in Bull. Mus. Hist. Natur. (Paris) 2, 7 (1896) 344; Fl. Tadzhik. 6 (1981) 158; Opred. rast. Sr. Azii [Key to Plants of Mid. Asia] 6 (1981) 155; Podl. in Mitt. Bot. Staatssamml. München, 25, 2 (1988) 761.—*A. mendax* Freyn in Bull. Herb. Boiss. 2 ser. 4 (1904) 770; Gontsch. and Boriss. in Fl. SSSR, 12 (1946) 200; Fl. Kirgiz. 7 (1957) 258; Fl. Kazakhst. 5 (1961) 140, Bait. Astrag. Tyan'-Shanya (1977) 52; Y.C. Ho in Bull. Bot. Research, 1, 3 (1981) 123; C.Y. Yang in Claves pl. Xinjiang, 3 (1985) 137.—*A. pamiroalaicus* Lipsky in Acta Horti Petrop. 26 (1907) 147; p.p. nom. illeg.; O. et B. Fedtsch. Konsp. fl. Turk. 2 (1909) 208.

—**Ic.:** Podl. l.c. fig. 251.

Described from Mid. Asia. Type in Paris (P).

On steppified rocky slopes of mountains, subalpine meadows and coastal pebble beds and sandy shoals of rivers and lakes.

IIA. Junggar: ***Tien Shan*** ("Nor. Sinkiang"—Y.C. Ho l.c.; "from Ili basin along southern slopes of Tien Shan"—C.Y. Yang l.c.).

General distribution: Nor. and Cen. Tien Shan; Mid. Asia (Pamiro-Alay).

Section 9 (34). **Gontscharoviella** R. Kam.

122. **A. alatavicus** Kar. et Kir. in Bull. Soc. Natur. Moscou, 15 (1842) 344; Bunge Gen. Astrag. Sp. Geront. 1 (1868) 34 and 2 (1869) 42; id. Astrag. Turk. (1880) 232; id. in Acta Horti Petrop. 7 (1880) 370; Lipsky in Acta Horti Petrop. 18 (1901) 34; O. et B. Fedtsch. Konsp. fl. Turk. 2 (1909) 206; Gontsch. and Boriss. in Fl. SSSR, 12 (1946) 224; Fl. Kirgiz. 7 (1957) 261; Fl. Kazakhst. 5 (1961) 145; Bait. Astrag. Tyan'-Shanya (1977) 54; Opred. rast. Sr. Azii [Key to Plants of Mid. Asia] 6 (1981) 168; Y.C. Ho in Bull. Bot. Research, 1, 3 (1981) 124; C.Y. Yang in Claves pl. Xinjiang, 3 (1981) 134; Podl. in Mitt. Bot. Staatssamml. München, 25, 2 (1988) 515.—*Tragacantha alatavica* (Kar. et Kir.) Kuntze, Rev. Gen. 2 (1891) 942.

—**Ic.:** Fl. Kazakhst. 5, Plate 19, fig. 1; C.Y. Yang l.c., tab. 9, fig. 1; Podl. l.c. fig. 158.

Described from East. Kazakhstan (Jung. Ala Tau). Type in St.-Petersburg (LE), isotypes in Moscow (MW) and Paris (P).

On rocky and rubbly slopes, subalpine herbage meadows, in sheep's fescue steppes, more rarely spruce forests in middle and upper hill belts. Plate III, fig. 5.

IIA. Junggar: ***Jung. Ala Tau*** (Junggar alps, Kul'den-daban pass, 2440–2740 m, May 26, 1878—A. Reg."Ala Tau region"—Y.C. Ho l.c., C.Y. Yang l.c.), ***Tien shan*** ("Nor. part of East. Tien Shan"—Y.C. Ho l.c., "Inin"—C.Y. Yang l.c.).

General distribution: Jung.-Tarb., Nor. and Cen. Tien Shan.

123. **A. pamiriensis** Franch. in Bull. Mus. Hist. Natur. (Paris) 2 (1896) 344; Opred. rast. Sr. Azii [Key to Plants of Mid. Asia] 6 (1981) 169; Fl. Tadzhik. 6 (1981) 175; Podl. Mitt. Bot. Staatssamml. München, 25, 2 (1988) 520.—*A. myriophyllus* Bunge in Izv. obshch. lyub. estestv., antr. i etnogr. 26, 2 (1880) 233, nom. illeg., non Pall.; Gontsch. and Boriss. in Fl. SSSR, 12 (1946) 24; Fl. Kirgiz. 7 (1957) 261; Ikonn. Opred. rast. Pam. [Key to Plants of Pamir] (1963) 162; C.Y. Yang in Claves pl. Xinjiang, 3 (1985) 134.—*A. alatavicus* var. *pamirensis* (Franch.) B. Fedtsch. in Acta Horti Petrop. 21, 3 (1903) 313.

—**Ic.:** Fl. Tadzhik. 6 (1981) Plate 27, fig. 1–7; Podl. l.c. fig. 159.

Described from East. Pamir. Type in Paris (P).

On sandy slopes, pebble beds in valleys of montane rivers, moraines, high mountains.

IIIC. Pamir (around Ucha pass, on clayey descents, June 17, 1909—Divn.; Pil'nen, 3000-4000 m., June 30, 1942—Serp.; "Pamir, vallis Jersil, 3000 m, July 5, 1930, leg. Persson [LD]"—Podl. l.c.).

General distribution: East. Pamir; Mid. Asia (Pamiro-Alay).

*A. **adpressipilosus** Gontsch. in Not. Syst. (Leningrad) 9 (1946) 128; Gontsch. and Boriss. in Fl. SSSR, 12 (1946) 230; Fl. Kirgiz. 7 (1957) 262; Kitam. Fl. West Pakist. and Afghan. (1964) 88; Bait. Astrag. Tyan'-Shanya (1977) 55; Podl. et Anders. in Mitt. Bot. Staatssamml. München, 13 (1977) 439; Opred. rast. Sr. Azii [Key to Plants of Mid. Asia] 6 (1981) 170; Fl. Tadzhik. 6 (1981) 180; Podl. in Mitt. Bot. Staatssamml. München, 25, 2 (1988) 534.

—**Ic.:** Fl. Tadzhik. 6, Plate 27, fig. 16, 17.

Described from Mid. Asia (Gissar mountain range). Type in St.-Petersburg (LE).

On rubbly slopes of hills, pebbly shoals, in juniper forests.

Reported from adjoining regions and is expected from Chinese Pamir.

General distribution: Mid. Asia (Pamiro-Alay, West. Tien Shan), Afghanistan, Pakistan.

*A. **dignus** Boriss. in Not. Syst. (Leningrad), 10 (1947) 44; Gontsch. and Boriss. in Fl. SSSR, 12 (1946) 228; Ikonn. Opred. rast. Pam. [Key to Plants of Pamir] (1963) 163; Podl. et Anders in Mitt. Bot. Staatssamml. München, 13 (1977) 439; Opred. rast. Sr. Azii [Key to Plants of Mid. Asia] 6 (1981) 170; Fl. Tadzhik. 6 (1981) 177; Podl. in Mitt. Bot. Staatssamml. München, 25, 2 (1988) 526.—*A. alatavicus* auct. non Kar. et Kir.; Y.C. Ho in Bull. Bot. Research, 1, 3 (1981) 124 p.p.; C.Y. Yang in Claves pl. Xinjiang, 3 (1985) 134 p.p.

—**Ic.:** Fl. Tadzhik. 6, Plate 27, fig. 10, 11; Podl. l.c. fig. 161.

Described from Mid. Asia (Shugnan). Type in St.-Petersburg (LE).

On rubbly slopes, pebble beds along river beds and terraces, moraine, talus, alpine meadows, in montane steppes.

Reported and collected several times in East. Pamir (Tajikistan), Hindukush (Afghanistan) and Chitral (Pakistan) adjoining the Chinese territory.

Not reported so far from Chinese portion of East. Pamir.

General distribution: East. Pamir; Mid. Asia (Pamiro-Alay), Afghanistan, Pakistan (Chitral).

124. **A. alaicus** Freyn in Bull. Herb. Boiss. 2 ser. 4 (1904) 766; Gontsch. and Boriss. in Fl. SSSR, 12 (1946) 27; Fl. Kirgiz. 7 (1957) 262; Fl. Kazakhst. 5 (1961) 146; Bait. Astrag. Tyan'-Shanya (1977) 55; Opred. rast. Sr. Azii [Key to Plants of Mid. Asia] 6 (1981) 169; Fl. Tadzhik. 6 (1981) 176; Podl. in Mitt. Bot. Staatssamml. München, 25, 2 (1988) 523.—*A. alatavicus* auct. non Kar. et Kir.: Gontsch. in Fl. Tadzhik. 5 (1937) 382, p.p.; Y.C. Yang in Claves pl. Xinjiang, 3 (1985) 134 p.p.

—**Ic.:** Fl. Tadzhik. 6, Plate 37, fig. 8–9; Podl. l.c. fig. 160.

Described from Mid. Asia (Alay). Type in Copenhagen [C].

On rocky and rubbly slopes, moraines, alpine grasslands, in juniper groves and montane steppes in middle and upper mountain belts.

IIA. Junggar: ***Jung. Ala Tau*** ("Ala Tau region"—Y.C. Ho l.c.), *Tien Shan* ("nor.-west. East. Tien Shan"—C.Y. Yang l.c.).

General distribution: Cen. Tien Shan; Mid. Asia (Pamiro-Alay).

Note. Reports also possible from Chinese portion of East. Pamir.

Subgenus 6. **Trimeniaeus** Bunge

1. Flowers yellow, in globose, loosely-capitate, 1–1.3 cm long racemes with 5–10 (15) flowers; standard 5.5–6.5 mm long. Pods 1–2 cm long, strongly falcate or helical, laterally compressed, crumpled-rugose, membranous, patently white hairy, aggregated in dense heads, nigrescent on maturity. Leaflets oblong-ovate or oval, (5) 8–12 mm long, emarginate, villous on both surfaces (section 1 (35). **Cycloglottis** Bunge) .... 125. **A. contortuplicatus** L.

\+ Flowers purple, violet, albescent, light-pink .... 2.

2. Racemes ovate, rather lax, many-flowered, 3–5 cm long, elongated after anthesis to (7) 10–15 cm; corolla lilac-purple; standard 11–14 (15) mm long, limb broadly-ovate. Pods erect, on short, 1.5 mm long stalk, narrowly-linear, (15) 20–25 mm long, 2–2.5 mm broad, falcate or straight, narrowed abruptly into subulate, straight, 1.5–2 mm long beak, keeled on back, membranous, bilocular, Leaflets oblong-elliptical or oblong-oval to laceolate, (7) 10–15 mm long, subglabrous above, mostly pilose beneath (section 2 (36). **Heterodontus** Bunge) .... 126. **A. dahuricus** (Pall.) D.C.

\+ Racemes few-flowered, lax; if many-flowered, capitate-aggregated, about 1 cm long, but never elongated; corolla violet or albescent .... 3.

3. Pods narrowly linear-cylindrical, arcuate, mostly moniliform, nutant, unilocular (section 3 (37). **Ophiocarpus** Bunge) .... 127. **A. ophiocarpus** Benth. ex Boiss.

\+ Pods not moniliform, totally or partly bilocular .... 4.

4. Pods sharply trigonous in cross-section, oblong or lanceolate, 15–19 mm long, 5–6.5 mm broad, glabrous, with developed oblong spiny-dentate keels at middle; serrulate prominently along keel. Flowers and pods in compressed, subcapitate racemes. Bracts deltoid-ovate or narrowly-ovate, with white

and black hairs (section 4 (38). **Seversovii** Bunge) .... 128. **A. vicarius** Lipsky

+ Pods oval, round or tri- or tetragonous in cross-section but without sharp corners, keels without spiny, dentate processes on valves .... 5.

5. Flowers and pods in loose racemes .... 6.

+ Flowers and pods in dense capitate racemes, with pods enlarged downward, obliquely erect or procumbent stellately upward in the same plane (section 8 (42). **Oxyglottis** Bunge) ..... 11.

6. Limb of standard not narrowed ligulately in upper part, emarginate or rounded at tip; wings rounded at tip, more rarely slightly emarginate .... 7.

+ Limb of standard with abruptly round enlargement at middle, sharply narrowed toward tip and base, obtuse or acuminate at tip; wings emarginate at tip (section 7 (41). **Ankylotus** (Stev.) Bunge) .... 8.

7. Pods with finely reticulate nerves, rugose, glabrous, submembranous, subtetragonal in cross-section, 10–20 mm long, 2–3 mm broad, acuminulate at tip. Leaflets 4–7 pairs, oblong-cuneate or narrowly-oblanceolate, 3–10 mm long, emarginate at tip (section 5 (39). **Reticulata** R. Kam.) .... ***A. reticulatus** M.B.

+ Pods glabrous, 12–25 mm long, 2–2.5 mm broad, flacate for up to 1/2 of circumference. Leaflets 2–4 pairs, ovate or obovate, 3–8 (12) mm long. Calyx 3–3.5 mm long, teeth as long as tube or somewhat shorter (section 6 (40). **Harpilobus** Bunge) .... 129. **A. harpilobus** Kar. et Kir.

8. Calyx teeth 2/3 as long as tube. Peduncle shorter than leaves .... 130. **A. stalinskyi** Sirj.

+ Calyx teeth 1/3–1/2 as long as tube. Peduncle as long as leaves or longer .... 9.

9. Standard ligulate-attenuated at tip, sharply and acutely narrowed, contorted at end after anthesis .... 131. **A. ankylotus** Fisch. et Mey.

+ Standard obtuse at tip, mostly emarginate .... 10.

10. Pods 2–4 cm long. Stipules deltoid-lanceolate. Calyx 6–8 mm long. Leaflets oblong-oval, oblong or linear-oblong .... 132. **A. commixtus** Bunge.

+ Pods 0.9–1.3 cm long. Stipules ovate-deltoid. Calyx 5–6 mm long. Leaflets oval or oblong-oval .... 133. **A. gracilipes** Benth. ex Bunge.

11. Pods erect, lanceolate or lanceolate-oblong, (8) 10–12 (16) mm long, 2.5–3 mm broad, with oblong obtuse keels at valve middle, subtetragonal in cross-section, stellately-procumbent. Calyx teeth 1/4–1/3 as long as tube; corolla light-pink .... 134. **A. oxyglottis** Stev.

\+ Pods mostly curved, valves without keel. Calyx teeth 2/3 as long as tube; corolla of different colour .... 12.

12. Racemes on well developed peduncles as long as leaves, more rarely slightly shorter. Stems erect, simple or branched .... 13.

\+ Racemes sessile or subsessile, considerably shorter than leaves, more rarely nearly as long. Stems decumbent or ascending, branched from base .... 14.

13. Pods linear or linear-oblong, 12–20 mm long, glabrous (not rugose), obliquely erect. Calyx campanulate, 6–7 (9) mm long; corrolla violet .... 135. **A. sesamoides** Boiss.

\+ Pods oblong, 7–10 mm long, 2–3 mm broad, reticulate-rugose, horizontally-procumbent. Calyx tubular, 3-4 mm long, corolla pale-violet .... 136. **A. filicaulis** Fisch. et Mey.

14. Pods stellate-procumbent, oblong, distinctly inflated at base, with 2 obtuse, horse-shaped tubercles, subobtuse at tip. Calyx narrowly-campanulate, 4–5 mm long, black- and white-hairy; teeth linear, as long as tube or 2/3 of it; corolla albescent, more rarely violet-coloured, standard 6–8 (10) mm long. Stipules glabrous, white-ciliate only along margin .... 137. **A. tribuloides** Delile.

\+ Pods in dense heads, obliquely erect, asymmetrically ovate, without tubercles in lower portion, acuminate at tip. Calyx short-tubular, about 2.5 mm long, with fine, white pubescence, teeth linear, (1/3) 1/2–2/3 as long as tube; corolla violet, standard 5–6 (6.5) mm long. Stipules pubescent with white and black hairs .... 138. **A. ammophilus** Kar. et Kir.

Section 1 (35). **Cycloglottis** Bunge

125. **A. contortuplicatus** L. Spl. pl. (1753) 758; Bunge Gen. Astrag. Sp. Geront. 1 (1868) 18 and 2 (1869) 20; id. Astrag. Turk. (1880) 207; O. et B. Fedtsch. Konsp. fl. Turk. 2 (1909) 193; Kryl. Fl. Zap. Sib. 7 (1933) 1642; Fl. Tadzhik. 5 (1937) 269; Gontsch. and M. Pop. in Fl. SSSR, 12 (1946) 281; Fl. Kirgiz. 7 (1957) 268; Fl. Kazakhst. 5 (1961) 153; Nasir et Ali, Fl. West Pakist. No. 100 (1977) 149; Bait. Astrag. Tyan'-Shanya (1977) 98; Opred. rast. Sr. Azii [Key to Plants of Mid. Asia] 6 (1981) 110; Fl. Tadzhik. 6 (1981) 200; Opred. rast. Tuv. ASSR [Key to Plants of Tuva

Autonomous Soviet Socialist Republic] (1984) 146; Kam et al. in Byul. Mosk. obshch. ispyt. prir., otd. biol. 90, 5 (1985) 115; C.Y. Yang in Claves pl. Xinjiang, 3 (1985) 113, Liou fil. in Fl. desert Sin. 2 (1987).

—**Ic.:** Fl. SSSR, 12, Plate 20, fig. 3; Fl. Kazakhst. 5. Plate 20, fig. 1.

Described from West. Siberia. Type in London (LINN).

In solonetzic meadows, solonchak and sandy soils of riverine valleys, in tugais along banks of rivers and lakes as well as weed in plantations.

IB. Kashgar: *Nor.* (between Maral-bashi and Aksu, around Chadyr-kul' station, among poplar forests, in glade, Aug. 6, 1929—Pop.; "Aksu"—C.Y. Yang l.c.; "Luntai"—Liou fil. l.c.), ***Takla-Makan*** ("Tarim basin"—Liou fil. l.c.).

IIA. Junggar: ***Cis-Alt.*** (Shara-Sume), 550 m, along fringes of farms, No. 2881, Sep. 8, 1956—Ching), ***Jung. Gobi*** (Bulgan river floodplain 30 km west of Bulgan somon settlement, Aug. 14, 1982—Gub.; "Junggar basin"—C.Y. Yang l.c., Liou fil. l.c.); ***Dzhark.*** ("Ili"—Liou fil. l.c.).

General distribution: Aralo-Casp., Fore Balkh., Nor. and Cen. Tien Shan; Europe, Caucasus, Mid. Asia, West. Siberia (south, Tuva), Afghanistan (Hindukush), Iran.

Section 2 (36). **Heterodontus** Bunge

126. **A. dahuricus** (Pall.) DC. Prodr. 2 (1825) 285; Ledeb. Fl. Alt. 3 (1831) 310; id. Fl. Ross. 1 (1842) 622; Turcz. Fl. baic.-dahur. 1 (1842) 769; Bunge Gen. Astrag. Sp. Geront. 1 (1868) 5 and 2 (1869) 3; (sub *A. dahuricus* DC.); Pavl. in Byull. Mosk. obshch. ispyt. prir., otd. biol. 38, 1–2 (1929) 90; Kryl. Fl. Zap. Sib. 7 (1933) 1641; Kitag. Lin. Fl. Mansh. (1939) 280; Gontsch. et M. Pop. in Fl. SSSR, 12 (1946) 285; Boriss. in Fl. Zabaik. 6 (1954) 572; Grub. Konsp. fl. MNR (1955) 183; Wang and Tang, Ill. treatm. princip. pl. China, Legum. (1955) 386; M. Pop. Fl. Sr. Sib. 1 (1957) 327; Fl. Krasnoyar. kr. 6 (1960) 34; Fl. Tsentr. Sib. 2 (1979) 599; Fl. pl. herb. Chinae bor.-or. 5 (1976) 95; Fl. Intramong. 3 (1977) 213 and 2 ed. 3 (1989) 269; Sanczir in Grub. Opred. rast. Mong. [Key to Plants of Mongolia] (1982) 156; Ulzij. in Tr. Inst. bot. AN MNR, 8 (1982) 14; Opred. rast. Tuv. ASSR [Key to Plants of Tuva Autonomous Soviet Socialist Republic] (1984) 148; Fl. desert Sin. 2 (1987) 265.—*Galega dahurica* Pall. Reise, 3 (1776) 742.—*Phaca dahurica* Pall. Reise (1776) 321.

—**Ic.:** Pall. Reise, 3 (1776) tab. W, fig. 1; Fl. Zabaik. 6, fig. 294; Wang and Tang l.c. fig. 386; Fl. Intramong. 3 (1977) tab. 108, fig. 1–7 and 2 ed. 3 (1989) ? tab. 104, fig. 1–6.

Described from East. Siberia (Trans-Baikal). Type in London (BM).

In steppe meadows, steppe and meadow-covered slopes, sandy steppes, along sand banks of rivers, as weed in fallow land, along banks of irrigation canals and boundaries.

IA. Mongolia: *Cen. Khalkha* (upper Kerulen, steppe near Erdeni hills, 1899—Pal.; knolls between Murin-gol river and Suchzhi-bulak [Tsetsenkhan] spring, July 27,1924—

Lis.; valley on right bank of Kerulen river facing Kherlen-Bayan-ula mountains, Aug. 9, 1969—Ulzij. [UBU]; Avzag somon in Bulgan ajmaq, along road to Ulan Bator, July 22, 1970—Banzragch, Karam. et al.), ***East. Mong.*** (Mongolia chinensis 1841—Kirilov; Muni-ula, 1871—Przew.; Tuchen town ruins near Khukh-khoto, Aug. 2, 1884—Pop.; Choibalsan somon, 20 km east of Enger-Shanda, Sumiin-khoolai area, Aug. 23, 1957—Dashnyam; Khaltszan somon, 5–7 km north of Khatabchin-khida, along road to Yugodzyr from Biruta, Sep. 17; Khalkhin-gola valley 13 km south-east of Khamar-Daba, in river bed part of floodplain, Aug. 11, 1949—Yun.; "Shilingol"—Fl. Intramong l.c.), ***Depr. Lakes*** (Urangom area, June 26, 1879); in Ulangom region, Kharkhira river valley, gently inclined slopes on left bank, Aug. 4; same locality, old abandoned ploughed field in rubbly-sandy steppe, Aug. 6–7; same locality, Kharkhira river valley, 20 km from Ulangom, Aug. 8; same locality, fringe of irrigation canal in abandoned ploughed field, Aug. 11; same locality, fringe of irrigation canal in wheat plantations, Sept. 2–1931, Bar. and Shukardin; Khobdossk state farm, in lower courses of Buyantu river, July–Aug. 1941 and 1942—Kondratenko), ***East. Gobi*** (Ikhe-bulak-gol river, near Ula-Obo-khuduk well, 50 km south-west of Khatan-Bulak somon, in gorge, July 23, 1974—Rachk. and Volk.; Bayan-Dkhag area, Aug. 11, 1984—Kam., Dariima); "Ulantsab etc."—Fl. Intramong. l.c.), ***Ordos*** (Ordos, No. 185, June; Huang He river valley, along river banks, mid-July—1871, Przew.; Echzin-khoro, on sandy soil, Aug. 17; valley of Chichirgan river, Aug. 19; Teshin-gol river valley, Aug. 19—1884, Pot.).

General distribution: West. Sib. (Altay south, Tuva), East. Sib. (Daur.), Far East (Ussur.), Nor. Mong. (Hang., Mong.-Daur.), China (Dunbei, North, North-West, Central), Korean peninsula.

Section 3 (37). **Ophiocarpus** Bunge

127. **A. ophiocarpus** Benth. ex Boiss. Fl. Or. 2 (1872) 224; Bunge Gen. Astrag. Sp. Geront. 1 (1868) 10 and 2 (1869) 6; id. in Acta Horti Petrop. 7 (1880) 368; Hook. f. Fl. Brit. Ind. 2 (1876) 122; Lipsky in Acta Horti Petrop. 26 (1907) 205; O. et B. Fedtsch. Konsp. fl. Turk. 2 (1909) 193; Fl. Tadzhik. 5 (1937) 255; Gontsch. and M. Pop. in Fl. SSSR, 12 (1946) 285; Fl. Kirgiz. 7 (1957) 267; Fl. Kazakhst. 5 (1961) 154; Ikonn. Opred. rast. Pam. [Key to Plants of Pamir] (1963) 159; Nasir et Ali, Fl. West Pakist. No. 100 (1977) 153; Bait. Astrag. Tyan'-Shanya (1977) 98; Fl. Tadzhik. 6 (1981) 202; Opred. rast. Sr. Azii [Key to Plants of Mid. Asia] 6 (1981) 96; Li et Ni in Fl. Xizang, 2 (1985) 846.—*A. paulseni* Freyn in Bull. Herb. Boiss. 2 ser. 4 (1904) 445.—*Trigonella komarovii* Lipsky in Acta Horti Petrop. 26 (1907) 25; O. et B. Fedtsch. Konsp. Fl. Turk. 2 (1909) 167.

—**Ic.:** Fl. SSSR, 12, Plate 21, fig. 1; Fl. Tadzhik. 6 (1981), Plate 33, fig. 1.

Described from West. Tibet. Type in London (K).

On rocky-rubbly slopes, coastal sand depositions, in foothills.

IIIB. Tibet: *Chang Tang* ("Tibeto occidentalis, alt. 11,000 ft (3353 m), T. Thomson !" —Bunge l.c., "***West. Tibet***"—Li et Ni l.c.).

IIIC. Pamir: Reported from the adjoining Tajikistan territory (Yashil'-Kul' lake and Murgab river valley).

General distribution: East. Pamir; Mid. Asia, Iran, Afghanistan.

Section 4 (38). **Seversovii** Bunge

128. **A. vicarius** Lipsky in Acta Horti Petrop. 18 (1900) 25; O. et B. Fedtsch. Konsp. fl. Turk. 2 (1909) 197; Fl. Tadzhik. 5 (1937) 272; Gontsch. and M. Pop. in Fl. SSSR, 2 (1946) 300; Fl. Kirgiz. 7 (1957) 272; Fl. Kazakhst. 5 (1961) 163; Bait. Astrag. Tyan'-Shanya (1977) 101; Opred. rast. Sr. Azii [Key to Plants of Mid. Asia] 6 (1981) 100; C.Y. Yang in Claves pl. Xinjiang, 3 (1985) 113.—*A. dubius* Krassn. Enum. pl. Tian-Schan Orient. (1887) 128, non DC. (1831).

—**Ic.:** Fl. Tadzhik. 5 (1937), Plate 26, fig. 6 and 5 (1978), Plate 53, fig. 2, 3; Fl. SSSR 12, Plate 20, fig. 6; Fl. Kazakhst. 5, Plate 21, fig. 3.

Described from Mid. Asia (Khodzha-kala in Turkmenia). Type in St.-Petersburg (LE).

On arid rocky, rubbly and melkozem slopes, foothills, sandy deserts, rarely in fallow lands and boghara (unirrigated) plantations.

IIa. Junggar: ? ***Jung. Ala Tau, Dzhark.*** (between Piluchi and gorge, 914-1219 m (3000–4000 ft), April 22, 1879—A. Reg.).

General distribution: Jung.-Tarb., Nor. Tien Shan; Mid. Asia (West. Tien Shan, Pamiro-Alay, Kopet-Dag).

Note. C.Y. Yang l.c. does not cite the exact location of report in Sinkiang territory.

Section 5 (39). **Reticulata** R. Kam.

***A. reticulatus** M.B. Fl. taur.-cauc. 3 (1819) 491; Bunge Gen. Astrag. Sp. Geront. 1 (1868) 14 and 2 (1869) 14; id. Astrag. Turk. (1880) 212; Gontsch. and M. Pop. in Fl. SSSR 12 (1946) 293; Fl. Kazakhst. 5 (1961) 158; Opred. rast. Sr. Azii [Key to Plants of Mid. Asia] 6 (1981) 101.—*A. oliganthus* Kar. et Kir. in Bull. Soc. Natur. Moscou, 15 (1842) 337.

—**Ic.:** Fl. Kazakhst. 5, Plate 20, fig. 6.

Described from European Russia (Sarepta vicinity). Type in St.-Petersburg (LE).

In solonchaks, solonetzes and saline sands in deserts and desert steppes.

Found frequently in regions adjoining Zaisan basin and probably will also be found in this territory of Sinkiang.

General distribution: Fore Balkh. (Zaisan basin, Kazakhstan hillocky area).

Section 6 (40). **Harpilobus** Bunge

129. **A. harpilobus** Kar. et Kir. in Bull. Soc. Natur. Moscou, 15, 2 (1842) 336; Gontsch. and M. Pop. in Fl. SSSR 12 (1946) 292; Fl. Kazakhst. 5 (1961) 157; Opred. rast. Sr. Azii [Key to Plants of Mid. Asia] 6 (1961) 114; C.Y. Yang in Claves pl. Xinjiang, 3 (1985) 115; Liou fil. in Fl. desert.

Sin. 2 (1987) 264.—*A. gyzensis* var. *harpilobus* Boiss. Fl. Or. 2 (1872) 234. —*A. drobovii* M. Pop. et Vved. in Bull. Univ. Asia Media, 14 (1926) 134, inadnot.; Fl. Kazakhst. 5 (1961) 157; Bait. Astrag. Tyan'-Shanya (1977) 99.—*A. gyzensis* auct. non Del.: Bunge Gen. Astrag. Sp. Geront. 1 (1868) 14 and 2 (1869) 16; id. Astrag. Turk. (1880) 212.

—**Ic.:** Bunge Icon. (1847) tab. 13, fig. 2; Fl. SSSR 12, Plate 21, fig. 8 (sub. nom. *A. drobovii*) and Plate 21, fig. 10; F1. Kazakhst. 5, Plate 20, fig. 4, 5.

Described from East. Kazakhstan (Balkhash lake). Type in Moscow (MW). Isotype in St.-Petersburg (LE).

On sand in submontane plain, sand-covered rocky and plastered soils of riverine valleys and along trails of montane residuals.

IIA. Junggar: ***Jung. Gobi*** ("Junggar basin, Mosavan"—C.Y. Yang l.c., Liou fil. l.c.), ***Dzhark.*** (in Ili river valley, Suidun, May 4; vicinity of Suidun, May 8, 1878—A. Reg.; "Ili region"—C.Y. Yang l.c.).

General distribution: Aralo-Casp., Fore Balkh., Cen. Tien Shan; Mid. Asia.

Section 7 (41). **Ankylotus** (Stev.) Bunge

130. **A. stalinskyi** Sirj. in Feddes Repert. 53 (1944) 75; Fl. Kirgiz. 7 (1957) 273; Fl. Kazakhst. 5 (1961) 164; Podl. et Deml. in Mitt. Bot. Staatssamml. München, 7 (1970) 340; Bait. Astrag. Tyan'-Shanya (1977) 101; Fl. Tadzhik. 6 (1981) 214; Opred. rast. Sr. Azii [Key to Plants of Mid. Asia] 6 (1981) 114; C.Y. Yang in Claves pl. Xinjiang, 3 (1985) 116; Liou fil. in Fl. desert Sin. 2 (1987) 101.—*A. brachymorphus* Nikif. in Not. Syst. (Leningrad) 10 (1947) 101; Gontsch. and M. Pop. in Fl. SSSR, 12 (1946) 304; Li et Ni in Fl. Xizang, 2 (1985) 844.

—**Ic.:** Fl. Kazakhst. 5, Plate 21, fig. 6; Fl. Xizang, 2, tab. 276, fig. 1–7.

Described from Mid. Asia. Type in Tashkent (TAK).

On rubbly, rocky and clayey slopes of foothills, low and residual mountains, rarely in fallow land.

IIA. Junggar: ***Tien Shan*** ("Tsitai [Guchen], Emushan'"—Liou fil. l.c.), ***Jung. Gobi*** ("Manas"—C.Y. Yang l.c.; "Savan [Yantszykhai], Urumchi"—Liou fil. l.c.), ***Zaisan*** ("Burchum"—C.Y. Yang l.c.).

IIIB. Tibet: ***South.*** ("Chzhada"—Li et Ni l.c.).

General distribution: Nor. Tien Shan; Mid. Asia, Iran.

Note. Finds possible in Tarbagatai.

131. **A. ankylotus** Fisch. et Mey. in Ind. Sem. Horti Petrop. 2 (1935) 27; Bunge Gen. Astrag. Sp. Geront. 1 (1868) 15 and 2 (1869) 17; id. Astrag. Turk. (1880) 221; Boiss. Fl. Or. 2 (1872) 637; O. et B. Fedtsch. Konsp. fl. Turk. 2 (1909) 195; Kryl. Fl. Zap. Sib. 7 (1933) 1642; Gontsch. and M. Pop. in Fl. SSSR, 12 (1946) 303; Fl. Kazakhst. 5 (1961) 164; Opred. rast. Sr. Azii [Key to Plants of Mid. Asia] 6 (1981) 113; Kam. et al. in Byull. Mosk. obshch. ispyt. prir., otd. biol. 90, 5 (1985) 115.

—**Ic.:** Bunge Icon. (1847) tab. 10, fig. 1A.

Described from European Russia (Inder lake). Type in St.-Petersburg (LE).

In gorges and clayey soils in desert.

IA. Mongolia: ***Mong. Alt.*** (in Dzun-Khada-ula low mountains—Gub., Kam. and Dariima; in lower course of Bayan-gol river, in gorges, July 24, 1984—Gub. et al.).

IIA. Junggar: ***Jung. Gobi*** (7–10 km nor.-nor.-east of Shaeda state farm, along road to Podai, fringes of irrigation canals, June 16, 1957—Yun., I-f. Yuan').

General distribution: Aralo-Casp., Fore Balkh.; West. Sib. (south).

Note. Plant from Jung. Gobi is very close to *A. commixtus* Bunge but the tip of standard abruptly narrowed as in *A. ankylotus* Fisch. et May.

132. **A. commixtus** Bunge in Arb. Natur. Ver. Riga, 1, 2 (1847) 146; id. Gen. Astrag. Sp. Geront. 1 (1868) 15 and 2 (1869) 17; id. Astrag. Turk. (1880) 211; Boiss. Fl. Or. 2 (1872) 235; O. et B. Fedtsch. Konsp. fl. Turk. 2 (1909) 195; Fl. Tadzhik. 5 (1937) 266; Gontsch. and M. Pop. in Fl. SSSR, 12 (1946) 302; Fl. Kirgiz. 7 (1957) 273; Kitam. Fl. Afghan. (1960) 218; Fl. Kazakhst. 5 (1961) 163; Bait. Astrag. Tyan'-Shanya (1977) 101; Opred. rast. Sr. Azii [Key to Plants of Mid. Asia] 6 (1981) 113; Fl. Tadzhik. 6 (1981) 211; C.Y. Yang in Claves pl. Xinjiang, 3 (1985) 115; Liou fil. in Fl. desert Sin. 2 (1987) 264.—*A. ankylotus* auct. non Fisch. et Mey.: Kryl. Fl. Zap. Sib. 7 (1933) 1642.

—**Ic.:** Bunge Icon. (1847) tab. 10, fig. 1B; Fl. Tadzhik. 5 (1937) Plate 24, fig. 5 and 6 (1981) Plate 34, fig. 1–7; Fl. SSSR 12, Plate 20, fig. 2.

Described from Mid. Asia. Type in St.-Petersburg (LE).

On clayey, clayey-rubbly slopes of foothills and submontane plains, outcrops of variegated rocks, more rarely in compacted sandy steppes, sandy and rocky deserts.

IIA. Junggar: ***Jung. Gobi*** ("Junggar basin: Zhimisar, Manas, Fukan, Savan, Khutubi"—Liou fil. l.c., C.Y. Yang l.c.), ***Zaisan*** ("Burchum"—C.Y. Yang l.c.).

General distribution: Aralo-Casp., Fore Blakh., Nor. and Cen. Tien Shan, East. Pamir; Balk.-Asia Minor, Fore Asia, Mid. Asia.

133. **A. gracilipes** Benth ex Bunge Gen. Astrag. Sp. Geront. 1 (1868) 15 and 2 (1869) 17; Fl. Tadzhik. 6 (1981) 212; Opred. rast. Sr. Azii [Key to Plants of Mid. Asia] 6 (1981) 114; Li et Ni in Fl. Xizang, 2 (1985) 845.—*A. schurae* Pavl. in Vest. AN KazSSR, 12 (1946) 53; Ikonn. Opred. rast. Pam. [Key to Plants of Pamir] (1963) 161.—*A. ninae* Gontsch. in Not. Syst. (Leningrad) 10, 1–12 (1947) 34; Gontsch. and M. Pop. in Fl. SSSR, 12 (1946) 303; Podl. et Deml. in Mitt. Bot. Staatssamml. München, 7 (1970) 333.

Described from West. Tibet. Type in London (K).

On melkozem-rubbly montane slopes and sandy soils, alpine desert.

IIIB. Tibet: ***Chang Tang*** ("West. Tibet"—Li et Ni l.c.).

General distribution: East. Pamir; Mid. Asia (Pamiro-Alay).

Note. The species is found in the adjoining border regions of Tajikistan and its reports are likely from East. Pamir in Sinkiang.

Section 8 (42). **Oxyglottis** Bunge

134. **A. oxyglottis** Stev. in M.B. Fl. taur.-cauc. 2 (1808) 192; Bunge Gen. Astrag. Sp. Geront. 1 (1868) 11 and 2 (1869) 9; id. Astrag. Turk. (1880) 208; Boiss. Fl. Or. 2 (1872) 229; Lipsky in Acta Horti Petrop. 26 (1907) 209; O. et B. Fedtsch. Konsp. fl. Turk. 2 (1909) 194; Kryl. Fl. Zap. Sib. 7 (1933) 1641; Fl. Tadzhik. 5 (1937) 258; Gontsch. and M. Pop. in Fl. SSSR, 12 (1946) 308; Fl. Kirgiz. 7 (1957) 256; Fl. Kazakhst. 5 (1961) 168; Bait. Astrag. Tyan'-Shanya (1977) 103; Nasir et Ali, Fl. West Pakist. No. 100 (1977) 158; Fl. Tadzhik. 6 (1981) 221; Opred. rast. Sr. Azii [Key to Plants of Mid. Asia] 6 (1981) 201; C.Y. Yang in Claves pl. Xinjiang, 3 (1985) 113; Liou fil. in Fl. desert Sin. 2 (1987) 263.

—**Ic.:** Fl. Tadzhik. 5 (1937) Plate 24, fig. 2 and 6 (1981) Plate 33, fig. 7; Fl. SSSR 12, Plate 21, fig. 6; Fl. Kazakhst. 5, Plate 22, fig. 4.

Described from Crimea. Type in Helsinki (H).

In melkozem-rubbly, clayey and sandy soils in submontane plains, foothills, low and residual mountains, sometimes in sandy areas.

IIA. Junggar: ***Cis-Alt.*** ("Fuyun' [Koktogai]"—Liou fil. l.c.); ***Jung. Gobi*** ("Manas, Khutube"—C.Y. Yang l.c.; "Junggar basin: Zhimisar, Mosavan, Savan, Fukan"—Liou fil. l.c.).

General distribution: Aralo-Casp., Fore Balkh., Jung.-Tarb., Nor. and Cen. Tien Shan; Europe (east.), Mediterr. (east.), Balk.-Asia Minor, Fore Asia, Caucasus, Mid. Asia.

135. **A. sesamoides** Boiss. Diagn. pl. or. nov. 1 ser. 9 (1849) 59; Bunge Gen. Astrag. Sp. Geront. 1 (1868) 12 and 2 (1869) 12; id. Astrag. Turk. (1880) 210; O. et B. Fedtsch. Konsp. fl. Turk. 2 (1909) 195; Fl. Tadzhik. 5 (1937) 261; Gontsch. and M. Pop. in Fl. SSSR, 12 (1946) 306; Fl. Kirgiz. 7 (1957) 274; Kitam. Fl. Afghan. (1960) 220; Fl. Kazakhst. 5 (1961) 167; Bait. Astrag. Tyan'-Shanya (1977) 102; Opred. rast. Sr. Azii [Key to Plants of Mid. Asia] 6 (1981) 101; Fl. Tadzhik. 6 (1981) 217; C.Y. Yang in Claves pl. Xinjiang, 3 (1985) 114.

—**Ic.:** Fl. Tadzhik. 5 (1937) Plate 26, fig. 8 and 6 (1981) Plate 33, fig. 6.

Described from Afghanistan. Type in Geneva (G).

On rubbly montane slopes, loessial foothills, sand-covered and pebbly river valleys.

IIA. Junggar: ***Dzhark.*** (Aktyube around Kul'dzha, No. 1491, May 3, 1877—A. Reg.).

General distribution: Fore Balkh., Jung.-Tarb., Nor. and Cen. Tien Shan; Mid. Asia, Afghanistan.

Note. C.Y. Yang l.c. does not cite the actual location of find in Sinkiang.

136. **A. filicaulis** Fisch. et Mey. in Kar. et Kir. in Bull. Soc. Natur. Moscou, 15, 2 (1842) 336 and in Ledeb. Fl. Ross. 1, 3 (1843) 637; Bunge Gen. Astrag. Sp. Geront. 1 (1868) 11 and 2 (1869) 9; id. Astrag. Turk. (1880) 208; id. in Acta Horti Petrop. 7 (1880) 368; Lipsky in Acta Horti Petrop. 26 (1907) 129, 208; O. et B. Fedtsch. Konsp. fl. Turk. 2 (1909) 194; Fl. Tadzhik. 5 (1937) 256; Gontsch. and M. Pop. in Fl. SSSR, 12 (1946) 307; Fl. Kirgiz. 7 (1957) 275; Kitam. Fl. Afghan. (1960) 220; Fl. Kazakhst. 5 (1961) 167; Nasir et Ali, Fl. West Pakist. 100 (1977) 149; Bait. Astrag. Tyan'-Shanya (1977) 102; Opred. rast. Sr. Azii [Key to Plants of Mid. Asia] 6 (1981) 101; Fl. Tadzhik. 6 (1981) 218; C.Y. Yang in Claves pl. Xinjiang, 3 (1985) 115.—*A. rytidolobus* Bunge Astrag. Turk. (1880) 209; id. in Acta Horti Petrop. 7 (1880) 368; Fl. Tadzhik. 5 (1937) 257; Gontsch. and M. Pop. in Fl. SSSR, 12 (1946) 308; Fl. Kirgiz. 7 (1957) 275; Fl. Kazakhst. 5 (1961) 168; Fl. Tadzhik. 6 (1981) 219.—*A. leptodermus* Bunge, Astrag. Turk. (1880) 210.

—**Ic.:** Fl. Tadzhik. 5 (1937) Plate 24, fig. 8 and 6 (1981) Plate 31, fig. 8.

Described from east. coast of Caspian Sea. Type in Berlin ? (B).

In submontane plains, foothills, rarely on sand.

IIA. Junggar: ***Jung. Gobi*** (left bank of Urungu river, Sulyugou area, between Shauzge state farm [in lower courses of Khobuk river] and Dinsan' [in Urungu], desert, July 12, 1959, Yun., I-f. Yuan'), ***Dzhark.*** (vicinity of Kul'dzha, May 13, 1877, A. Reg.).

General distribution: Aralo-Casp., Fore Balkh., Jung.-Tarb., Cen. Tien Shan, East. Pamir; Mid. Asia, Afghanistan, Pakistan.

Note. C.Y. Yang l.c. points out only generally to the distribution of this species in the southern and northern territories of Sinkiang.

137. **A. tribuloides** Delile, Fl. Aegypt. Illustr. (1813) 70; Bunge Gen. Astrag. Sp. Geront. 1 (1868) 10 and 2 (1869) 7; id. Astrag. Turk. (1880) 208; Boiss. Fl. Or. 2 (1872) 224; O. et B. Fedtsch. Konsp. fl. Turk. 2 (1909) 194; Fl. Tadzhik. 5 (1937) 256; Gontsch. and M. Pop. in Fl. SSSR, 12 (1946) 312; Kitam. Fl. Afghan. (1960) 220; Fl. Kazakhst. 5 (1961) 169; Nasir et Ali, Fl. West Pakist. 100 (1977) 146; Bait. Astrag. Tyan'-Shanya (1977) 103; Fl. Tadzhik. 6 (1981) 103; C.Y. Yang in Claves pl. Xinjiang, 3 (1985) 114.—*A. kirgisicus* Schtschegleev in Bull. Soc. Natur. Moscou, 27 (1854) 161.

—**Ic.:** Bunge Icon. (1847) tab. 14, fig. 1; Fl. Tadzhik. 5 (1937) Plate 26, fig. 7 and 6 (1981) Plate 33, fig. 8; Fl. SSSR, 12, Plate 21, fig. 5; Fl. Kazakhst. 5, Plate 22, fig. 5.

Described from Egypt. Type in Paris (P).

In clayey and clayey-rubbly slopes of foothills, sandy and rocky deserts, solonchak-clayey submontane plains, in pebble beds along river valleys, rarely as weed in plantations.

IIA. Junggar: *Tarb.* ?, *Tien Shan* ?.

IIIC. Pamir (C.Y. Yang l.c.).

General distribution: Aralo-Casp., Fore Balkh., Jung.-Tarb., Nor. and Cen. Tien Shan, East. Pamir; Mid. Asia, Europe (south-east), Mediterr. (east.), Balk.-Asia Minor, Caucasus, Mid. Asia.

Note. C.Y. Yang l.c. points to the distribution of this species in the northern and southern territories of Sinkiang.

138. **A. ammophilus** Kar. et Kir. in Bull. Soc. Natur. Moscou, 15, 2 (1842) 355; Bunge Gen. Astrag. Sp. Geront. 1 (1868) 11 and 2 (1869) 10 id. Astrag. Turk. (1880) 209; Boiss. Fl. Or. 2 (1872) 228; O. et B. Fedtsch. Konsp. fl. Turk. 2 (1909) 195; Fl. Tadzhik. 5 (1937) 261; Gontsch. and M. Pop. in Fl. SSSR, 12 (1946) 313; Kitam. Fl. Afghan. (1960) 220; Fl. Kazakhst. 5 (1961) 170; Nasir et Ali, Fl. West Pakist. No. 100 (1977) 150; Bait. Astrag. Tyan'-Shanya (1977) 103; C.Y. Yang in Claves pl. Xinjiang, 3 (1985) 114.—*A. vachanicus* Boriss. et A. Korol. In Fl. Tadzhik. 5 (1937) 655 and 261; Gontsch. and M. Pop. in Fl. SSSR, 12 (1946) 314; Fl. Tadzhik. 6 (1981) 223, in Fl. Tadzhik. 6 (1981) 222; Opred. rast. Sr. Azii [Key to Plants of Mid. Asia] 6 (1981) 103.

—**Ic.:** Fl. Tadzhik. 5 (1937) Plate 24, fig. 3–3a and 6 (1981) Plate 33, fig. 8; Fl. SSSR, 12, Plate 21, fig. 4; Fl. Kazakhst. 5, Plate 22, fig. 6.

Described from East. Kazakhstan (Arganaty mountains). Type in Moscow (MW), isotype in St.-Petersburg (LE).

On sandy, rubbly, rocky and clayey slopes of foothills and low hills, frequently on gypseous outcrops of variegated rocks.

IIA. Junggar: *Zaisan* ?, *Balkh.-Alak.* ?

General distribution: Aralo-Casp., Fore Balkh., East. Pamir; Mid. Asia, Iran, Afghanistan.

Note. C.Y. Yang l.c. points to the distribution of this species in the sandy deserts of northern Sinkiang.

Subgenus 7. **Calycophysa** Bunge

1. Flowers in dense globose or oval, more rarely in very dense, shortly-cylindrical racemes, on well developed peduncles; more rarely racemes sessile, concentrated in upper part of stem. Calyx not inflated, herbaceous, without reticulate nerves, rarely attenuate, semitransparent toward end of anthesis but then breaking off with pod. Pods sessile. Corolla pilose or glabrous. Leaflets usually 12–30 pairs; if 5–9 (10) pairs, petals of corolla pubescent (section 1 (43). **Alopecias** (Stev.) Bunge) .... 2.

\+ Flowers in loose or somewhat dense, large, oblong or obovate sessile racemes, more rarely on short (up to 2 cm long) peduncles arranged all along stem. Calyx inflated cystlike, membranous. Pods on 2–4 (9) mm long stalk. Corolla glabrous. Leaflets 4–9 (11) pairs (section 2 (44). **Eremophysa** Bunge) ..... 5.

2. Inflorescence on short or long peduncles, ovate or ovate-oblong, 4–6 cm long, 3–5 cm broad. Leaflets 12–15 pairs .... 3.

\+ Inflorescence sessile or subsessile, oval or cylindrical, (3) 5–15 (20) cm long. Leaflets 15–25 (30) pairs .... 4.

3. Bracts 10–20 mm long. Limb of standard oblong-obovate, 28 mm long, gradually narrowed toward base into a claw 1.5 times longer than limb. Racemes sessile or on very short peduncles up to 0.5 mm long, dense. Leaflets broadly-ovate or obcordate, 8–23 mm long, 5–20 mm broad, rounded at tip, covered with appressed hairs beneath ...... 139. **A. vulpinus** Willd.

\+ Bracts 5–7 mm long. Limb of standard orbicular-ovate, 20–26 mm long, abruptly narrowed toward base into claw and nearly as long. Racemes on 0.5–2 cm long peduncles. Leaflets orbicular-ovate, obcordate or oval, distinctly emarginate at tip, or obtuse, long hairy beneath along midrib, with crispate ciliate along margin .... 140. **A. pseudovulpinus** Sancz. ex Ulzij.

4. Inflorescence 5–9 cm long, 3.5–4 cm broad, ovate or ovate-oblong, 1/3–1/2 as long as leaf. Calyx campanulate, mostly inflated, 12–17 mm long, shorter than standard, teeth 2/3 as long as tube; limb of standard oblong or elliptical, emarginate at tip. Leaflets oblong-lanceolate, lanceolate or ovate-lanceolate, (10) 20–30 (45) mm long, (2) 10–15 (20) mm broad, diffusely red hairy beneath .... 141. **A. alopecurus** Pall.

\+ Inflorescence (5) 10–15 (20) cm long, cylindrical or ovate-cylindrical. Calyx tubular-campanulate, 20–25 mm long, as long as standard or somewhat longer, teeth slightly longer than tube; limb of standard ovate, obtuse. Leaflets broadly-elliptical or obovate, (5) 10–15 (25) mm long, 4–10 mm broad, with densely white villous beneath .... 142. **A. alopecias** Pall.

5. Racemes on up to 2 cm long peduncles, rather dense, (7) 9–14 cm long. Calyx initially tubular, 11–15 mm long, ovate- or almost globose-cystiform in fruit, 17–22 mm long, velutinous. Pods oblong-linear, densely velutinous, on 2–3 mm long stalks. Leaves 15–27 cm long; leaflets 6–11 pairs, orbicular or nearly so .... 143. **A. lehmannianus** Bunge.

\+ Racemes sessile, dense, 3–7 cm long. Calyx campanulate or tubularly-campanulate at anthesis, 12–14 mm long, orbicular-ovate in fruit, cystiform, 15–20 mm long, white villous. Pods glabrous, oblong or oblong-ovate on slender 3–9 mm long stalk. Leaves (6) 10–15 (20) cm long; leaflets 3–5 pairs, broadly-ovate or orbicular .... 144. **A. sphaerophysa** Kar. et Kir.

Section 1 (43). **Alopecias** (Stev.) Bunge

139. **A. vulpinus** Willd. Sp. pl. 3, 2 (1800) 1259; DC. Prodr. 2 (1825) 296; Ledeb. Fl. Alt. 3 (1831) 318; id. Fl. Ross. 1 (1842) 635; Bunge in Arb. Naturf. Ver. Riga, 1, 2 (1847) 250; id. Gen. Astrag. Sp. Geront. 1 (1868) 60 and 2 (1869) 100; id. Astrag. Turk. (1880) 246; Boiss. Fl. Or. 2 (1872) 414; Lipsky in Acta Horti Petrop. 26 (1907) 247; O. et B. Fedtsch. Konsp. fl. Turk. 2 (1909) 214; Kryl. Fl. Zap. Sib. 7 (1933) 1669; Gorschk. in Fl. SSSR, 12 (1946) 390; Fl. Kazakhst. 5 (1961) 178; Bait. Astrag. Tyan'-Shanya (1977) 57; Opred. rast. Sr. Azii. [Key to Plants of Mid. Asia] 6 (1981) 118; K.T. Fu in Acta Bot. Bor.-Occ. Sin. 1, 1 (1981) 22; Jager et al. in Flora, 177 (1985) 69; C.Y. Yang in Claves pl. Xinjiang, 3 (1985) 118; Liou f. in Fl. desert Sin. 2 (1987) 260.—*A. clausii* C.A. Mey. in Goebel, Reise in Steppen Sudl. Russl. 2 (1838) 265; Ledeb. Fl. Ross. 1, 3 (1843) 624.—*A. lagocephalus* Fisch. et Mey. ex Schrenk. in Bull. Phys.-Math. Ac. Sci. Petersb. 2 (1844) 197; Bunge Gen. Astrag. Sp. Geront. 1 (1868) 60 and 2 (1869) 100; id. Astrag. Turk. (1880) 246; O. et B. Fedtsch. Konsp. fl. Turk. 2 (1909) 214.—*A. alopecuroides* auct. non L.: Pall. Astrag. (1880) 9.

—**Ic.:** Fl. Kazakhst. 5, Plate 24, fig. 3.

Described from West. Siberia. Type in Berlin [B].

In steppes in solonetzic, clayey and rocky sites, meadows, sandy banks of rivers and brooks covered profusely with sand dunes.

IIA. Jungger: *Cis-Alt.* ("Altay, Fuyun' [Koktogai]"—K.T. Fu l.c.; C.Y. Yang l.c.; Liou f. l.c.), ***Jung. Gobi*** (Trockenbett des Bodoncin-gol-Aue, ca. 25 km südlich Altai-Sum, No. 3699, 1964—Danert et al. [UBA, GAT]; Ikhe-Khavtagiin-nur mountain range, 35 km east of Deeg border post, Aug. 31, 1979; 20 km nor.-west of Tsargin border post in Takhin-Shara-nur mountain range foothills, July 12, 1984—Gub. [MW]; "Unterlauf des Bodoncin-gol 20 km unterhal Altaj-sume, 1240 m, 1982—Jager [HAL]"—Jager et al.), ***Zaisan*** ("Burchum, Khaba-khe [Kaba river]"—K.T. Fu l.c.; C.Y. Yang l.c.; Liou f. l.c.).

General distribution: Aralo-Casp., Fore Balkh., Nor. Tien Shan; Mid. Asia.

140. **A. pseudovulpinus** Sancz. ex Ulzij. in Bull. Soc. Natur. Moscou ser. biol. 95, 1 (1990) 115.—*A. pseudovulpinus* Sancz. in Grub. Opred. rast. Mong. [Key to Plants of Mongolia] (1982) 157; nom. subnud. (descr. ross. in clave); Grub. in Novosti sist. vyssh. rast. 21 (1984) 207; Nemeth in Studia Bot. Hungarica, 21 (1989) 45, 47.—*A. vulpinus* auct. non Willd.: Ulzij. in Tr. Inst. bot. AN MNR, 8 (1982) 14.

Described from Mongolia (Jung. Gobi). Type in Ulan Bator (UBA).

On sandy and sandy-pebbly trails and valleys as well as in kitchen gardens and garbage as weed.

IIA. Junggar: ***Jung. Gobi*** (Khuren-Bogdyn-nuru mountain range, 15 km west and south-west of Tsargin border post, on pebbly trails, 1220 m, Aug. 13, 1977, No. 7473, Volk. and Rachk.—typus ! [UBA]; "Ongon: a shepherd's shelter on the right side of Bulgan river in the foreground of Mongol Altay about 20 km from Chinese border and 60 km to west of Bulgan sum, Aug. 2, 1986—F. Nemeth."—F. Nemeth l.c.).

General distribution: endemic.

141. **A. alopecurus** Pall. Sp. Astrag. (1800) 11; Bunge Gen. Astrag. Sp. Geront. 1 (1868) 59 and 2 (1869) 96; id. Astrag. Turk. (1880) 243; id. in Acta Horti Petrop. 7 (1880) 372; O. et B. Fedtsch. Konsp. fl. Turk. 2 (1909) 212; Gorschk. in Fl. SSSR, 12 (1946) 388; Fl. Kazakhst. 5 (1961) 177; Bait. Astrag. Tyan'-Shanya (1977) 57; Opred. rast. Sr. Azii [Key to Plants of Mid. Asia] 6 (1981) 117; K.T. Fu in Acta Bot. Bor.-Occ. Sin. 1, 1 (1981) 21; C.Y. Yang in Claves pl. Xinjiang, 3 (1985) 117; Liou f. in Fl. desert. Sin. 2 (1987) 256.— *A. alopecuroides* auct. non L.: DC. Prodr. 2 (1825) 394, p.p.; Ledeb. Fl. Alt. 3 (1831) 318; id. Fl. Ross. 1 (1842) 633.

—**Ic.:** Fl. Kazakhst. 5, Plate 24, fig. 2; Acta Bot. Bor.-Occ. Sin. 1, 1 (1981) tab. 2, fig. 1–7.

Described from Sakmara river. Type in London (BM).

Along steppes, steppe meadows, forest margins and river banks.

IIA. Junggar: ***Cis-Alt.*** ("Altay"—K.T. Fu l.c.; C.Y. Yang l.c.; Liou f. l.c.), ***Tarb.*** ("Dachen"—C.Y. Yang l.c.), ***Jung. Ala Tau*** (Urtak-Sary west of Sairam lake, July 7, 1878—Fet.; Borotala river basin, south. slope of Jung. Ala Tau, before Koketau pass near picket, July 21, 1909—Lipsky; mountains not far from Toli town, No. 2558, Aug. 6, 1957 —Kuan), ***Tien Shan*** (Talki-bashi, 2134–2743 m, Sairam lake, July 1877; upper Borotala, 1829 m, Aug. 1878—A. Reg.; Urtak-Aksu in Kul'dzha region, June 17, 1878—Fet.; "Bogdo hills, Guchen town, Inin [Kul'dzha] town, ? Tulei; Urumchi et al."—K.T. Fu l.c.; C.Y. Yang l.c.; Liou f. l.c.), ***Zaisan*** ("Burchum"—C.Y. Yang l.c.), ***Dzhark.*** (Suidun region, July 16, 1877—A. Reg.).

General distribution: Aralo-Casp., Fore Balkh., Jung.-Tarb.; Europe (south-east); West. Sib. (Altay, south), East. Sib. (Sayans).

142. **A. alopecias** Pall. Sp. Astrag. (1800) 12; DC. Prodr. 2 (1825) 294; Ledeb. Fl. Alt. 3 (1831) 317; id. Fl. Ross. 1 (1842) 633; Bunge Gen. Astrag. Sp. Geront. 1 (1868) 59 and 2 (1869) 97; id. Astrag. Turk. (1880) 244; id. in Acta Horti Petrop. 7 (1880) 372; Boiss. Fl. Or. 2 (1872) 411; O. et B. Fedtsch. Konsp. fl. Turk. 2 (1909) 213; Kryl. Fl. Zap. Sib. 7 (1933) 1669; Fl. Tadzhik. 6 (1937) 402; Fl. SSSR, 12 (1946) 387; Fl. Kirgiz. 7 (1957) 279; Kitam. Fl. Afghan. (1960) 186; Fl. Kazakhst. 5 (1961) 176; Bait. Astrag. Tyan'-Shanya (1977) 56; Fl. Tadzhik. 6 (1981) 224; Opred. rast. Sr. Azii [Key to Plants of Mid. Asia] 6 (1981) 117; K.T. Fu in Acta Bot. Bor.-Occ. Sin. 1, 1 (1981) 21; C.Y. Yang in Claves pl. Xinjiang, 3 (1985) 117; Liou f. in Fl. desert Sin. 2 (1987) 259.—*A. leucospermus* Bunge in Arb. Naturf. Ver. Riga, 1, 2 (1847) 250.

—**Ic.:** Pall. l.c. tab. 9; Fl. Tadzhik. 5 (1937) Plate 45 and 6 (1981) Plate 35, fig. 1–6; Fl. SSSR, 12, Plate 26, fig. 1; Fl. Kazakhst. 5, Plate 24, fig. 1; K.T. Fu l.c. tab. 1, fig. 1–7.

Described from East. Kazakhstan (Alakul' lake). Type in London (BM).

On slopes of foothills, submontane plains, fixed sand, meadow-covered slopes and fallow lands, solonetzic wormwood deserts.

IB. Kashgar: ? ***Takla-Makan*** ("Tarim basin"—Liou fil. l.c.).

IIA. Junggar: ***Tien Shan*** (Kul'dzha, July 4, 1877—A. Reg.; in the vicinity of Kul'dzha town, June 20, 1878—Larionov; "Gunlyu [Tokkuztara], Inin"—K.T. Fu l.c.; C.Y. Yang l.c.; "Ili basin"—Liou fil. l.c.), ***Dzhark.*** (Suidun, July 18, 1877—A. Reg.).

General distribution: Aralo-Casp., Fore Balkh., Jung.-Tarb., nor. Tien Shan; Mid. Asia, West. Sib. (Altay, south), Iran.

Section 2 (44). **Eremophysa** Bunge

143. **A. lehmannianus** Bunge in Arb. Naturf. Ver. Riga, 1, 2 (1847) 352; id. Gen. Astrag. Sp. Geront. 1 (1868) 62 and 2 (1869) 106; id. Astrag. Turk. (1880) 284; Boiss. Fl. Or. 2 (1872) 420; O. et B. Fedtsch. Konsp. fl. Turk. 2 (1909) 216; Gontsch. in Fl. SSSR, 12 (1946) 407; Fl. Kazakhst. 5 (1961) 181; Opred. rast. Sr. Azii [Key to Plants of Mid. Asia] 6 (1981) 173; K.T. Fu in Acta Bot. Bor.-Occ. Sin. 1, 1 (1981) 22; C.Y. Yang in Claves pl. Xinjiang, 3 (1985) 119; Liou fil. in Fl. desert Sin. 2 (1981) 261.—*A. sphaerophysa* α *lehmannianus* Kuntze in Acta Horti Petrop. 10 (1887) 184.

—**Ic.:** Bunge Icon. (1847) tab. 15; Fl. SSSR, 12, Plate 27, fig. 3; Fl. Kazakhst. 5, Plate 25, fig. 1; K.T. Fu l.c. tab. 3, fig. 15–21.

Described from Aral Sea coastal region. Type in St. Petersburg (LE).

On compacted sand, more rarely on sand dunes and sandy river terraces.

IIA. Junggar: ***Jung. Gobi*** ("Junggar basin: Tsitai town [Guchen town]"—C.Y. Yang l.c.; Liou f. l.c.; "West. Sinkiang"—K.T. Fu. l.c.).

General distribution: Aralo-Casp., Fore Balkh; Caucasus (Dagestan), Mid. Asia.

144. **A. sphaerophysa** Kar. et Kir. in Bull. Soc. Natur. Moscou, 15 (1842) 338; Bunge Gen. Astrag. Sp. Geront. 1 (1868) 62 and 2 (1869) 106; id. Astrag. Turk. (1880) 146; O. et B. Fedtsch. Konsp. fl. Turk. 2 (1909) 215; Gontsch. in Fl. SSSR, 12 (1946) 410; Fl. Kazakhst. 5 (1961) 181; Opred. rast. Sr. Azii. [Key to Plants of Mid. Asia] 6 (1961) 174; K.T. Fu in Acta Bot. Bor.-Occ. Sin. 1, 1 (1981) 22; C.Y. Yang in Claves pl. Xinjiang, 3 (1985) 118; Liou f. in Fl. desert. Sin. 2 (1987) 260.—*A. sphaerophysa* α *normalis* Kuntze and γ *multifoliolatus* Kuntze. in Acta Horti Petrop. 10 (1887) 183, 184.

—**Ic.:** Fl. Kazakhst. 5, plate 25, fig. 2; Liou f. l.c. tab. 93, fig. 1–6; K.T. Fu l.c. tab. 3, fig. 7–14.

Described from East. Kazakhstan (Arganaty mountains). Type in St.-Petersburg (LE).

On compacted and hummocky sand.

IIA. Junggar: ***Jung. Gobi*** ("Guchen [Tsitai] town, on sand"—K.T. Fu l.c.; C.Y. Yang l.c.; Liou fil. l.c.).

General distribution: Fore Balkh.

Note. Sinkiang plant is evidently introduced.

Subgenus 8. **Cercidothrix** Bunge

1. Spiny golbose-pulvinoid dwarf shrub up to 30 cm tall, leaf rachis persistent and rigescent. Flowers 1–2 each in leaf axils. Pods trigonous in cross-section, subglabrous and cross-rugulose (section 1 (45). **Bulimioides** Bunge) .... 145. **A. unijugus** Bunge.
+ Herbs or nonspiny shrubs .... 2.
2. Whole corolla sericeous, pale-pinkish, almost as long as calyx. Inflorescence dense-capitate (section 2 (46). **Tanythrix** Bunge) .... 146. **A. roseus** Ledeb.
+ Corolla glabrous .... 3.
3. Calyx tubular, tube mostly long, appressed- or patent-hairy. Plants mostly with woody caudex .... 4.
+ Calyx short-tubular, tubular-campanulate (teeth not more than 1/3–1/2 as long as tube) or campanulate .... 23.
4. Leaves and stems pubescent with forked, asymmetrically-double-ended, patent or semipatent hairs. Stems short, 0.5–3 cm long. Leaflets 9–16 pairs, 8–16 mm long, (3) 4–6 mm broad, obovate, or elliptical. Peduncles 2–8 cm long. Racemes short, 2–4 cm long, many-flowered. Calyx 12–16 mm long, with dense black and white stiff hairs, mostly with abundant black hairs along nerves, thus appearing banded. Pods pubescent white villous (section 3 (47). **Tamias** Bunge) .... 147. **A. pilutshensis** Gontsch. ex Ulzij.
+ Leaves and stems pubescent with double-ended appressed hairs. Plants mostly with woody caudex. Pods narrow or somewhat thickened but not shorter than 25 mm and not broader than 4.5 mm, pubescent or glabrous .... 5.
5. Pods linear, linear-oblong .... 6.
+ Pods oblong-oval or nearly cylindrical-oblong, 3–6.5 cm long, with long attenuated beak, densely white lanate-villous. Peduncles longer than leaves (section 7 (51). **Cytisodes** Bunge) .... 22.
6. Pods oblong or linear-oblong, 3–4 cm broad, patently pilose (section 4 (48). **Paraxiphidium** R. Kam.) .... 7.

\+ Pods narrowly-linear, with appressed, sometimes semipatent hairs .... 8.

7\. Pods erect, linear-oblong, 10–18 mm long, 3–3.5 mm broad, with obliquely deflexed subulate 2–4 mm long beak, pubescent with white semipatent and fine black hairs, rapidly glabrescent. Racemes capitate, compressed, with 10–20 flowers, 2–4 cm long. Calyx teeth linear-subulate, 3–3.5 mm long. Corolla violet-purple or red, 18–20 mm long. Leaflets 3–9 pairs, narrowly-linear, or lanceolate-linear, 10–30 mm long, 1.5–4 mm broad. Stipules 4–6 mm long. Dwarf shrubs 30–75 cm tall .... 148. **A. cornutus** Pall.

\+ Pods somewhat curved, oblong, 10–17 mm long, (3) 3.5–4 mm broad, with erect subulate, 1–3 mm long beak and dense patent white hairs. Racemes semiumbellate, short, with 5–8 flowers, 2–2.5 cm long. Calyx teeth subulate, 1–2 mm long. Corolla reddish-violet, (18) 20–23 mm long. Leaflets (5) 6–9 pairs, lanceolate-linear, more rarely oblong or linear, (5) 10–20 (30) mm long, (1) 2–3 (4) mm broad. Stipules 2–4 mm long. Shrub 20–60 (90) cm tall, with deep-brown bark .... 149. **A. suffruticosus** DC.

8\. Shrubs, dwarf shrubs or subshrubs with distinct erect woody caudex (section 5 (49). **Xiphidium** Bunge) .... 9.

\+ Perennial or subshrub with shortened, branched, underground caudex or latter woody at base. Racemes dense, short. Flowers (15) 18–28 mm long. Leaflets 5–11 pairs; if 3–4 pairs, flowers pale-yellow or sometimes lilac-purple (section 6 (50). **Ceratoides** Ulzij.) .... 12.

9\. Racemes with somewhat distant flowers. Peduncles 1.5–2 times longer than leaves. Corolla 21 mm long, purple-coloured. Calyx 10–12 mm long, teeth 2–2.5 (3) mm long. Pods subulate-linear, nutant, 23–30 mm long, 1.5–2 mm broad. Leaflets 2–3 pairs, linear or linear-oblong, 12–20 (30) mm long, (1) 2–4 mm broad, with white hairs diffusely above and densely beneath. Shrub 30–55 cm tall .... 150. **A. polyceras** Kar. et Kir.

\+ Racemes capitate-compressed .... 10.

10\. Leaflets (2) 3–4 pairs, linear-lanceolate or broadly-linear, pubescent above, sometimes very densely pubescent, (8) 15–40 mm long, (1) 1.5–3 mm broad. Peduncles 2–3 times longer than leaves. Racemes 2–4 cm long, dense, many-flowered. Corolla reddish-violet, 18–20 mm long, calyx 7–11 mm long, teeth filiform-subulate, 1.5–2 mm long. Pods linear-subulate or narrowly-linear, (15) 20–30 mm long, (1.5) 2 mm broad, coriaceous. Shrub up to 100 (120) cm tall .... 151. **A. arbuscula** Pall.

\+ Leaflets 4–6 pairs .... 11.

11. Leaflets lanceolate, 1.5–2 mm broad. Pods lanceolate-oblong, 25–30 mm long, 2.5–3 mm broad. Branching distinctly dichotomous .... 152. **A. subuliformis** DC.

\+ Leaflets oblong, elliptical or oblong-lanceolate, 2–7 mm broad. Branching different .... 153. **A. gontscharovii** Vass.

12. Flowers pale-yellow, albescent .... 13.

\+ Flowers bright-pink, lilac-purple, reddish-lilac or violet, rarely bicoloured, with more pale standard and intensely coloured tip of keel; sometimes white when racemes are rather loose and capitate .... 14.

13. Corolla pale-yellow. Pods linear-subulate, falcate, 25–30 mm long, 2–3 mm broad, densely blackish-hairy, canescent due to mixed black and white sparse hairs .... 154. **A. dsharkenticus** M. Pop.

\+ Corolla albescent. Pods linear-oblong, erect, 15–23 mm long, 4 mm broad, with dense appressed black and white hairs .... *__A. pycnolobus__ Bunge.

14. Racemes lax, capitate, 4–5 cm long, with 7–15 flowers. Flowers white or lilac-violet. Pods linear, subtrigonous-cylindrical, somewhat curved, (17) 20–30 mm long, 2–4 mm broad, bilocular. Perennials (5) 10–20 (50) cm tall, with numerous, branched underground caudices. Annual stems (1.5) 2–8 cm long, silvery-albescent .... 15.

\+ Racemes dense, shortened, umbellate-capitate or umbellate, 2–4 cm long, with 4–10 (15) flowers. Flowers of different shades. Pods of different form. Perennials or subshrubs ...... 16.

15. Leaflets narrowly-oblong, oblong-elliptical or linear-lanceolate, subacute, 5–12 mm long, 1.5–3 (4) mm broad, greyish due to appressed puberulence, (4) 5–7 pairs. Calyx 9–12 mm long, appressed-pilose, teeth 1/6–1/4 as long as tube; standard oblong-obovate, somewhat auriculate at base; limb of wings narrowly-oblong or lanceolate-oblong, emarginate at tip .... 155. **A. macrolobus** M.B.

\+ Leaflets oblong, oblong-elliptical or lanceolate-elliptical, short-acuminate at tip, (5) 10–20 mm long, 3–8 mm broad, greyish-green due to stiff appressed long hairs, (2) 3–4 (6) pairs. Calyx appressed- or semiappressed-pilose, teeth 1/4–1/3 as long as tube; standard obovate or oblong-obovate; limb of wings linear-lanceolate or linear-oblong, subobtuse at tip, undivided .... 156. **A. polozhiae** Timoch.

16. Peduncles together with dense shortened racemes considerably (by 2–4 times) longer than leaves. Racemes 3–5 cm long, with 5–14 flowers. Calyx tubular, 9–10 (13) mm long, pubescent with black hairs mixed with white; teeth short, 1–2 (2.5) mm long. Corolla bicoloured with white or pink standard and bright tip of keel. Standard 22–24 mm long, gently emarginate. Pods linear, about 3.5 cm long, acuminate, covered with black and white hairs. Leaflets 5–11 pairs, somewhat oblong, ovate-oblong or linear, 3–16 mm long .... 157. **A. karkarensis** M. Pop.

\+ Peduncles with umbellate (rarely capitate) racemes as long as leaves or 1.5 (2) times longer. Corolla single-coloured, pink, lilac or lilac-violet .... 17.

17. Wings nearly as long as standard; latter 26–28 mm long; corolla albescent-pink. Calyx 13–15 (17) mm long, with 1.5–2 mm long subulate teeth, 1/10–1/7 as long as tube. Racemes umbellate-capitate, with 4–8 flowers. Pods subulate-linear, 25–33 mm long, 1.5–2 mm broad, erect or somewhat curved, cylindrical, bilocular. Leaflets 4–7 pairs, linear-oblong or lanceolate, 5–12 (15) mm long, 1–3 mm broad, appressed-pilose. Caudex together with short old branches immersed in soil .... 158. **A. ortholobiformis** Sumn.

\+ Wings distinctly shorter than standard: latter 18–27 mm long .... 18.

18. Calyx (11) 13–15 mm long. Standard 24–27 mm long, with distinct ligulate taper at tip. Leaflets 7–9 pairs, lanceolate or linear-lanceolate. Peduncles white- and black-hairy, with subumbellate-divaricate raceme of pink-violet flowers .... 159. **A. macrotropis** Bunge.

\+ Calyx 5–10 mm long. Standard 18–23 mm long, tip not tapered or rounded .... 19.

19. Calyx 6–7 mm long, with subulate teeth. Corolla lilac-violet; standard 18–22 mm long. Pods linear, long-acuminate, 25–35 mm long, up to 2 mm broad, shallow-sulcate on back, bilocular. Stems and leaves sparsely pubescent, green. Perennial, 12–30 cm tall .... 160. **A. ceratoides** M.B.

\+ Calyx 8–15 mm long with subulate or linear teeth. Corolla lilac-purple. Stems and leaves with dense white pubescence. Subshrubs .... 20.

20. Leaflets 5–7 pairs, (1) 2–3 mm broad, elongated-elliptical or sublanceolate. Racemes umbellate. Pods subulate-linear, 2–2.5 mm broad, erect or barely curved, semibilocular .... 161. **A. stenoceras** C.A. Mey.

\+ Leaflets 3–4 pairs. Racemes capitate. Pods linear, 2.5–3 mm broad, bilocular .... 21.

21. Leaflets linear, 1–1.5 mm broad. Calyx 8–10 mm long. Pods linear, 20–25 mm long, erect .... 162. **A. compressus** Ledeb.

\+ Leaflets linear-lanceolate, 3–4 mm broad. Calyx 10–15 mm long. Pods narrowly-linear, 40–50 mm long, somewhat curved .... 163. **A. kifonsanicus** Ulbr.

22 (5). Peduncles 2–3 times longer than leaves (up to 10 cm long), greyish-green due to white appressed pubescence; flowers in subcapitate racemes; calyx 11–13 mm long; corolla pale-violet, 17–18 mm long. Pods compressed-cylindrical, arcuately curved upward, 3.5–5 (6.5) cm long, 4.5–5 mm broad, with beak up to 6 mm long, narrow, pubescent with simple white hairs, borne on tubercles. Leaflets 5–7 pairs, oblong-linear, or elongated-elliptical. Subshrubs .... 164. **A. pavlovianus** Gamajun.

\+ Peduncles somewhat longer than leaves, sturdy, 5–12 cm long, with rather sparse patent white pubescence; flowers in subumbellate racemes; calyx 13–15 mm long; corolla yellow, up to 25 mm long. Pods subulate-cylindrical, suberect, up to 5 cm long, with attenuated, 5–8 mm long beak, pubescent with white stiff patent hairs. Leaflets 6–8 pairs, elliptical. Perennial .... 165. **A. ornithorrhinchus** M. Pop.

23 (3). Calyx short-tubular, (7) 8–15 mm long (section 8 (52). **Pseudohelmia** (M. Pop.) R. Kam.) .... 24.

\+ Calyx campanulate or tubular-campanulate, 2–7 mm long, sometimes 8–9 (10) mm long; in latter case, with long, linear or filiform teeth; if (very rarely) short-tubular, pods oblong ..... 29.

24. Pods sessile or subsessile .... 25.

\+ Pods on 1–3 mm long stalks .... 27.

25. Leaflets 3–4 pairs. Calyx 7–8 mm long, teeth subulate, 1.5–2 mm long. Standard 14–15 mm long. Pods nutant, linear-oblong, 10–20 mm long, 2.5–3 mm broad, rounded on back, keeled in front. Bracts oblong-ovate, 1–1.5 mm long .... ***A. psilopus** Schrenk.

\+ Leaflets 2–3 pairs. Calyx 8–12 mm long. Standard longer than 17 mm. Pods erect, 2 mm broad .... 26.

26. Leaflets linear, 1.5–2 mm broad. Bracts ovate, 2–2.5 mm long, with white pubescence. Corolla dark-pink, sometimes purple. Calyx teeth lanceolate-linear. Pods narrowly-linear, 21–23 mm long, somewhat sulcate on back, compressed-trigonous .... 166. **A. sogotensis** Lipsky

\+ Leaflets narrowly-linear, 1–1.5 mm broad. Bracts lanceolate, about 2 mm long, with white and black hairs. Corolla purple-red. Calyx teeth subulate. Pods linear-oblong or linear, 10–15 mm long, sulcate on back .... 167. **A. yumenensis** S.B. Ho

27. Stipules connate at base, 3–4 mm long. Flowers pale-violet. Leaf rachis rigescent and persistent in large numbers after leaflets perish. Leaflets 5–6 pairs, linear or lanceolate-linear, subacute, 8–15 mm long, 1–2 mm broad. Peduncles 2–3 times longer than leaves, strong, virgate; racemes 5–10 cm long, with distant flowers. Large perennial plant, 20–30 cm tall .... 168. **A. kessleri** Trautv.

\+ Stipules mostly connate in sheath and adnate to petiole. Flowers pink or pale-pink. Leaf rachis not rigescent and rarely persistent after leaflets perish .... 28.

28. Corolla 25 mm long, dirty-pink; calyx 11–12 mm long, with lanceolate-linear 2 mm long teeth. Leaflets 3–4 pairs, ovate, oblong or lanceolate, obtuse, 5–14 mm long, 2–3 mm broad. Pods 13–14 mm long .... 169. **A. chorgossicus** Lipsky

\+ Corolla 16 mm long, pale-pink; calyx up to 10 mm long, with very short (0.5 mm long) teeth. Leaflets 3–5 pairs, small, linear or oblong-linear, subacute or subobtuse, 3–6 mm long, 0.5–1.5 mm broad. Pods 6–10 mm long ..... 170. **A. kendyrlyki** M. Pop.

29. Psammophilic unarmed shrubs or subshrubs with well-developed erect albescent shoots; leaf rachis mostly persistent and rigescent, but not spiny. Flowers 5–7 each in loose raceme or compressed racemose inflorescences. Pods oblong or oval, laterally compressed (section 9 (53). **Ammodendron** Bunge) .... 30.

\+ Plant with different characteristics .... 34.

30. Petiole together with leaf rachis 8–10 (15) cm long. Leaflets quite distant on 5–8 (12) cm long rachis, 3–4 pairs, oval or oblong-oval. Racemes lax, few-flowered, 4–10 cm long. Pods 6–8 (10) mm long, 3–4 (6) mm broad, ovate or oblong-ovate, inflated .... 171. **A. cognatus** Schrenk.

\+ Petiole together with leaf rachis 0.5–5 (7) cm long. Leaflets on 0.2–3 (5) cm long rachis, 1–2 (3) pairs, linear, or oblong ...... 31.

31. Petiole together with leaf rachis (3) 5–7 (10) cm long. Leaflets distant on 2–3 (5) cm long rachis. Racemes 2–4 cm long, with 4–6 flowers. Standard 13–14 mm long, limb broadly-rhombic, twice as long as claw. Pods ovate, 5–7 mm long, with densely white villous .... 172. **A. gebleri** Fisch. ex Bong. et Mey.
+ Petiole together with leaf rachis up to 3 cm long. Leaflets approximate on very short (upto 2 cm long) rachis. Racemes elongated, 4–12 cm long, many-flowered .... 32.
32. Calyx campanulate, 3.5–4 mm long. Limb of standard ovate. Pods oblong-ovate, 4–5 mm long, densely silky white-hairy. Racemes elongated, lax, many-flowered, (5) 6–12 cm long .... 173. **A. iliensis** Bunge.
+ Calyx tubular-campanulate .... 33.
33. Calyx 6–7 (8) mm long. Standard 13–15 mm long, limb broadly- or orbicular-ovate. Pods oblong, 5–8 mm long, with densely villous .... 174. **A. brachypus** Schrenk.
+ Calyx 4–6 mm long. Standard 8–12 mm long, limb oblong-obovate. Pods initially linear, 10–15 mm long, later falcate, with appressed silvery pubescence .... 175. **A. hotanensis** S.B. Ho
34. Procumbent, forming caespitose mats, plants of sandy regions having shortened stems with white pubescence; leaflets few-paired, approximated subflabellately; stipules connate for much of their length; pink or pale-pink flowers sessile 1–2 each in leaf axils. Pods 4–5 mm long, 2.5–3 mm broad, with dense white pubescence (section 10 (54). **Ammodytes** (Stev.) Bunge) .... 176. **A. ammodytes** Pall.
+ Leaves with distant, sometimes single leaflets. Flowers in well-developed inflorescences or subradical in acauline plants .... 35.
35. Pods inflated cystlike, membranous .... 36.
+ Pods of different form, not inflated; if inflated, not cystiform .... 43.
36. Acauline perennials with dense racemose inflorescences on long peduncles (section 11 (55). **Cystium** Bunge) .... 37.
+ Plants with well-developed stems or subacauline but then 2–5-flowered inflorescences on short (shorter than leaves) peduncles .... 39.
37. Ovary and pods glabrous .... 38.

\+ Ovary pubescent. Pods with diffuse semiappressed white hairs. Leaflets 11–13 pairs, lanceolate or oblong-elliptical, acute, 6–10 mm long, sparsely pilose on both surfaces. Peduncles with white and black hairs in upper part .... 177. **A. skorniakovii** B. Fedtsch.

38\. Leaflets glabrous on both surfaces or only above, with sparse appressed hairs beneath only along midrib and along margin or (very rarely) allover surface, ovate or oval, 8–13 pairs, (8) 10–20 mm long, 5–12 mm broad. Peduncles glabrous .... 178. **A. physocarpus** Ledeb.

\+ Leaflets appressed-pilose above and beneath, lanceolate or elliptical, (10) 13–20 (22) pairs, (5) 8–14 mm long, acute. Peduncles with appressed white hairs .... ***A. kurdaicus** Saposhn. ex Sumn.

39\. Stems well-developed, usually taller than 10 cm, sometimes less; in the latter case, decumbent or ascending, white-lanate. Inflorescence with (5) 10–15 flowers. Standard up to 20 mm long. Pods densely lanate (section 13 (57). **Leucophysa** Bunge) .... 40.

\+ Plant subacauline, 5–10 cm tall, canescent. Inflorescence with 2–4 (rarely 5) flowers. Pods pubescent with small appressed and long patent hairs. Calyx teeth deltoid-lanceolate, bases connivent, 1/6–1/5 as long as tube. Leaflets linear-oblong or oblong-oval, more rarely oblong-obovate, (3) 4–8 (10) mm long, glabrous above, pilose beneath (section 12 (56). **Paracystium** Gontsch.) .... 179. **A. lasiophyllus** Ledeb.

40\. Leaflets small, up to 8 mm long, suborbicular, with dense semipatent and small white hairs on both surfaces. Peduncles as long as leaves or only slightly shorter. Bracts lanceolate. Standard 16–17 mm long, wings 14–16 mm long, keel 13–14 mm long. Pods globose, acuminate into curved, 4–7 mm long beak, with dense and patent white hairs .... 180. **A. candidissimus** Ledeb.

\+ Leaflets with densely appressed or patent stiff long hairs on both surfaces (sometimes sparse above). Peduncles considerably shorter than leaves .... 41.

41\. Pods 13–15 mm long, globose or subglobose with slender, short, 1–2 (3) mm long beak. Inflorescence with (3) 5–8 flowers. Calyx teeth 1.5–2 mm long. Leaflets (5) 7–12 (15) mm long. Bracts linear or lanceolate-linear, 3–7 mm long .... 181. **A. steinbergianus** Sumn.

\+ Pods longer than 15 mm, ovate, with broad, firm, attenuated, 4–6 mm long beak. Calyx teeth 2–3.5 mm long .... 42.

42. Inflorescence with 9–15 flowers. Bracts linear-lanceolate or linear-subulate, 6–10 (11) mm long. Leaflets 6–14 pairs, 10–24 mm long, 6–11 mm broad, broadly-elliptical, more rarely suborbicular. Stems 8–20 cm tall .... 182. **A. urunguensis** Ulzij.

\+ Inflorescence with 7–10 flowers. Bracts lanceolate. Leaflets 5–8 pairs, 4–10 mm long, 3–9 mm broad, orbicular-ovate. Stems 3–8 cm tall .... 183. **A. toksunensis** S.B. Ho

43 (35). Plant with well-developed stems; even in small plants, stems 2–4 cm tall. Flowers on long peduncles .... 44.

\+ Plant acauline or almost so but sometimes with lignescent caudex branches for a noticable height. Flowers in inflorescences on long or shortened peduncles or subradical .... 67.

44. Long-stemmed herb with many-flowered dense racemose inflorescence on long peduncle; at least lower flowers nutant, pendent. Flowers pale-greenish, canescent, sometimes with partial purple-brownish colouration. Pods nutant, more rarely obliquely or horizontally patent (section 14 (58). **Euodmus** Bunge) .... 45.

\+ Inflorescence lax or dense but without nutant (pendent) lower flowers or pods. Flowers dark coloured .... 47.

45. Ovary and pods glabrous. Pods 9–13 mm long, 3.5–4 mm broad, obliquely erect, oblong-ovate or oblong, with beak declinate laterally, (1.5) 2–3 mm long. Racemes 3–6 cm long, dense, many-flowered, flowers pale-greenish-yellow, later somewhat erubescent. Leaflets (7) 10–14 pairs, (10) 20–40 mm long, 5–15 mm broad, long-elliptical .... 184. **A. uliginosus** L.

\+ Ovary and pods pubescent. Pods nutant. Racemes lax or somewhat lax, many-flowered .... 46.

46. Pods 11–15 (20) mm long, oblong, abruptly narrowed into up to 1–2 mm long beak. Flowers brownish-purple, standard 15–16 mm long, keel 10–11 mm long, with obtuse limb. Calyx tubular, 8–10 mm long, with deltoid-subulate, 1–1.5 mm long teeth .... 185. **A. peduncularis** Royle

\+ Pods 8–9 mm long, lanceolate-oblong, with curved, slender, 1.5–2 mm long beak. Flowers albescent, standard 9–12 mm long, keel 7–8 mm long, limb semiorbicular, subacute. Calyx campanulate-tubular, 4–4.5 mm long, with subulate-deltoid teeth about 1 mm long .... 186. **A. odoratus** Lam.

47. Pods narrowly-linear, long, arcuate. Flowers 12–18 mm long, pink-violet or pale-yellow with pale-purple tip; calyx 6–7 mm long. Leaflets single or 2–5 pairs (section 15 (59). **Gobicus** Ulzij.) .... 48.

\+ Pods oblong or ovate; if linear, wings laciniate .... 50.

48. Stems dichotomously or highly sinuately-branched from base. Leaves with single or, more rarely with 3 leaflets; latter elliptical or lanceolate, acuminate, (25) 30–35 mm long, 5–7 mm broad. Racemes 4–6 (10) cm long, with 6–12 flowers; corolla 12–14 mm long, red-violet. Pods arcuate or suborbicular, declinate laterally or recurved, 20–30 (40) mm long, 2–2.5 mm broad, bilocular .... 187. **A. gobicus** Hanelt et Davazamc.

\+ Stems moderately branched from base, suberect. Leaves not paripinnate, leaflets 3–5 pairs, oblong or elliptical. Corolla 12–17 mm long. Pods usually erect, semibilocular .... 49.

49. Leaflets 9–17 pairs, small, 5–10 mm long, 1–3 mm broad. Racemes 1–3 cm long, with 5–8 flowers; corolla blue-violet, standard oblong. Pods 20–30 mm long, 2–3 mm broad, arcuate .... 188. **A. leansanicus** Ulbr.

\+ Leaflets (3) 7–9 pairs, larger, 15–30 (35) mm long, 6–11 mm broad. Racemes 2–4 cm long, with 8–15 flowers; corolla pale-yellow with purple tip, standard narrowly-obovate. Pods 30–45 mm long, 1.5–2 (2.5) mm broad, suberect .... 189. **A. hamiensis** S.B. Ho

50. Racemes dense, capitate or few-flowered, compressed, subumbellate .... 51.

\+ Racemes lax or short and cylindrical, axillary, with distant or approximated flowers and pods. Flowers purple, pink or violet. Ovary and pods pubescent, sometimes glabrous. Leaflets pilose on both surfaces (section 19 (63). **Craccina** (Stev.) Bunge) .... 61.

51. Standard subrhombic, distinctly narrowed or even ligulate toward tip. Corolla purple-violet, red, bright-pink, bright-blue-violet, more rarely milky-white, flavescent; white in albinos. Pods with short white pubescence or subglabrous. Perennials with long, well-foliate stems upward, not woody in lower part (section 18 (62). **Onobrychium** Bunge) .... 55.

\+ Standard ovate, enlarged toward tip. Pods densely hirsute .... 52.

52. Plant with only white hairs in pubescence. Wings undivided at tip. Calyx 9–10 mm long. Leaflets obovate, round. Stems sinuate (section 16 (60). **Ammotrophus** Bunge) .... 190. **A. albicans** Bong.

\+ Plant with white and black hairs in pubescence (especially pods). Wings partite at tip (section 17 (61). **Pseudoammotrophus** Gontsch.) .... 53.

53. Calyx 10–14 mm long, slightly inflated in fruit and shedding with pod. Standard 19–24 mm long. Pods bilocular. Leaflets oval, elliptical, orbicular-elliptical or suborbicular. Limb of standard oblong or oblong-elliptical. Stems erect .... 191. **A. saratagius** Bunge.

\+ Calyx 8–10 mm long, not inflated. Standard 14–18 mm long. Pods unilocular .... 54.

54. Calyx predominantly white-hairy, with narrowly-lanceolate 2 mm long teeth, 1/4–1/3 as long as tube. Flowers 10–15 mm long, pale-violet; standard 2 mm longer than keel. Bracts lanceolate. Leaflets elliptical or oblong, 5–6 mm long, subacute .... *A. **djilgensis** Franch.

\+ Calyx predominantly black-hairy, with deltoid 1–3 mm long teeth, 1/8–1/5 as long as tube. Flowers 15–18 mm long, reddish; standard 5 mm longer than keel. Bracts oblong-ovate. Leaflets oblong-elliptical, 3–5 mm long, subobtuse .... *A. **tranzschelii** Boriss.

55. Standard oblong-spathulate or oblong-obovate, broadest in upper third, bilobed at tip, narrowed toward base, usually twice longer than calyx .... 56.

\+ Standard subrhombic, (13) 16–28 mm long, entire, enlarged below middle, narrowed upward, twice longer than wings. Calyx tubular-campanulate, usually white-coloured, rarely with sparse black hairs, (5) 7–9 mm long; teeth 3–5 mm long. Inflorescence dense, globose-capitate or oblong raceme. Corolla lilac-purple. Plant 35–80 cm tall .... 192. **A. onobrychis** L.

56. Corolla yellowish, isabelline or canescent with faint violet shade .... 57.

\+ Corolla purple or light-violet, sometimes milky-white or yellow .... 59.

57. Standard (15) 16–21 mm long, (6) 7–8 mm broad, oblong-obovate or oblong-rhombic; (13) 14–17 mm long. Calyx short-tubular or campanulate-tubular, (7) 8–10 mm long; teeth linear, nearly as long as tube or 1/2 as long. Bracts linear-lanceolate

or lanceolate, nearly as long as calyx or 1/2 as long .... 193. **A. viridiflavus** Ulzij.

\+ Standard 13–15 mm long, 4–5 (6) mm broad, oblong-spathulate; wings 12–13 mm long. Calyx campanulate, 7–8 mm long, teeth filiform, somewhat shorter or 1/2 as long as tube. Bracts filiform, somewhat shorter than calyx tube .... 194. **A. inopinatus** Boriss.

58. Leaflets obovate with tip subobtuse, truncated or even emarginate, 3–8 pairs, 2–6 mm long, 1–2 mm broad. Corolla light-reddish or yellowish, standard 9–10 mm long, 4 mm broad .... 195. **A. laspurensis** Ali

\+ Leaflets and corolla with different characteristics .... 59.

59. Mats dense, pulvinoid. Stems strongly shortened, (2) 3–5 cm tall. Leaflets with appressed white hairs on both surfaces, 3–7 (8) mm long, 1–2 (3) mm broad. Racemes short, 1–2 cm long, with 9–13 (15) flowers .... 196. **A. potaninii** Ulzij.

\+ Mats more lax, multicaulis. Stems 10–50 cm long, arcuately ascending. Leaflets (5) 10–25 (30) mm long, 3–8 (10) mm broad, usually glabrous above. Racemes long, with many (over 15) flowers .... 60.

60. Bracts linear-lanceolate, covering calyx almost completely or at least half. Calyx 7–9 (10) mm long, with linear, acute teeth as long as tube or half as long. Corolla light-violet or, more rarely, milky-white, 14–16 mm long; standard 6–7 mm broad. Pods ovate, obtusely trigonous, pubescent with appressed white and black hairs, sometimes with preponderance of either of them, 6–7 mm long, 2.5 mm broad. Plant 10–25 cm tall. Tap root robust, multiheaded ...... 197. **A. austrosibiricus** Schischk.

\+ Bracts short, 2–3 mm long, ovate or ovate-lanceolate, 1/3–1/2 as long as calyx tube. Calyx 5–6 (7) mm long; teeth bristly, 1/5–1/3 (1/2) as long as tube. Corolla purple or red-violet, 15 mm long; standard 5–6 mm broad. Pods oblong-ovate, or trigonous-cylindrical, covered with brown hairs. Plant 20–45 cm tall. Roots fibrous, usually robust, flexible .... 198. **A. adsurgens** Pall.

61 (50). Pods on stalks longer than calyx; calyx teeth very short, 1/7–1/5 as long as tube. Calyx tubular or campanulate-tubular, (3) 4–7 mm long, predominantly black-hairy; corolla bluish-violet, 10–12 mm long. Pods oblong or linear-lanceolate, 10–20 mm long. Leaflets 5–13 pairs, oblong, obtuse, 6–10 (13) mm long, pilose on both surfaces, more rarely diffusely pilose above .... 199. **A. discolor** Bunge.

\+ Pods sessile or subsessile; calyx teeth (1/4) 1/3–1/2 as long as tube .... 62.

62. Standard (14) 15–17 mm long, corolla light-purple or lilac-violet. Calyx 6–7 mm long, black-hairy. Leaflets 5–7 pairs, oblong or oblong-elliptical, obtuse, 5–8 mm long, 2–3 mm broad, appressed-pilose. Bracts lanceolate, acuminate, 2–3 times longer than pedicels. Pods oblong, about 9 mm long, 3 mm broad, with appressed black hairs .... 200. **A. argutensis** Bunge.

\+ Standard less than 10 mm long, more rarely 10–13 mm long but then calyx (3) 4–6 mm long .... 63.

63. Corolla lilac-pink, speckled; calyx campanulate, 5–6 mm long, teeth 1/3 as long as tube. Standard about 10 (12) mm long .... 201. **A. variabilis** Bunge ex Maxim.

\+ Corolla pink-red, light-purple or violet. Calyx 2–3 mm long, teeth 1/3–1/2 as long as tube; standard 6–9 mm long, rarely 10–13 mm long but then calyx 3–4 mm long .... 64.

64. Racemes short, globose-ovate, 1.5–2 cm long, mostly with approximate flowers. Corolla light-purple; standard (9) 10–13 mm long, with ovate limb, bilobed at tip; calyx 3–4 mm long, teeth lanceolate-deltoid, 1/2–2/3 as long as tube or almost as long, acuminate. Leaflets 4–7 pairs, linear, 3–10 mm long, 0.5–1 mm broad, obtuse, lax above, densely appressed-pilose beneath. Pods oblong, 9–20 mm long, about 2 mm broad, thin-valved .... 202. **A. brachybotrys** Bunge.

\+ Racemes elongate, oblong, 3–7 cm long, more rarely ovate, 2–4.5 cm long but then standard about 9 mm long, oval or ovate. Calyx 2–3 mm long; teeth deltoid or linear-subulate .... 65.

65. Flowers pink-red, in ovate or oblong-ovate lax racemes. Corolla about 9 mm long; wings bilaciniate at tip; calyx predominantly white-hairy with mixture of black hairs, teeth deltoid, 1/4–1/3 as long as tube. Pods linear, 8–12 mm long, 2 mm broad, sulcate on back, leptodermatous. Leaflets (3) 4–5 pairs, narrowly-linear, 8–12 mm long, 1 mm broad; hairs double-ended medifixed. Perennial, 7–17 cm tall plants .... 203. **A. miniatus** Bunge.

\+ Flowers pale-violet, in oblong, lax racemes. Corolla 6.5–8 (9) mm long. Pods sulcate on back .... 66.

66. Wings slightly emarginate at tip. Pods oblong, 9–11 mm long, about 2 mm broad, membranous. Leaflets 8–11 pairs, linear-oblong, sometimes oblong-elliptical, 10–25 mm long, 1–7 mm

broad; hairs double-ended attached at very end, thus appearing simple. Young plants 30–60 (80) cm tall .... 204. **A. sulcatus** L.

\+ Wings rounded at tip. Corolla about 8 mm long. Pods linear, 7–8 mm long, 1–1.5 mm broad, leptodermatous. Leaflets 6–9 pairs, linear, 6–12 (18) mm long, 2–3 mm broad, glabrous above. Perennial 30–60 cm tall plants .... 205. **A. consanguineus** Bong. et Mey.

67 (43). Calyx gibbous at base, usually with 2 bracteoles. Flowers yellow, rapidly erubescent, more rarely purple-violet. Racemes short, oval-capitate, 5–10 cm long. Perennial, acauline, generally sparsely pubescent, green plant, 10–35 cm tall, with 5–6 pairs of elliptical or suborbicular leaflets and large herbaceous stipules connate for much of their length. Pods broadly-ovate, trigonous, enlarged at base, 10–13 mm long, 4 mm broad (section 20 (64). **Proselius** (Stev.) Bunge) .... 206. **A. platyphyllus** Kar. et Kir.

\+ Calyx not gibbous at base, without bracteoles. Flowers white to dark-pink or lilac. Generally diffusely pubescent plants with free or connate stipules .... 68.

68\. Pods with slender recurved beak. Flowers in dense capitate inflorescences. Standard rhomboid, ligulate-narrowed in upper part (section 26 (70). **Hololeuce** Bunge) .... 102.

\+ Pods with erect beak. Flowers in lax, racemose or subumbellate, more rarely capitate inflorescences. Standard broad in upper part, ligulate not narrowed .... 69.

69\. Flowers on distinctly manifest peduncles .... 70.

\+ Flowers radical or subradical; if on short peduncles, in leaf axils, stems short .... 103.

70\. Stipules connate for half or more. Leaflets with appressed silvery hairs. Stems shortened, woody, dwarf or subaculine perennials. Peduncles 3–7 cm long. Inflorescence capitate-umbellate; calyx invariably appressed-pilose (section 21 (65) **Helmia** Bunge) .... 71.

\+ Stipules free or connate only at base, very rarely up to half .... 75.

71\. Pods linear-oblong or oblong, 18–20 (22) mm long, 3–5 mm broad .... 72.

\+ Pods ovate-oblong or ovate, 10–15 mm long, 5–6 mm broad. Calyx teeth linear-lanceolate, 2/5–1/2 as long as tube .... 207. **A. helmii** Fisch.

72. Corolla pale-purple or white .... 73.
+ Corolla pale-purple. Standard 17–25 mm broad, broadly-elliptical, rounded at tip or barely emarginate. Leaflets 2–4 pairs, obovate or oblong-obovate, 2–3 (5) mm long. Stipules 2–2.5 mm long, with appressed white hairs. Pods narrowly-linear-oblong or linear-oblong, acuminate, 18–20 mm long, 3–5 mm broad, with dense, white, patent hairs .... 208. **A. heptapotamicus** Sumn.
73. Corolla ivory-white or yellow; standard 17–22 mm long, 6–9 mm broad. Leaflets 1.5–4 mm broad .... 74.
+ Corolla white, violet-coloured keel at tip; standard 22–25 mm long, 10–12 mm broad, oblong-obovate, emarginate at tip. Leaflets 2–4 (5) pairs, oblong-elliptical or orbicular-elliptical, (5) 7–13 mm long, 3–6 mm broad. Stipules 4–5 mm long, 2 with dense, white hairs. Pods linear-oblong, 18–20 mm long, 3.5–4 mm broad, somewhat curved, with densely lanate, bilocular .... 209. **A. tuvinicus** Timoch.
74. Stipules 4–5 mm long, with appressed white or black and white hairs. Leaflets 2–6 pairs, lanceolate or oblong-elliptical, 5–10 mm long, 1.5–3 mm broad, acute, with silvery and dense appressed hairs; petiole as long as rachis or 1/2–2/3 as long. Racemes lax, with 3–5 flowers. Corolla ivory-white, standard 18–22 mm long, 8–9 mm broad (in upper part) .... 210. **A. depauperatus** Ledeb.
+ Stipules 2–4 mm long, with appressed white hairs. Leaflets 1–2 (3) pairs, lanceolate or broadly-lanceolate, (5) 7–10 (15) mm long, 2–4 (5) mm broad, with appressed white hairs on both surfaces; petiole 2–3 times longer than rachis or as long. Racemes dense, with 2–3 (4) flowers. Corolla pale-yellow, standard 17–20 mm long, narrower (6 mm broad) .... 211. **A. kasachstanicus** Golosk.
75. Plants with robust caudex, latter short, branched and underground or shortened and woody on surface. Stems usually geniculately curved .... 76.
+ Plant loosely and finely caespitose; if densely caespitose or with underground branched caudex, plant acauline, small or with rather low stems .... 78.
76. Flowers 8–18 mm long; calyx short-tubular or campanulate-tubular, 5–10 mm long. Pods 6–14 mm long, oblong or elliptically-oblong, compressed (section 22 (66). **Pseuderioceras** Ulzij.) .... 77.

\+ Flowers very large, 18–25 mm long. Calyx tubular, 10–14 mm long. Pods 17–30 mm long, linear, cylindrical (section 23 (67). **Erioceras** Bunge) .... 79.

77\. Calyx short-tubular, 8–10 mm long, teeth linear-subulate or lanceolate, (1) 1.5–2 (2.5) mm long, (1/6) 1/4–1/3 as long as tube; corolla (13) 14–18 mm long. Pods oblong or linear-oblong, 10–14 mm long, about 3 mm broad, distinctly curved. Leaflets (9) 11–20 mm long .... 212. **A. rudolfii** Ulzij.

\+ Calyx campanulate-tubular, 5–8 mm long, teeth subulate-filiform, (2.5) 3–4 mm long, nearly as long as tube or oval-oblong or elliptical-oblong, 6–8 (9) mm long, 2–3 mm broad, erect or somewhat curved. Leaflets 5–10 (12) mm long .... 213. **A. granitovii** Sancz. ex Ulzij.

78\. Wings undivided; if slightly emarginate, leaves with broad elliptical or oblong-elliptical leaflets (section 24 (68). **Chomutoviana** B. Fedtsch. emend. Sancz.) .... 86.

\+ Wings emarginate or bidentate. Leaves with linear, linear-filiform, more rarely lanceolate leaflets; leaves simple, undivided (section 25 (69). **Corethrum** Bunge) .... 94.

79\. Stems geniculately curved, brittle .... 80.

\+ Stems not curved, not brittle .... 81.

80\. Leaflets (1) 2–3 (4) pairs, broadly-elliptical or obovate, (6) 10–15 (20) mm long, (4) 6–8 (12) mm broad, with appressed canescent hairs; terminal leaflet usually larger and broader than rest. Pods curved, angular .... 214. **A. neo-popovii** Golosk.

\+ Leaflets 5–8 pairs, oblong-ovate or elliptical, 5–10 mm long, 2.5–4 mm broad, densely semipatently-pilose. Pods erect, cylindrical .... ***A. infractus** Sumn.

81\. Leaflets linear, linear-lanceolate, elliptical or oblong-elliptical .... 82.

\+ Leaflets orbicular-ovate, oblong-ovate, obovate or broadly elliptical .... 84.

82\. Racemes with 10–18 flowers, orbicular-ovate. Corolla violet. Calyx tube 8–10 mm long. Leaflets 4–7 pairs, with appressed dense, white hairs on both surfaces .... 83.

\+ Racemes with 5–7 flowers, capitate, 2–3 cm long. Corolla purple-violet. Calyx tube 11–14 mm long. Leaflets 2–3 (4) pairs, lanceolate or linear-lanceolate, 5–10 mm long, loosely pilose above and densely, patently beneath. Pods linear, 17–25 mm long, somewhat curved, pubescent only with white hairs .... 216. **A. arcuatus** Kar. et Kir.

83. Leaflets elliptical or oval, 3–7 mm broad. Calyx tube with appressed white hairs mixed with black hairs .... 215. **A. petraeus** Kar. et Kir.

\+ Leaflets linear or linear-lanceolate, up to 3 mm broad. Calyx tube distinctly black-hairy mixed with white hairs .... 217. **A. kaschgaricus** M. Pop. ex Ulzij.

84. Leaflets small, 2–2.5 mm long, 1–1.5 mm broad, 5–6 pairs, orbicular-obovate, appressed-pilose, barely subacute at tip .... *A. **innominatus** Boriss.

\+ Leaflets 2–4 mm long, 4–6 mm broad .... 85.

85. Leaflets 3–4 pairs, oblong-obovate, more rarely oblong, with canescent and short appressed hairs on both surfaces. Pods lanceolate-oblong, 10–17 mm long, 3.5–4 mm broad, with short (1–1.5 mm) beak, densely lanate with predominance of white hairs on sides and black hairs on sutures, specially on back, pod thus appearing with a large black band on back. Standard 19–21 mm long, wings 18–19 mm long, keel 14–15 mm long. Plant subacauline, with short-branched underground caudex .... ***A. alitschuri** O. Fedtsch.

\+ Leaflets 5–7 pairs, obovate, oblong-obovate or orbicular-ovate, diffusely villous above, densely so below. Pods linear, 25–30 mm long, 3.5–4 mm broad, falcate in upper half, acuminate into subulate, 2–3 mm long beak, short-villous only with white hairs. Standard 22–28 mm long, wings 20–23 mm long, keel 19–22 mm long. Plant acauline, caudex underground, woody, short .... ***A. arganaticus** Bunge.

86. Flowers large, 25–30 mm long, albescent, purple along margin. Calyx 10–12 mm long. Standard oblong-obovate, constricted at middle; wings emarginate at tip. Leaflets 4–9 pairs, narrowly-elliptical or lanceolate, 5–10 mm long, 2–4 mm broad .... 218. **A. wensuensis** S.B. Ho

\+ Flowers smaller, up to 22 mm long, violet or blue .... 87.

87. Flowers violet, 10–20 (22) mm long. Calyx (4) 6–11 mm long, teeth 1.5–2.5 mm long. Leaflets 5–24 mm long .... 88.

\+ Flowers blue, 8–10 mm long. Calyx 3–5 mm long, teeth 1–2 mm long. Leaflets 3–6 mm long, sometimes 6–10 mm long .... 90.

88. Standard orbicular-oval or ovate, 14–15 mm long, without constriction. Pods cylindrical, somewhat inflated, 9–13 mm long, with appressed white and black hairs, distinctly bilocular .... 219. **A. saichanensis** Sancz.

+ Standard oblong-elliptical, (10) 15–20 (22) mm long, constricted at middle, gradually narrowed toward base. Pods oblong, conspicuously inflated, (6) 8–9 (10) mm long, villous with short white hairs, almost entirely unilocular .... 89.

89. Calyx 6–8 mm long, with deltoid-lanceolate teeth, 1/4–1/3 as long as tube. Inflorescence as long as leaves or barely longer .... 220. **A. chomutovii** B. Fedtsch.

+ Calyx 8–11 mm long, with linear-lanceolate teeth, 2/5–2/3 as long as tube. Inflorescence 2–2.5 times longer than leaves .... ***A. tekessicus** Bajt.

90. Racemes with (3) 4–20 flowers. Pods 7–18 mm long, curved .... 91.

+ Racemes with 1–4 flowers. Pods 3–7 mm long, not curved .... 93.

91. Mats dense, large, pulvinoid. Pods highly curved ringlike, narrowly-linear, 15–18 mm long. Leaflets linear or linear-lanceolate, small, up to 5 mm long, not more than 1 (1.5) mm broad, with silvery pubescence. Peduncles 3–5 times longer than leaves .... 221. **A. caudiculosus** Kom.

+ Mats small, loose, sometimes dense but small pads. Pods up to 12 mm long .... 92.

92. Peduncles short. Racemes dense, 8–12 mm long, with (3) 4–8 flowers. Corolla violet, blue or blue-violet, standard 7–8 mm long. Bracts deltoid or deltoid-ovate, sometimes 3-lobed, 1.5–2.5 mm long, white-ciliate along margin. Leaflets 5–7 (9) pairs, narrowly-elliptical or oblong-lanceolate, 4–6 mm long. Pods unilocular, flattened .... 222. **A. roborowskyi** Ulzij.

+ Peduncles ascending, 3–5 times longer than leaves. Racemes rather lax, 1–2 cm long, later elongated to 4 cm, with 8–20 flowers. Corolla double-coloured, pale-blue or yellowish with violet tip of keel; standard 9–11 mm long. Bracts lanceolate, 1–1.5 mm long, with black pubescence outside, black-ciliate along margin. Leaflets 9–11, oblong-elliptical, 6–10 mm long. Pods almost entirely bilocular, keeled .... 223. **A. divnogorskajae** Ulzij.

93. Stipules adnate to petiole upto middle. Leaflets 2–3 (4) pairs, 3–6 mm long. Peduncle with 2–4 flowers. Calyx 4–5 mm long, teeth broadly-lanceolate, 1/2–2/3 as long as tube. Corolla 8–10 mm long, wings 6–8 mm long, nearly as long as keel. Pods 5–7 mm long, 3 mm broad, semiorbicular or oblong-semiovate, semibilocular .... 224. **A. arnoldii** Hemsl. et Pearson

+ Stipules adnate to petiole at base. Leaflets 2–3 pairs, 3–5 mm long. Peduncle with 1–2 flowers. Calyx 3–4 mm long, teeth deltoid, 1/2 as long as tube. Corolla 8–9 mm long, wings 5–6 mm long, keel 4–5 mm long. Pods 3–5 mm long, about 2 mm broad, oblong, unilocular .... 225. **A. monticola** P.C. Li et Ni

94 (78). Leaflets filiform-linear, not more than 1 mm broad, 1–3 pairs, with canescent hairs. Plant subacauline, forming small loose mats, 6–15 (18) cm tall. Flowers dark-purple; corolla 9–10 mm long; Calyx 5–7 mm long, teeth longer than tube, rarely as long. Pods 11–16 mm long, somewhat falcate, slightly pubescent with patent white hairs .... 226. **A. nematodes** Bunge ex Boiss.

+ Leaflets linear, lanceolate or oblong, 1 mm or more broad. Mats larger or plant with well developed stem .... 95.

95. Pods inflated, oblong-ovate, 6–9 mm long, with slightly recurved beak. Inflorescence dense, capitate; corolla violet, standard (11) 16–25 mm long. Leaflets 3–5 pairs, (4) 7–12 (15) mm long, 1–1.3 mm broad, narrowly linear, subobtuse .... 227. **A. kronenburgii** B. Fedtsch.

+ Pods not inflated .... 96.

96. Racemes 1–2 cm long, with 5–7 flowers. Wings gently emarginate, with limb enlarged in upper portion. Pods 8–9 mm long, oblong, falcate, convex on back, horizontally declinate or obliquely erect, acuminate into subulate beak, pubescent with white hairs. Plant 5–10 cm tall, with robust, profusely-branched underground caudex .... 228. **A. dschangartensis** Sumn.

+ Racemes longer, lax and profusely flowered .... 97.

97. Wings deeply bilaciniate at tip. Plant smaller .... 98.

+ Wings undivided, rounded or emarginate at tip. Plant very large, 25–80 cm tall .... 99.

98. Plant acauline, 10–15 (20) cm tall. Leaflets 2–3 (4) pairs, acute; calyx campanulate, 5 mm long. Corolla pink, standard 7–9 mm long, wings deeply (for 1/3 of blade length) laciniate at tip. Pods 7–10 mm long, oblong-ovate, sessile .... 229. **A. semenovii** Bunge.

+ Plant with short stems or subacauline, 20–40 cm tall. Leaflets 3–4 pairs, lanceolate or linear-lanceolate, acute. Calyx tubular, 9–11 mm long. Corolla pale-violet, standard 12–14 mm long, wings deeply (for 1/4 of limb length) laciniate at tip. Pods 11–12 mm long, about 2 mm broad, oblong, subsessile .... ***A. schachdarinus** Lipsky

99. Pods glabrous, sometimes with sparse, appressed white hairs along dorsal suture, 15–20 mm long, 3–4 mm broad, ablong, bilocular, on stalk as long as calyx tube. Calyx 4–6 mm long; corolla violet-pink, standard 15–19 mm long. Leaflets 3–5 pairs, linear-lanceolate, 10–40 mm long, 1–3 mm broad. Peduncles virgate, twice longer than leaves .... *A. **terektensis** Fisjun.

\+ Pods pubescent, 6–18 mm long .... 100.

100. Pods white- and black-hairy. Leaflets with canescent hairs on both surfaces. Peduncles slender, virgate, 1.5–2.5 times longer than leaves .... 101.

\+ Pods white-hairy, linear-oblong, mostly curved, 10–15 mm long, 2.5–3.5 mm broad, with 2–3 mm long recurved beak. Leaflets 1–3 pairs, lanceolate or oblong, acute or obtuse, (6) 8–15 (20) mm long, (2) 3–5 (7) mm broad, with appressed silvery hairs on both surfaces. Peduncles stout, 2–3 times longer than leaves. Limb of standard obovate, more rarely oblong-oval .... 230. **A. pseudoscoparius** Gontsch.

101. Leaflets 4–6 pairs, oblong or lanceolate, acute, 5–15 mm long. Pods oblong, 6–10 mm long, 3–3.5 mm broad, about 2 mm thick, with slender 3–4 mm long beak mostly bent at tip, compressed laterally. Mat fairly dense .... 231. **A. scoparius** Schrenk.

\+ Leaflets 3–4 (5) pairs, linear or linear-lanceolate, 10–20 (23) mm long, 1–2 (3) mm broad. Pods linear-cylindrical, 14–18 mm long, 2 mm broad, with short, 1–2 mm long acuminate beak, not flattened. Mat more dense .... 232. **A. hesiensis** Ulzij.

102 (68). Pods black- and white-hairy, 9–12 mm long, oblong-ovate. Leaflets narrowly-linear, (2) 3–5 pairs, (13) 20–30 mm long, 1–2 (3) mm broad. Standard 12–13 mm long. Calyx campanulate, 7–15 mm long, teeth 1/4–1/2 as long as tube. Plant with stems woody for a considerable height in lower part .... 233. **A. angustissimus** Bunge.

\+ Pods exclusively white-hairy. Leaflets 5–12 pairs, oblong or oblong-elliptical, 10–20 mm long, 2–6 mm broad. Standard 19–25 mm long. Calyx campanulate, 12–15 mm long, teeth 1/2 as long as tube .... 234. **A. kuldshensis** Bunge.

103 (69). Plant with short but distinct, up to 5 cm long stems. Inflorescence dense, many-flowered, on shortened peduncles or subsessile in leaf axils. Flowers small, 10–11 mm long. Calyx campanulate-tubular, 9–10 mm long, with filiform teeth nearly

as long as tube. Pods semibilocular, 7–8 mm long, 3 mm broad, sublinear-oblong (section 27 (71). **Pseudorosei** Ulzij.) .... 235. **A. pseudoroseus** Ulzij.

\+ Plant acauline or nearly so. Inflorescence lax, dense, many-flowered or few- (rarely single-) flowered, radical or subradical .... 104.

104. Calyx pubescent with white and black hairs (section 28 (72). **Mixotricha** Ulzij.) .... 105.

\+ Calyx pubescent exclusively with white hairs, sometimes with black hairs; in latter case, leaflets 2–3 pairs .... 107.

105. Calyx slightly inflated toward end of anthesis and usually shedding with pod. Leaflets 9–12 pairs, oblong-elliptical or lanceolate, 5–10 (15) mm long. Peduncles 1/3–2/3 as long as leaves. Pods white-lanate, 9–10 (15) mm long, ovate or oblong-ovate .... 236. **A. megalanthus** DC.

\+ Calyx changing its form toward end of anthesis .... 106.

106. Pods oval, ovate or orbicular-ovate, with patent, stiff, white hairs, 9–18 mm long, 8–9 mm broad. Leaflets 7–13 pairs, dense, semiappressed-pilose on both surfaces. Bracts lanceolate, longer than pedicels .... 237. **A. testiculatus** Pall.

\+ Pods oblong-obovate, with soft white tomentum. Leaflets 10–12 pairs, with dense, semipatent hairs on both surfaces. Bracts broadly-cordate, acute, very short .... 238. **A. lactiflorus** Ledeb.

107. Pods oblong-ovate, attenuated at tip into firm and long, subulate beak 3–5 mm long or as long as pod and standing erect from calyx (section 29 (73). **Scabriseta** R. Kam.) .... 108.

\+ Pods lanceolate, linear, cylindrical or oblong, with short (much shorter than pod) beak .... 109.

108. Corolla white, standard and keel violet-coloured at tip, standard (14) 16–20 mm long; calyx 8–12 mm long, tubular, teeth (1/3) 1/2–2/3 as long as tube, linear-subulate. Leaflets (2) 3–8 (9) pairs, elliptical or obovate, subobtuse, more rarely subacute, 5–10 (14) mm long, 2.5–8 mm broad, with dense, appressed, stiff hairs on both surfaces, albescent .... 239. **A. scabrisetus** Bong.

\+ Corolla purple; standard 20–22 mm long; calyx (13) 15–18 mm long, teeth linear-subulate, as long as tube or 1/2 as long. Leaflets 6–13 pairs, suborbicular, orbicular-oval or orbicular-ovate, obtuse, 5–10 (13) mm long, 3–7 (10) mm broad, with densely appressed or semipatent stiff hairs on both surfaces .... 240. **A. grubovii** Sancz.

109. Leaflets 4–12 (15) pairs (section 30 (74). **Trachycercis** Bunge) .... 110.

\+ Leaves with 1, 3 or 5 leaflets .... 125.

110. Calyx with appressed or semiappressed hairs .... 111.

\+ Calyx densely, white-villous or densely lanate with white hairs .... 117.

111. Flowers 10–12 mm long; calyx (5) 6–9 mm long, teeth filiform, as long as tube or somewhat longer. Pods asymmetrical, semioval-oblong, white-villous, up to 6 mm long, 2.5 mm broad, bilocular. Leaflets 7–11 pairs, (2) 3–6 mm long, (1) 1.5–2 (2.5) mm broad, elliptical, oblong or obovate .... 241. **A. pseudotesticulatus** Sancz. ex Ulzij.

\+ Flowers larger, calyx teeth linear-lanceolate, filiform or subulate, invariably (1/5) 1/3–1/2 as long as tube .... 112.

112. Standard 16–18 mm long, limb oblong, angular at base. Calyx 8–9 mm long, with densely appressed and semiappressed, stiff, white hairs. Pods oblong, 11–13 mm long, with dense white-lanate or villous .... 242. **A. salsugineus** Kar. et Kir.

\+ Standard 18–30 mm long; pubescence of calyx different .... 113.

113. Calyx with dense, long and short white hairs, 8–14 mm long, teeth short, 1/7–1/5 as long as tube. Corolla pinky-white, 18–22 (24) mm long, standard oblong-obovate, gradually narrowed into beak. Leaflets (2) 3–5 (7) pairs, lanceolate, elliptical or oblong, subacute, 8–16 mm long, 2–4 (5) mm broad, with appressed or semiappressed hairs. Pods 3–7 mm long, 3–5 (7) mm broad, with 1 mm long beak, orbicular-ovate or subglobose. Plant 5–15 (20) cm tall .... 243. **A. junatovii** Sancz.

\+ Calyx with rather sparse, short, white hairs (not lanate), 8–11 mm long. Leaflets (4) 5–9 pairs .... 114.

114. Limb of standard oblong .... 116.

\+ Limb of standard different in form .... 115.

115. Standard spathulate. Corolla ivory-white. Leaflets elliptical or oblong-elliptical, with dense semipatent hairs. Stipules deltoid-ovate. Bracts lanceolate, Pods oblong, slightly curved, 15 mm long, with slender beak .... 244. **A. pseudoscaberrimus** Wang et Tang

\+ Standard ovate, corolla yellow, sometimes with violet colouration on keel and standard. Leaflets lanceolate or oblong-elliptical, with appressed, stiff hairs, terminal leaflet usually larger than rest. Pods lanceolate or oblong, falcate, 10–17 mm long, acute .... 245. **A. scaberrimus** Bunge.

116. Leaflets 4–6 pairs, obovate, obtuse or slightly emarginate at tip, 7–15 mm long, 4–9 mm broad, with scattered, glaucescent, short, appressed white hairs. Calyx 8–11 mm long, teeth subulate, 1/2 as long as tube, corolla pinky-lilac, standard 18–25 mm long. Pods linear-oblong, about 15 mm long .... 246. **A. glomeratus** Ledeb.

\+ Leaflets 3–4 (5) pairs, oblong-oval or lanceolate, subacute, all similar, appressed-pilose on both surfaces, 4–10 (12) mm long, 1–3 (4) mm broad. Calyx 8–10 (15) mm long, with dense, short, appressed white hairs, teeth linear-lanceolate, more rarely nearly subulate, 1/5–1/3 as long as tube. Corolla sulphureous; standard 20–30 mm long. Pods oblong, sessile, curved .... 247. **A. brevifolius** Ledeb.

117. Leaflets glabrous above, 5–9 (11) pairs, lanceolate or oblong-lanceolate, 3–8 mm long, 1–2.5 mm broad. Calyx short-tubular, 8–10 mm long, densely villous due to patent white hairs. Corolla pale-yellow or albescent, 22–28 mm long, limb of standard oblong. Plant 3–5 cm tall, forming mats .... 248. **A. galactites** Pall.

\+ Leaflets pilose on both surfaces; if glabrous above, leaflets broader than 3.5 mm, not lanceolate but ovate; (3) 4–12 (14) pairs, patently or semipatently hirsute. Corolla ivory-white .... 118.

118. Leaflets 3–4 pairs, 4–7 mm long, appressed white-pilose on both surfaces. Calyx 8–11 mm long .... 119.

\+ Leaflets 4–12 (15) pairs, 5–15 mm broad, patently or semipatently hirsute on both surfaces. Calyx 10–18 mm long .... 120.

119. Leaflets oblong, 3–5 mm broad. Corolla white; standard oblanceolate, 16–23 mm long, emarginate at tip; keel 2/3 of wing length, calyx teeth 1/2 as long as tube .... 249. **A. parvicarinatus** S.B. Ho

\+ Leaflets ovate or obovate, 3–5 mm broad. Corolla ivory-white, sometimes with violet colouration along margin; standard obovate, tip obtuse, slightly emarginate; keel slightly shorter than wings. Calyx teeth as long as tube or somewhat shorter .... 250. **A. jiuquanensis** S.B. Ho

120. Leaflets 4–6 (8) pairs, obovate .... 121.

\+ Leaflets 6–12 (15) pairs, ovate, oblong, oval or narrowly-elliptical .... 122.

121. Leaflets 10–15 mm long, 5–9 mm broad. Standard oblong, (27) 32–38 mm long, 7–9 mm broad; wings emarginate at tip. Pods subglobose, 5–6 mm long, conspicuously inflated, with short, 1–1.5 mm long beak .... 251. **A. hypogaeus** Ledeb.

\+ Leaflets 8–10 mm long, 4–6 mm broad. Standard narrowly-oblong, 15–18 mm long, 4–5 mm broad; wings undivided at tip. Pods 10–15 mm long, slightly bent, with 4–7 mm long beak .... 252. **A. pseudohypogaeus** S.B. Ho

122. Racemes with 1–3 flowers .... 123.

\+ Racemes many-flowered .... 124.

123. Racemes with 2–3 flowers. Wings bidentate at tip. Leaflets 5–10 pairs, oval, 3–4 (5) mm long, up to 3 mm broad, bristly above, appressed canescent-pilose beneath .... 253. **A. koburensis** Bunge.

\+ Racemes with 1–2 flowers. Wings undivided at tip. Leaflets 10–17 pairs, obovate or broadly-elliptical, 6–12 mm long, 3–6 mm broad, semipatently-pilose on both surfaces .... 254. **A. ordosicus** H.C. Fu

124. Calyx 10–14 (17) mm long. Standard oblong-obovate, 17–28 mm long. Pods oblong-ovate, 10–15 mm long, 4–6 mm broad, with strong, 3–6 (8) mm long beak. Leaflets ovate or oblong .... 255. **A. hsinbaticus** P.Y. Fu et Y.A. Chen

\+ Calyx 6–8 mm long. Standard oblanceolate, about 15 mm long. Pods oblong, 15 mm long, 7 mm broad, with short beak. Leaflets narrowly-elliptical .... 256. **A. hebecarpus** Cheng f.

125 (109). Flowers pale-yellow or albescent, 1–2 or 2–7 each on well-developed pedicels. Pods oblong-cylindrical, oblong-elliptical or oblong-ovate, 20–30 mm long, 6–8 (10) mm broad, lanate, white-villous, completely bilocular (section 31 (75). **Macrotrichoides** Ulzij.) .... 126.

\+ Flowers pink or pinkish-white, subradical, 2–8 each in leaf axils. Pods sessile, orbicular-elliptical, 4–10 mm long, 3–6 mm broad, inflated, white-lanate but not villous, semibilocular or subunilocular (section 32 (76). **Borodiniana** B. Fedtsch.) .... 128.

126. Leaves simple, i.e. with a single terminal leaflet, very rarely with 3 leaflets; latter orbicular- or broadly-ovate or broadly-oval, 15–25 mm broad, rather thick, obtuse, lateral, acuminate, stiff, both surfaces with dense and stiff appressed, silvery hairs. Peduncles short, with 1–2 flowers. Pods ovate or oblong-ovate, up to 2.5 mm broad, 6–8 mm long. Plant up to 5 cm tall, finely-caespitose .... 257. **A. monophyllus** Bunge.

\+ Leaves invariably with 3 or 5 leaflets; latter elliptical, oblong-obovate, orbicular-elliptical, more rarely oblong-oval, acuminate, stiff, with densely-appressed, white hairs on both surfaces .... 127.

127. Peduncles as long as leaves, up to 10 (12) cm long. Racemes with 3–6 (7) large flowers; corolla 20–26 mm long, calyx 13–15 mm long, campanulate-tubular. Leaves 10 (12) cm long, long-petiole, leaflets usually 5, more rarely 3. Leaflets 10–25 mm long, up to 18 mm broad, elliptical or oblong, acuminate at tip. Plant 5–10 cm tall. Densely-caespitose .... 258. **A. gubanovii** Ulzij.

\+ Peduncles slightly shorter than leaves. Racemes with 1–2 small flowers; corolla 15–18 mm long, calyx 13–15 mm long, tubular. Leaves 2–4 cm long; leaflets usually 3, more rarely single, petioles as long as rachis or slightly longer, leaflets 7–22 mm long, 7–15 mm broad, elliptical or orbicular-elliptical, acuminate. Pods oblong, arcuate, (2) 2.5–3.5 mm broad, 9–11 mm long, dense white- or yellowish-lanate. Plant 3–5 cm tall, small, loosely caespitose .... 259. **A. macrotrichus** Peter-Stib.

128. Leaves with 3 or 5 broad, obovate, oblong or elliptical leaflets .... 129.

\+ Leaves with 1 or 3 narrow, linear, lanceolate or oblong leaflets .... 131.

129. Leaves with 5, more rarely 3 obovate, broadly-elliptical leaflets, latter 3–8 mm long, 1.5–3.5 mm broad. Corolla white, standard 14–15 mm long with limb oblong; limb of wings 1.5–2 times longer than claw. Calyx short-tubular, 7–11 mm long, teeth nearly as long as tube or 1/2–2/3 as long .... 260. **A. baischanticus** Ulzij.

\+ Leaves with 3 or 5 oblong-obovate leaflets; latter 8–20 mm long .... 130.

130. Corolla pink, standard 27–30 mm long, limb oblong-obovate; calyx tubular, 12–15 mm long, teeth 1/6–1/5 as long as tube .... 261. **A. borodinii** Krassn.

\+ Corolla yellowish, standard 10–18 mm long, limb narrowly-oblong; calyx tubular-campanulate, 7–12 mm long, teeth filiform-linear, nearly as long as tube .... 262. **A. pseudoborodinii** S.B. Ho

131. Leaves entirely simple, linear-filiform or linear, 2–12 cm long, 1–2 mm broad, acuminate but barely spiny. Racemes with 2–5 flowers; calyx 5–7 mm long, corolla 8–12 mm long, purple-violet, standard about 11 mm long, oblong, with constriction at

middle, keel 7 mm long. Pods oblong or lanceolate-arcuate, about 10 mm long, semibilocular .... 263. **A. efolialatus** Hand.-Mazz.

\+ Leaves with single, more rarely 3 leaflets. Latter lanceolate, lanceolate-elliptical or oblong. Calyx 8–17 mm broad, 13–30 mm long .... 132.

132\. Leaves with single leaflet .... 133.

\+ Leaves with 3 oblong-obovate leaflets. Standard about 30 mm long with oblong-obovate limb; wings 26–28 mm long, keel 23 mm long; calyx 14–17 mm long, tube 12–15 mm long, teeth about 2 mm long .... 264. **A. muschketovii** B. Fedtsch.

133\. Corolla pale-pink, standard linear-oblong, wings narrowly-linear, slightly emarginate, keel about 10 mm long; calyx 10–11 mm long, teeth linear-subulate, as long as tube. Leaflets 10–30 mm long, lanceolate or lanceolate-elliptical .... 265. **A. alberti** Bunge.

\+ Corolla pinkish-white; standard oblong, wings oblong, undivided; keel 17–18 mm long; calyx 8–12 (15) mm long, teeth lanceolate, slightly longer than tube or as long. Leaflets 7–11 (17) mm long, elliptical, narrowly oblong, more rarely lanceolate .... 266. **A. vallestris** R. Kam.

Section 1 (45). **Bulimiodes** Bunge

145\. **A. unijugus** Bunge Gen. Astrag. Sp. Geront. 1 (1868) 130 and 2 (1869) 228; id. Astrag. Turk. (1880) 287; O. et B. Fedtsch. Konsp. fl. Turk. 2 (1909) 239; Gontsch. in Fl. SSSR, 12 (1946) 780; Opred. rast. Sr. Azii [Key to Plants of Mid. Asia] 6 (1981) 274; S.B. Ho in Bull. Bot. Research, 3, 1 (1983) 70; C.Y. Yang in Claves pl. Xinjiang, 3 (1985) 146; Liou f. in Fl. desert Sin. 2 (1987) 276.—*A. oligophyllus* Schrenk in Bull. Phys.-Math. Ac. Sci. Petersb. 2 (1844) 197, non Boiss. (1843); Fisch. in Bull. Soc. Natur. Moscou, 26, 4 (1853) 420.

—**Ic.:** Fl. Kazakhst. 5, Plate 37, fig. 5; Liou fil. l.c., tab. 97, fig. 1–7.

Described from East. Kazakhstan (Balkhash lake). Type in St.-Petersburg (LE).

In deserts and steppes, solonetzes, puffed solonchaks, floors of sandy gullies, rocky and rubbly slopes of knolls, plains and low mountains.

IIA. Junggar: ***Tarb.*** ("Dachen"—C.Y. Yang l.c.), ***Jung. Gobi*** ("Fukhai [Bulen-Tokhoi], Sanchuan', Susuchuan'"—Liou f. l.c.), "Gurban bulak east of Urumchi"—S.B. Ho l.c., "Qinhe [Chingil']"—C.Y. Yang l.c.).

General distribution: Aralo-Casp. (nor.-east.), Fore Balkh.

Section 2 (46). **Tanythrix** Bunge

146. **A. roseus** Ledeb. Fl. Alt. 3 (1831) 330; id. Fl. Ross. 1, 3 (1843) 623; Bunge Gen. Astrag. Sp. Geront. 1 (1868) 114 and 2 (1869) 195; id. Astrag. Turk. (1880) 271; O. et B. Fedtsch. Konsp. fl. Turk. 2 (1909) 224; Kryl. Fl. Zap. Sib. 7 (1933) 1686; Gontsch. in Fl. SSSR, 12 (1946) 568; Fl. Kazakhst. 5 (1961) 230; Opred. rast. Sr. Azii [Key to Plants of Mid. Asia] 6 (1981) 255; Ulzij. in Tr. Inst. bot. AN MNR, 8 (1982) 25; S.B. Ho in Bull. Bot. Research, 3, 1 (1983) 51; C.Y. Yang in Claves pl. Xinjiang, 3 (1985) 147; Liou f. in Fl. desert Sin. 2 (1987) 280.—*A. dasycephalus* Bess. ex Stev. in Bull. Soc. Natur. Moscou, 4 (1832) 264.

—**Ic.:** Ledeb. Icon. pl. fl. Ross. 3 (1831) 28, tab. 300; Fl. Kazakhst. 5, Plate 30, fig. 2; Liou f. l.c. tab. 98, fig. 21–25.

Described from Altay (Irtysh valley). Type in St.-Petersburg (LE).

On fixed, hummocky sand, solonetzic-sandy banks of rivers and lakes.

IIA. Junggar: ***Cis-Alt.*** ("Altay—all over the region"—S.B. Ho l.c.), ***Tarb.*** ("Zimunai" —C.Y. Yang l.c., Liou f. l.c.), ***Zaisan*** ("Burchum"—C.Y. Yang l.c.; Khaba-khe [Kaba river]—Liou f. l.c.).

General distribution: Fore Balkh.; West. Sib. (Altay, south).

Section 3 (47). **Tamias** Bunge

147. **A. pilutshensis** Gontsch. ex Ulzij., Novosti sist. vyssh. rast. 33 (2001) 137.

Described from Sinkiang (Junggar). Type in St.-Petersburg (LE). Map 3.

Habitat not reported.

IIA. Junggar: ***Jung. Ala Tau*** (Urtak-Sary west of Sairam lake, July 10, 1878—Fet.), ***Dzhark.*** (between Piluchi and gorge, 914–1219 m) (3000–4000 ft), April 22, 1879—A. Reg., typus !).

General distribution: endemic.

Note. So far, no more of these plants have been collected. Evidently rare.

Section 4 (48). **Paraxiphidium** R. Kam.

148. **A. cornutus** Pall. Reise 1, Anhang. (1771) 499; Kryl. Fl. Zap. Sib. 7 (1933) 1694, incl. var. *angustifolius* Kryl. et Serg.; Gontsch. and M. Pop. in Fl. SSSR, 12 (1946) 704; Fl. Kazakhst. 5 (1961) 259; Bait. Astrag. Tyan'-Shanya (1977) 79; Opred. rast. Sr. Azii [Key to Plants of Mid. Asia] 6 (1981) 186; C.Y. Yang in Claves pl. Xinjiang, 3 (1985) 150.—*A. vimineus* Pall. Astrag. (1800) 24; Bunge Gen. Astrag. Sp. Geront. 1 (1868) 124 and 2 (1869) 217; id. Astrag. Turk. (1880) 289.

—**Ic.:** Pall. Astrag. (1800) tab. 21.

Described from Europ. Russia (Lower Volga). Type in St.-Petersburg (LE).

In steppes, limestones, granite outcrops, more rarely along sandy banks.

IIA. Junggar: ***Cis-Alt.*** ("Altay"—C.Y. Yang l.c.).

General distribution: Aralo-Casp., Jung.-Tarb.; Europe (east.), Caucasus, West. Sib. (Irt.).

149. **A. suffruticosus** DC. Astrag. (1802) 103.—*A. fruticosus* Pall. Astrag. (1800) 21, non Forskal (1775); Ledeb. Fl. Ross. 1, 3 (1843) 632, p.p.; Bunge Gen. Astrag. Sp. Geront. 1 (1868) 24 and 2 (1869) 216; O. et B. Fedtsch. Konsp. fl. Turk. 2 (1909) 233, p.p.; Pavl. in Byul. Mosk. obshch. ispyt. prir., otd. biol. 38, 1–2 (1929) 92; Kryl. Fl. Zap. Sib. 7 (1933) 1693; Gontsch., M. Pop. and Boriss. in Fl. SSSR, 12 (1946) 706; Boriss. in Fl. Zabaik. 6 (1954) 509; Grub. Konsp. fl. MNR (1955) 184; M. Pop. Fl. Sr. Sib. 1 (1957) 335; Fl. Krasnoyar. kr. 6 (1960) 41; Fl. Kazakhst. 5 (1961) 261; Ulzij. in Opred. rast. okrestn. Ulan-Batora [Key to Plants in the Vicinity of Ulan Bator] (1972) 173; Fl. Tsentr. Sib. 2 (1979) 600; Sanczir in Grub. Opred. rast. Mong. [Key to Plants of Mongolia] (1982) 160; Ulzij. in Tr. Inst. bot. AN MNR, 8 (1982) 29; Opred. rast. Tuv. ASSR [Key to Plants of Tuva Autonomous Soviet Socialist Republic] (1984) 148; C.Y. Yang in Claves pl. Xinjiang, 3 (1985) 151.

—**Ic.:** Pall. (1800) l.c. tab. 19; Fl. Zabaik. 6, fig. 303; Fl. Kazakhst. 5, Plate 34, fig. 6.

Described from East. Siberia (from Lena river). Type in Geneva (G).

Along steppe slopes, larch and birch forest borders, scrubs, on rocks and precipices.

IA. Mongolia: ***Mong. Alt.*** (south-east.: Zantaishir mountain range, upper Shine-Usu nor. of Khalium somon, 2380–2450 m, larch forest on nor. slope, along rocks near summit, July 18, 1971—Grub., Ulzij. and Dariima), ***Cen. Khalkha*** (Undzhul somon, Ikhe-Khairkhan mountain 33 km east of somon centre, montane steppe, June 13, 1973—Sanczir et al. [UBA], same locality, Ara-Undzhul-ula 30 km nor. of Undzhul somon, asp-birch grove, June 22, 1974—Dariima [UBA]), ***Gobi-Alt.*** (Dzun-Saikhan mountains, on steppe slope, July 24; same locality, summit of a creek valley in Elo ravine, along mountain slope among willow and birch forests, Aug. 25, 1931, Ik.-Gal.; Khongor-obo somon, Dzun-Saikhan mountain range, nor. part, upper third of slope, on bank, June 19, 1945—Yun.).

IIA. Junggar: ***Cis-Alt.*** ("Altay [Shara-Sume town]"—C.Y. Yang l.c.), ***Tarb.*** ("Saur"—C.Y. Yang l.c.).

General distribution: West. Sib. (Alt.), East. Sib. (Sayans, Daur.), Far East, Nor. Mong. (Fore Hubs., Hent., Hang., Mong.-Daur.).

Section 5 (49). **Xiphidium** Bunge

150. **A. polyceras** Kar. et Kir. in Bull. Soc. Natur. Moscou, 15 (1842) 332; Bunge Gen. Astrag. Sp. Geront. 1 (1868) 125 and 2 (1869) 219; id.

Astrag. Turk. (1880) 285; O. et B. Fedtsch. Konsp. fl. Turk. 2 (1909) 232, Gontsch. and M. Pop. in Fl. SSSR 12 (1946) 670; Fl. Kazakhst. 5 (1961) 246; Bait. Astrag. Tyan'-Shanya (1977) 75; Opred. rast. Sr. Azii [Key to Plants of Mid. Asia] (1981) 201.

—**Ic.:** Fl. Kazakhst. 5, Plate 32, fig. 6.

Described from East. Kazakhstan. Type in Moscow (MW), isotype in St.-Petersburg (LE).

In rubbly and clayey solonetzic soils, along sand fringes in plains and foothills.

IIA. Junggar: *Tien Shan* (Davankou [Davanchin] pass, arid slope, among stones, No. 1567, Aug. 8, 1956—Ching).

General distribution: Aralo-Casp., Fore Balkh., Jung.-Tarb.

151. **A. arbuscula** Pall. Astrag. (1800) 19; Ledeb. Fl. Ross. 1, 3 (1843) 632; Bunge Gen. Astrag. Sp. Geront. 1 (1868) 124 and 2 (1869) 217; id. Astrag. Turk. (1880) 290; O. et B. Fedtsch. Konsp. fl. Turk. 2 (1909) 235; Kryl. Fl. Zap. Sib. (1933) 1695, incl. var. *microphyllus* Kryl. et Serg.; Gontsch. and M. Pop. in Fl. SSSR, 12 (1946) 667; Fl. Kazakhst. 5 (1961) 241; Vassilcz. in Novosti sist. vyssh. rast. 6 (1969) 148; Bait. Astrag. Tyan'-Shanya (1977) 74; Opred. rast. Sr. Azii [Key to Plants of Mid. Asia] 6 (1981) 200; S.B. Ho in Bull. Bot. Research, 3, 1 (1983) 62; C.Y. Yang in Claves pl. Xinjiang, 3 (1985) 150; Liou f. in Fl. desert Sin. 2 (1987) 270.—*A. horizontalis* Kar. et Kir. in Bull. Soc. Natur. Moscou, 14 (1841) 406.—*A. eremothamnus* Kar. et Kir. ibid. 5 (1842) 354; Bunge Gen. Astrag. Sp. Geront. 1 (1868) 124 and 2 (1869) 217; id. Astrag. Turk. (1880) 289, excl. pl. ex Ala Tau Transil.; O. et B. Fedtsch. Konsp. fl. Turk. 2 (1909) 235, p.p.

—**I.c.:** Pall. l.c. tab. 17; Fl. Kazakhst. 5, Plate 32, fig. 4; Liou f. l.c. tab. 95, fig. 12–18.

Described from East. Kazakhstan (east. Fore Balkhash). Type in London (BM). Plate IV, fig. 5.

On rocky and rubbly slopes of mountains and knolls, gorges, coastal pebble beds and sand, wet meadows, outcrops of red clays, plains and foothills.

IIA. Junggar: *Cis-Alt.* (Katun' area, foothills, June 9, 1903—Gr.-Grzh.; "Fuyun' [Koktogoi town]"—Liou f. l.c.), ***Tarb.*** (Tarbagatai, Aksu-Sary-bulak, Aug. 5, 1876—Pot.; "Dachen [Chuguchak town]"—S.B. Ho l.c.; C.Y. Yang l.c.; Liou f. l.c.), ***Tien Shan*** (Aktyube near Kul'dzha, May 13, 1877—A. Reg.; "Tien Shan: Urumchi: near Yar-bo"—S.B. Ho l.c.), ***Jung. Gobi*** ("Dzhimisar"—Liou f. l.c.); ***Dzhark.*** (Khorgos, Almaty in Kul'dzha region, April 22; Khoyur-Sumun south of Kul'dzha, 549–610 m, May 26; Kul'dzha, June 15; Piluchi near Kul'dzha, July—1877; between Kegen and Khorgos rivers, 610–914 m, May 21, 1878; Togustorau near Kul'dzha, April 1879—A. Reg.; "Inin [Kul'dzha]"—S.B. Ho l.c.); C.Y. Yang l.c.; "Khuochen [Khetszin]" Liou f. l.c.).

General distribution: Aralo-Casp., Fore Balkh., Jung.-Tarb., Nor. Tien Shan; West. Sib. (Altay, Irt.).

152. **A. subuliformis** DC. Astrag. (1802) 107; Ali in Kew Bull. (1958) 316 and (1973) 303; id. in Nasir, Fl. West Pakistan No. 100, Papilionac. (1977) 211; S.B. Ho in Bull. Bot. Research, 3, 1 (1983) 62.—*A. subulatus* Pall. Astrag. (1800) 22, non Desf.—*A. subulatus* auct. non M.B.: Baker in Hook. f. Fl. Brit. Ind. 2 (1872) 136.—*A. suffulcatus* Bunge Gen. Astrag. Sp. Geront. 1 (1868) 125 and 2 (1869) 219.—*A. gladiatus* Boiss. Diagn. Pl. Or. nov. ser. 1, 2 (1843) 45; Li et Ni in Fl. Xizang, 2 (1985) 809.

—**Ic.:** Ali l.c. (1977) tab. 28.

Described from Crimea. Type in Geneva (G)*.

On rubbly-rocky montane slopes, 3400–3500 m alt.

IIIB. Tibet: ***South.*** (Ali:"Chzhada"—Li et Ni l.c.).

General distribution: Himalayas (west.: Afghanistan, Pakistan).

153. **A. gontscharovii** Vass. in Fl. URSS, 12 (1946) 887 and 671; Fl. Kazakhst. 5 (1961) 246; Bait. Astrag. Tyan'-Shanya (1977) 75; Opred. rast. Sr. Azii [Key to Plants of Mid. Asia] 6 (1981) 201.—*A. eremothamnus* auct. non Kar. et Kir.: Bunge Astrag. Turk. (1880) 289, quoad pl. ex Ala Tau Transil.; O. et B. Fedtsch. Konsp. fl. Turk. 2 (1909) 235, p. min. p.

Described from East. Kazakhstan (Jung. Ala Tau). Type in St.-Petersburg (LE).

In montane meadows.

IIA. Junggar: ***Tien Shan*** (7 km south-south-east of Urumchi, near Yan-Ervo settlement, brow of terrace II of Urumchinka river, May 31, 1957—Yun. and I.-f. Yuan'; near Yan-Ervo settlement around Urumchi, on slope, No. 572, May 31, 1957—Kuan), ***Dzhark.*** (Togustorau west of Kul'dzha, Almaty gorge, 914 m, April 21, 1878—A. Reg.).

General distribution: Jung.-Tarb., Nor. Tien Shan.

Note. *A. gontscharovii*, so far regarded as endemic in Kazakhstan, has been reported as new record for the flora of People's Republic of China (Sinkiang). The plants cited here do not practically differ from the type specimen of *A. gontscharovii.*

Section 6 (50). **Ceratoides** Ulzij.

154. **A. dsharkenticus** M. Pop. in Not. Syst. (Leningrad) 10 (1947) 11; Gontsch. and M. Pop. in Fl. SSSR, 12 (1946) 686; Fl. Kazakhst. 5 (1961) 249; Bait. Astrag. Tyan'-Shanya (1977) 76; Opred. rast. Sr. Azii [Key to Plants of Mid. Asia] 6 (1981) 209; S.B. Ho in Bull. Bot. Research, 3, 1 (1983) 62 incl. var. *dsharkenticus* S.B. Ho and *gongliuensis* S.B. Ho: C.Y. Yang in Claves pl. Xinjiang, 3 (1985) 150.

—**Ic.:** Fl. Kazakhst. 5, Plate 33, fig. 1.

Described from East. Kazakhstan. Type in Alma-Ata (AA).

---

*The type habitat does not correspond to the distribution range of the species. There is some error here—Ed. (Russ. ed.).

On steppe slopes of mountains, among rocks, on knolls in foothills, lower and middle mountain belts.

IIA. Junggar: ***Tarb.*** ("Tomur [Dzhamur]"—C.Y. Yang l.c.), ***Tien Shan*** (Ili Kazak Zizhizhou, Gonglin Xian [Tokkuztarau], Mohelin-chang in arvis arenosis, 1120 m, No. 650201, May 5, 1965—T.Y. Chow et al., typus var. *gongliuensis* S.B. Ho; "Tekes ad Zhaosu, July 25, 1974, in viatico, No. 3597, C.W. Chang et al.", "Aksu", "Zhaosu"—S.B. Ho l.c.; "Inin"—C.Y. Yang l.c.).

General distribution: Jung.-Tarb. (Jung. Ala Tau), Nor. Tien Shan.

***A. pycnolobus** Bunge in Mém. Ac. Sci. St.-Petersb. Sav. Etrang. 2 (1835) 594; id. Gen. Astrag. Sp. Geront. 1 (1868) 127 and 2 (1869) 224; id. Astrag. Turk. (1880) 287; O. et B. Fedtsch. Konsp. fl. Turk. 2 (1909) 234; Kryl. Fl. Zap. Sib. 7 (1933) 1702; Fl. Kazakhst. 5 (1961) 265; Opred. rast. Sr. Azii [Key to Plants of Mid. Asia] 6 (1981) 211.

Described from East. Kazakhstan (Zaisan basin). Type in St.-Petersburg (LE).

On steppe slopes, in gorges, along river banks in plains and foothills.

Known from areas adjoining Zaisan basin.

General distribution: endemic in Zaisan basin.

Note. So far not reported from our territory. In all probability, judging from habitat conditions, this species may be found in the Chinese part of Zaisan basin.

155. **A. macrolobus** M.B. Fl. taur.-cauc. 3 (1819) 493 ? non Ledeb. (1831); DC. Prodr. 2 (1825) 285; Ledeb. Fl. Alt. 3 (1831) 307; p.p.; id. Fl. Ross. 1 (1842) 613, p.p.; Bunge Gen. Astrag. Sp. Geront. 1 (1868) 127 and 2 (1869) 222; Kryl. Fl. Zap. Sib. 7 (1933) 1700.—*A. macroceras* C.A. Mey. in Bong. et Mey. Verzeichniss. Saissang-Nor pfl. (1841) 24, nomen; Gontsch. and M. Pop. in Fl. SSSR, 12 (1946) 688; Grub. Konsp. fl. MNR (1955) 185; Fl. Krasnoyar. kr. 6 (1960) 40; Fl. Kazakhst. 5 (1961) 251; Fl. Tsentr. Sib. 2 (1979) 602; Sanczir in Grub. Opred. rast. Mong. [Key to Plants of Mongolia] (1982) 160; Ulzij. in Tr. Inst. bot. AN MNR, 8 (1982) 30; Opred. rast. Tuv. ASSR [Key to Plants of Tuva Autonomous Soviet Socialist Republic] (1982) 149; S.B. Ho in Bull. Bot. Research, 3, 1 (1983) 65; C.Y. Yang in Claves pl. Xinjiang, 3 (1985) 150; Ulzij. and Gub. in Byull. Mosk. obshch. ispyt. prir., otd. biol. 92, 2 (1987) 117.—*A. gregorii* B. Fedtsch. et N. Basil. in Gr.-Grzh. Zap. Mongoliya i Uryankhaiskii krai, 3, 2 (1930) 815; Grub. Konsp. fl. MNR (1955) 184; Sanczir in Grub. Opred. rast. Mong. [Key to Plants of Mongolia] (1982) 162; Ulzij. in Tr. Inst. bot. AN MNR, 8 (1982) 34; Grub. in Novosti sist. vyssh. rast. 21 (1984) 204.

—**Ic.:** Pl. Astrag. (1800) tab. 20 B.

Described from South. Altay. Type in St.-Petersburg (LE).

On rocky and rubbly steppe slopes and along banks of rivers and brooks, in steppe and alpine meadows.

IA. Mongolia: ***Mong.-Alt.*** (Dayan-nur lake, June 28; same locality, between Dayan-Nur and Ak-korum lakes, June 29, 1903, Gr.-Grzh.—Sub nom. *A. gregorii* B. Fedtsch. et N. Basil.; 60 km south of Tonkhil settlement near Tamch-daba pass, July 9; Sutai-ula mountains, 12 km south-south-west of Dariv somon settlement, Aug. 8; 35 km south-south-west of Khalkhyum settlement, July 13 [MW]), ***Depr. Lakes*** (around irrigation canal 10 versts (1 verst = 1.067 km) from Ubsa-nur lake, July 3, 1892—Kryl.), ***Val. Lakes*** ([Basin of Beger-nur lake] Tsagan-Dugyu, alongside of irrigation canal, July 10, 1877—Pot.).

IIA. Junggar: ***Cis-Alt.*** ("Altay"—C.Y. Yang l.c.), ***Tarb.*** ("Tomur [Dzhamur]"—C.Y. Yang l.c.), ***Jung. Gobi*** (Gobi, in Urungu river valley, on pebble beds—April 22, 1879, Przew.; "Bai-chen"—S.B. Ho l.c.), ***Zaisan*** ("Burchum"—C.Y. Yang l.c.).

General distribution: Fore Balkh., Jung.-Tarb.; West. Sib. (Alt., south).

156. **A. polozhiae** Timochina in Bot. zh. 12 (1980) 1796; Opred. rast. Tuv. ASSR [Key to Plants of Tuva Autonomous Soviet Socialist Republic] (1984) 146.—*A. squarrosulus* Sancz. in Grub. Opred. rast. Mong. [Key to Plants of Mongolia] (1982) 160, descr. ross. in clave, Grub. in Novosti sist. vyssh. rast. 21 (1984) 207.

—**Ic.:** Opred. rast. Tuv. ASSR [Key to Plants of Tuva Autonomous Soviet Socialist Republic] fig. 138.

Described from Tuva (Ubsanur basin). Type in Novosibirsk (NS).

In rocky-rubbly hill trails in desert steppes.

IA. Mongolia: ***Khobd.*** (Ulan-Lonkh-ula hill 65 km nor.-nor.-east of Ulgii town, knolls with feather grass-biurgun vegetation, July 20, 1988—Karam. and Sanczir, typus *A. squarrosulus* Sancz. !), ***Mong. Alt.*** (Uenchi river around Uenchi somon, July 28, 1987—Kam. and Dariima).

General distribution: West. Sib. (Suva).

157. **A. karkarensis** M. Pop. in Not. Syst. (Leningrad), 10 (1947) 17; Gontsch. and M. Pop. in Fl. SSSR, 12 (1946) 691, deser. ross.; Fl. Kirgiz. 7 (1957) 322; Fl. Kazakhst. 5 (1961) 253; Bait. Astrag. Tyan'-Shanya (1977) 78; Opred. rast. Sr. Azii [Key to Plants of Mid. Asia] 6 (1981) 209; S.B. Ho in Bull. Bot. Research, 3, 1 (1983) 64; C.Y. Yang in Claves pl. Xinjiang, 3 (1985) 154.

—**I.c.:** Fl. Kazakhst. 5, Plate 33, fig. 4.

Described from Kirgizstan (Kungei-Ala Tau). Type in St.-Petersburg (LE). Plate IV, fig. 1.

On rocky slopes of mountains, outcrops of variegated rocks, alluvial deposits, alpine meadows, on sand along river banks, in foothills, lower, middle and upper mountain belts.

IIA. Junggar: ***Tien Shan*** (Karagaitu south of Borokhudzir, June 3, 1878—Fet.; Sary-bulak nor.-west of Kul'dzha, April 24; Khanakhai, 914–1219 m, No. 427, June 15–1878, A. Reg.; "Guchen [Tsitai]"—S.B. Ho l.c.), ***Jung. Gobi*** ("Kuitun, Manas, Urumchi"—Liou f. l.c.), ***Dzhark.*** (between Piluchi and gorge, 914–1219 m, April 22, 1879—A. Reg.; "Khuachen [Khetszin]"—Liou f. l.c.; "Inin [Kul'dzha]"—C.Y. Yang l.c.).

General distribution: Nor. and Cen. Tien Shan; Mid. Asia (Pamiro-Alay).

Note. The plant from Khanakhai in Tien Shan occupies an intermediate position between *A. karkarensis* M. Pop. and *A. amabilis* M. Pop. Its identification requires confirmation on the basis of adequate samples.

158. **A. ortholobiformis** Sumn. in Animadv. Syst. Herb. Univ. Tomsk. 9–10 (1936) 8; Gontsch. and M. Pop. in Fl. SSSR, 12 (1946) 689; Fl. Kirgiz. 7 (1957) 322; Fl. Kazakhst. 5 (1961) 252; Bait. Astrag. Tyan'-Shanya (1977) 77; Opred. rast. Sr. Azii [Key to Plants of Mid. Asia] 6 (1981) 209; S.B. Ho in Bull. Bot. Research, 3, 1 (1983) 63; C.Y. Yang in Claves pl. Xinjiang, 3 (1985) 151.

—**Ic.:** Fl. Kazakhst. 5, Plate 33, fig. 3.

Described from Kirghizstan (Chu river valley). Type in Tomsk (TK).

On rocky slopes of mountains, fallow lands, beds of arid ravines, alluviums, in river valleys, foothills and lower mountain belt.

IA. Mongolia: ***Khesi*** ("from Dun'khuan to Aksai"—S.B. Ho l.c.).

IIA. Junggar: ***Tien Shan*** (Chapchal pass, south-east. Kul'dzha, 1524–2134 m—A. Reg.; south-east of Urumchi, in mountains, meadow, No. 182, July 14, 1956—Ching; <Chzhaosu, Nilki et al.—S.B. Ho l.c.), ***Dzhark.*** ("Inin"—C.Y. Yang l.c.).

General distribution: Nor. Tien Shan.

Note. The Khesi collection has probably not been correctly identified. I had no occasion to scrutinise it.

159. **A. macrotropis** Bunge Gen. Astrag. Sp. Geront. 1 (1868) 127 and 2 (1869) 223; id. Astrag. Turk. (1880) 286; id. in Acta Horti Petrop. 7 (1880) 376; Fl. Tadzhik. 5 (1937) 439; Gontsch. and M. Pop. in Fl. SSSR, 12 (1946) 686; Fl. Kirgiz. 7 (1957) 321; Fl. Kazakhst. 5 (1961) 250; Bait. Astrag. Tyan'-Shanya (1977) 77; Opred. rast. Sr. Azii [Key to Plants of Mid. Asia] 6 (1981) 208; S.B. Ho in Bull. Bot. Research, 3, 1 (1983) 65.—*A. stenoceras* var. *macrantha* Bunge ex Regel et Herd. in Bull. Soc. Natur. Moscou, 39, 2 (1866) 25.

Described from East. Kazakhstan (Arganaty mountains). Type in St.-Petersburg (LE).

On rocky and rubbly montane slopes, loessial mounds, abandoned fallow lands, in pebble beds on river banks and in scrubs.

IIA. Junggar: ***Tien Shan*** ("Tekes"—S.B. Ho l.c.), ***Jung. Gobi*** ("Manas, Urumchi"—S.B. Ho l.c.).

General distribution: Fore Balkh., Jung.-Tarb., Nor. and Cen. Tien Shan; Mid. Asia (Pamiro-Alay).

160. **A. ceratoides** M.B. Fl. taur.-cauc. 3 (1819) 429; DC. Prodr. 2 (1825) 284; Ledeb. Fl. Alt. 3 (1831) 306; Gontsch. and M. Pop. in Fl. SSSR, 12 (1946) 693; Fl. Kazakhst. 5 (1961) 256; Bait. Astrag. Tyan'-Shanya (1977) 78; Opred. rast. Sr. Azii [Key to Plants of Mid. Asia] 6 (1981) 210; S.B. Ho in Bull. Bot. Research, 3, 1 (1983) 63; C.Y. Yang in Claves pl. Xinjiang, 3 (1985) 151; Liou f. in Fl. desert. Sin. 2 (1987) 257.—*A. stenolobus* Bunge in Mém. Sav. Etrang. Ac. Sci. Petersb. 2 (1835) 593.

—**Ic.:** Fl. Kazakhst. 5, Plate 33, fig. 7.

Described from Altay. Type in St.-Petersburg (LE).

On arid rocky slopes, more rarely in steppe meadows.

IB. Kashgar: ***East.*** ("Turfan"—S.B. Ho l.c., Liou f. l.c.).

IIA. Junggar: ***Cis-Alt.*** ("Altay"—C.Y. Yang l.c.), ***Tarb.*** ("Saur"—C.Y. Yang l.c.), ***Tien Shan*** ("Gunlyu Dzhinkhe [Dzhin river]"—S.B. Ho l.c.), ***Jung. Gobi*** ("Savan, Urumchi"—S.B. Ho l.c., Liou f. l.c.), ***Zaisan*** ("Burchum, Kaba river"—C.Y. Yang l.c.).

General distribution: Jung.-Tarb.; West. Sib. (Altay, south).

161. **A. stenoceras** C.A. Mey. in Bong. et Mey. Verzeichniss Saissang-Nor. Pfl. (1841) 24; Ledeb. Fl. Ross. 1, 3 (1843) 629; Bunge Gen. Astrag. Sp. Geront. 1 (1868) 126 and 2 (1868) 221; id. Astrag. Turk. (1880) 287; id. in Acta Horti Petrop. 7 (1880) 376; O. et B. Fedtsch. Konsp. fl. Turk. 2 (1909) 233; Kryl. Fl. Zap. Sib. 7 (1933) 1699, incl. var. *angustissimus* Kryl.; Fl. Tadzhik. 5 (1937) 441; Gontsch. and M. Pop. in Fl. SSSR, 12 (1946) 694; Fl. Kazakhst. 5 (1961) 256; Opred. rast. Sr. Azii [Key to Plants of Mid. Asia] 6 (1981) 210; Ulzij. in Tr. Inst. bot. AN MNR, 8 (1982) 30; S.B. Ho in Bull. Bot. Research, 3, 1 (1983) 64, incl. var. *stenoceras* and var. *longidentatus* S.B. Ho; Opred. rast. Tuv. ASSR [Key to Plants of Tuva Autonomous Soviet Socialist Republic] (1984) 149; C.Y. Yang in Claves pl. Xinjiang, 3 (1985) 153; Liou f. in Fl. desert. Sin. 2 (1987) 251.—*A. ceratoides* M.B. α *campestris* Ledeb. Fl. Alt. 3 (1831) 306.

—**Ic.:** Pall. l.c. tab. 20 A, var. β; Fl. Kazakhst. 5, Plate 34, fig. 1; C.Y. Yang l.c. tab. 8, fig. 5.

Described from East. Kazakhstan (Zaisan lake basin). Type in St.-Petersburg (LE).

Along steppes and steppified meadows, along river banks, in sandy deserts, more rarely along rocky slopes of mountains, in plain, foothills, lower and middle mountain belts.

IA. Mongolia: ***Depr. Lakes*** (south. fringe of Ubsa-nur basin, Borig-Del sand near south. fringe [Tsagan-Del area], desert steppe, July 20, 1971—Grub., Ulzij. et al.; 30 km nor.-west of Ulangom town, along bank of Turgen' river, Aug. 31, 1984—Gub.), ***Khesi*** (Loukhu-shan' mountain range, south. slope, middle and lower belts, on sand with rubble, July 17, 1907—Czet.; Lanzhou, Beita Shan, in declivitatibus, 1600 m, No. 1961, June 24, 1957—Y.W. Tsui var. *longidentatus* S.B. Ho, typus !; id. Lang Gon, No. 1362, May 30, 1958; id. Tienzhu, Sun Shan Tan, in argilla deserts, 2600 m, No. 139, June 20, 1964, P.Y. Chang et Q.C. Chen—S.B. Ho l.c.).

IB. Kashgar: ***East.*** (Toksun district, Baklimon, on river terrace, No. 7229, June 10, 1958—A.R. Lee (1958)).

IIA. Junggar: ***Cis-Alt.*** ("Altay"—C.Y. Yang l.c.), Tarb. ("Saur, Tomurte [Dzhamur]"—C.Y. Yang l.c.), ***Tien Shan*** (Biangou, west of Urumchi town, in upper courses of Tasenku river, rocky slopes in spruce belt, Sep. 25, 1929—Pop.; "Inin [Kul'dzha]"—S.B. Ho l.c.).

General distribution: Aralo-Casp., Fore Balkh., Jung.-Tarb.; West. Sib. (Altay, Irt.), East. Sib. (Sayans).

162. **A. compressus** Ledeb. Fl. Alt. 3 (1831) 304; Bunge Gen. Astrag. Sp. Geront. 1 (1868) 126 and 2 (1869) 221; id. Astrag. Turk. (1880) 285; O. et B. Fedtsch. Konsp. fl. Turk. 2 (1909) 232; Kryl. Fl. Zap. Sib. 7 (1933) 1697; Gontsch. and M. Pop. in Fl. SSSR, 12 (1946) 692; Fl. Kazakhst. 5 (1961) 254; Opred. rast. Sr. Azii [Key to Plants of Mid. Asia] 6 (1981) 210; S.B. Ho in Bull. Bot. Research 3, 1 (1983) 65; C.Y. Yang in Claves pl. Xinjiang, 3 (1985) 153; Liou f. in Fl. desert. Sin. 2 (1987) 271.

—**Ic.:** Ledeb. Icon. fl. Ross. 3 (1831) ? tab. 289, Fl. Kazakhst. 5, Plate 33, fig. 6.

Described from East. Kazakhstan (Kurchum river). Type in St.-Petersburg (LE).

On rocky and rubbly mountain slopes and knolls, sand, in desert, along river banks in valleys and foothills.

IA. Mongolia: ***Khesi*** ("from Khesizul to Yuimyn'"—Liou f. l.c.).

IIA. Junggar: ***Cis-Alt.*** ("Altay [Shara-Sume town], Fuyun' [Koktokai]"—S.B. Ho l.c.; C.Y. Yang l.c.; Liou f. l.c.), ***Tarb.*** ("Tomurte [Dzhamur]"—C.Y. Yang l.c.), ***Jung. Gobi*** (upper Urungu river, May 1879—Prezhew.; "Fukhai"—S.B. Ho l.c., Liou f. l.c.).

General distribution: Fore Balkh.; West. Sib. (Altay, south).

163. **A. kifonsanicus** Ulbr. in Bot. Jahrb. 36, Beil. 82 (1905) 64; Peter-Stib.* in Acta Horti Gotoburg, 12 (1937–38) 68; S.B. Ho in Bull. Bot. Research, 3, 1 (1983) 65.

—**Ic.:** Icon. Cormoph. Sinic. 2 (1972) 418, fig. 2565.

Described from Nor.-West China (Shensi). Type in London (?).

IA. Mongolia: ? ***Khesi*** ("Gansu"**—S.B. Ho l.c.).

General distribution: China (Nor.: Shansi; Nor.-West Shensi, south. part of Gansu; Cen.: Henan).

Note. *Peter-Stibal incorrectly placed this species in section **Xiphidium** Bunge **I examined some specimens from Gansu in Beijing herbarium of the Institute of Botany, Academia Sinica, People's Republic of China, which were identified by S.B. Ho.

Section 7 (51). **Cytisodes** Bunge

164. **A. pavlovianus** Gamajun. in Fl. Kazakhst. 5 (1961) 492 and 286; Bait. Asrag. Tyan'-Shanya (1977) 86; Opred. rast. Sr. Azii [Key to Plants of Mid. Asia] 6 (1981) 219; C.Y. Yang in Claves pl. Xinjiang, 3 (1985) 161. —*A. pavlovianus* Gamajun. var. *longirostris* S.B. Ho in Bull. Bot. Research, 3, 1 (1983) 67.

Described from East. Kazakhstan (Jung. Ala Tau). Type in Alma Ata (AA).

Along south. rocky slopes in middle mountain belt (750–1400 m).

IIA. Junggar: ***Jung. Gobi*** ("Urumqi, Yanerwo, in declivitatem sicco, No. 3510, May 17, 1962—typus var. *longirostris* S.B. Ho; ib. in glareosis, No. 177, May 15, 1969, S.-m. Su;

Manas Xiang, Manas lingchang, in arena, 750 m, no. 760031, June 6, 1976—C.Y. Yang"—S.B. Ho l.c.; "Qinhe"—C.Y. Yang l.c.).

General distribution: Jung.-Tarb. (Jung. Ala Tau).

165. **A. ornithorrhynchus** M. Pop. in Not. Syst. (Leningrad), 10 (1947) 19; Gontsch. and M. Pop. in Fl. SSSR, 12 (1946) 749, deser. ross.; Fl. Kazakhst. 5 (1961) 286; Bait. Astrag. Tyan'-Shanya (1977) 86; Opred. rast. Sr. Azii [Key to Plants of Mid. Asia] 6 (1981) 219; S.B. Ho in Bull. Bot. Research, 3, 1 (1983) 67; C.Y. Yang in Claves pl. Xinjiang, 3 (1985) 161.

Described from East. Kazakhstan (Jung. Ala Tau). Type in Alma-Ata (AA).

On rocky-clayey slopes of foothills.

IIA. Junggar: ***Tien Shan*** (18–20 km south-east of Urumchi town, along road to Davanchin-daban, desertified ridges, No. 53, June 2—typus var. *urumqiensis* Ulzij. !; vicinity of Urumchi town, south. extremity of Yao mountain range, No. 82, June 3—1957, Yun. and I-f. Yuan'; "Inin, Bai-shildum"—S.B. Ho l.c.; "Ven'syan to In'li"—C.Y. Yang l.c.).

General distribution: Fore Balkh. (Arganaty and Arkharly hills), Jung.-Tarb. (Jung. Ala Tau).

Note. Var. *urumqiensis* Ulzij. var. nov. differs from type in the following characteristics: flowers violet or rather sordid violet, standard undivided or almost without notch at tip. *A. ornithorrhynchus* var. *urumqiensis* Ulzij. Corolla violacea vel sordide violaceae, vexillum apice integrum vel fere intergruum (non emarginatum).

Typus: Orientali-Tian-Schani in clivo septentrionale: 18–20 km ad austro-orientem Urumqi (ad viarum) in itinere ad trajectum Davancxin-davan, ad subdesertos No. 53, June 2—1957, ynatov et Yuani I-Feni.

Section 8 (52). **Pseudohelmia** (M. Pop.) R. Kam.

***A. psilopus** Schrenk in Bull. Ac. Sci. St.-Petersb. 10 (1842) 254; Ledeb. Fl. Ross. 1, 3 (1843) 787; Gontsch. and M. Pop. in Fl. SSSR, 12 (1946) 727; Fl. Kazakhst. 5 (1961) 272; Bait. Astrag. Tyan'-Shanya (1977) 82; Opred. rast. Sr. Azii [Key to Plants of Mid. Asia] 6 (1981) 193; Golosk. Fl. Jung. Alatau (1984) 74.—*A. spartioides* auct. non Kar. et Kir.; Bunge Gen. Astrag. Sp. Geront. 2 (1869) 219, quoad syn. *A. psilopus;* id. Astrag. Turk. (1880) 285, quoad syn. *A. psilopus* et pl. Schrenk.

—**Ic.:** Fl. Kazakhst. 5, Plate 35, fig. 5.

Described from East. Kazakhstan (Alakul' lake). Type in St.-Petersburg (LE).

On sand mountain trails, banks of lakes, foothills.

Reports likely from:

IIA. Junggar: ***Balkh.-Alak.*** (Alakul' lake region).

General distribution: Fore Balkh., Jung.-Tarb.

166. **A. sogotensis** Lipsky in Acta Horti Petrop. 26 (1907) 178; O. et B. Fedtsch. Konsp. fl. Turk. 2 (1909) 219; Gontsch. and M. Pop. in Fl. SSSR, 12 (1946) 701; Fl. Kazakhst. 5 (1961) 258; Bait. Astrag. Tyan'-Shanya (1977) 78; Opred. rast. Sr. Azii [Key to Plants of Mid. Asia] 6 (1981) 192; S.B. Ho in Bull. Bot. Research, 3, 1 (1983) 66; C.Y. Yang in Claves pl. Xinjiang, 3 (1985) 154.—*A. kessleri* auct. non Trautv.: Bunge in Acta Horti Petrop. 7 (1880) 376; O. et B. Fedtsch. Konsp. fl. Turk. 2 (1909) 232 p.p.

—**Ic.:** Fl. Kazakhst. 5, Plate, 34, fig. 3.

Described from East. Kazakhstan (Syugaty mountains). Type in St.-Petersburg (LE).

On sandy and rocky-sand soils, coastal sand and pebble beds, more rarely in fallow lands, in plains and foothills.

IIA. Junggar: ***Cis-Alt.*** ("Fuyun'"—S.B. Ho l.c.), ***Jung. Gobi*** ("Guchen"—S.B. Ho l.c.).

General distribution: Fore Balkh. (Ili river lowland), Nor. Tien Shan (Syugaty mountains).

167. **A. yumenensis** S.B. Ho in Bull. Bot. Research, 3, 1 (1983) 65, tab. 18, fig. 1–11.

Described from China (Khesi). Type in Beijing (PE).

In arid valleys on montane slopes.

IA. Mongolia: ***West. Gobi*** (Bugat somon 30 km east of old Khair-khan somon centre, hillocky area, Aug. 23, 1984—Buyan-Orshikh [UBA]), ***Khesi*** ("Gansu, Jiuquan ad Yumen, May 19, 1957, No. 421, K.J. Kuan—typus !; Sunan Yugurzu Zuzhi Xian, dahetangeltan, in declivitate sicco, alt. 2540 m, Aug. 2, 1967, No. 126, Hexi Exped.").

IIA. Junggar: ***Jung. Gobi*** (Khabtag-ula mountains 82 km south-east of Altay somon, east of Khar-Tolgoin-bulak, on montane slopes, 2200–2400 m, Aug. 16, 1983—Rachk. [UBA]; same locality, nor. macro slope of Khabtag-ula mountain 80 km south of Altay somon, 2750 m, Aug. 21, 1984—Buyan-Orshikh [UBA]).

General distribution: endemic.

168. **A. kessleri** Trautv. in Bull. Soc. Natur. Moscou, 33, 1 (1860) 496; Bunge Gen. Astrag. Sp. Geront. 1 (1868) 125 and 2 (1869) 219; id. Astrag. Turk. (1880) 284; O. et B. Fedtsch. Konsp. fl. Turk. 2 (1909) 232, excl. pl. ex angust. Almaatinsk.; Gontsch. and M. Pop in Fl. SSSR, 12 (1996) 725; Fl. Kazakhst. 5 (1961) 270; Opred. rast. Sr. Azii [Key to Plants of Mid. Asia] 6 (1981) 192; C.Y. Yang in Claves pl. Xinjiang, 3 (1985) 154.

Described from East. Kazakhstan (Bektau-ata mountains). Type in St.-Petersburg (LE).

On rocky montane slopes and granite rocks.

IIA. Junggar: ***Tien Shan*** (Ili valley 89 km east of Ili town [Kul'dzha], along right bank of Kunges, rocky bank of valley, July 29, 1957—Yun. and I-f. Yuan'), ***Dzhark.*** ("Kul'dzha"—Gontsch. and M. Pop. l.c.; "Inin [Kul'dzha]"—C.Y. Yang l.c.

General distribution: Fore Balkh.

169. **A. chorgossicus** Lipsky in Acta Horti Petrop. 26 (1907) 257; Gontsch. and M. Pop. in Fl. SSSR, 12 (1946) 718; Fl. Kazakhst. 5 (1961)

267; Bait. Astrag. Tyan'-Shanya (1977) 80; Opred. rast. Sr. Azii [Key to Plants of Mid. Asia] 6 (1981) 192; C.Y. Yang in Claves pl. Xinjiang, 3 (1985) 154.

Described from East. Kazakhstan (Jung. Ala Tau). Type in St.-Petersburg (LE). Plate IV, fig. 3.

On rocky montane slopes, in variegated beds, along river banks, in foothills and lower mountain belt.

IIA. Junggar: ***Dzhark.*** (Kul'dzha vicinity, 1878; Bayandai in Kul'dzha region, 600–1219 m, May 6, 1878—A. Reg.; between Suidun and Ili, May 7; Almaty gorge nor. of Kul'dzha, May, 1878 A. Reg.; "Leichin"—C.Y. Yang l.c).

General distribution: Jung-Tarb. (Jung. Ala Tau).

170. **A. kendyrlyki** M. Pop. in Not. Syst. (Leningrad), 10 (1974) 14; Gontsch. and M. Pop. in Fl. SSSR, 12 (1946) 719, descr. ross.; Fl. Kazakhst. 5 (1961) 267; Opred. rast. Sr. Azii [Key to Plants of Mid. Asia] 6 (1981) 192; C.Y. Yang in Claves pl. Xinjiang, 3 (1985) 153.

Described from East. Kazakhstan (Saur mountain range). Type in St.-Petersburg (LE).

Along southern slopes of mountains.

IIA. Junggar: ***Tarb.*** ("Saur mountain range"—C.Y. Yang l.c.).

General distribution: Jung.-Tarb. (Saur.), endemic.

Section 9 (53). **Ammodendron** Bunge

171. **A. cognatus** Schrenk in Fisch. et Mey. Enum. pl. nov. 1 (1841) 81; Ledeb. Fl. Ross. 1, 3 (1843) 611; Bunge Astrag. Turk. (1880) 295; Gontschy., M. Pop. and Boriss. in Fl. SSSR, 12 (1946) 770; Fl. Kazakhst. 5 (1961) 292; Opred. rast. Sr. Azii [Key to Plants of Mid. Asia] 6 (1981) 269; C.Y. Yang in Claves pl. Xinjiang, 3 (1983) 148; Liou f. Fl. desert Sin. 2 (1987) 277.

—**Ic.:** Fl. Kazakhst. 5, Plate 38, fig. 2; Fl. desert Sin. 2, tab. 97, fig. 22–28.

Described from East. Kazakhstan (in Fore Balkhash region). Type in St.-Petersburg (LE).

On hummocky and dune sand, along the bottom of arid sandy river beds, more rarely in solonetzes, pebble beds and loamy sand, in plains and foothills.

IIA. Junggar: ***Jung. Gobi*** (east. part of Dzostyn-elis sand, 86 km nor. of Guchen, along road to Alatai, ridge sand with saxaul, July 16, 1956—Yun. and I-f. Yuan'; "Jung. basin, Tsitai, Fukhai"—Liou f. l.c.), ***Dzhark.*** (Suidun in Ili river valley, July 1878—A. Reg.; "Tsavchir, Khuochen [Khetszin] in Ili vicinity"—C.Y. Yang l.c.: Liou f. l.c.: "Ili"—S.B. Ho l.c.).

General distribution: Fore Balkh., Jung.-Tarb.

172. **A. gebleri** Fisch. ex Bong. et Mey. Verzeichn. Saisang-Nor. Pfl. (1841) 24; Ledeb. Fl. Ross. 1, 3 (1843) 611; Bunge Gen. Astrag. Sp. Geront. 1 (1868) 128 and 2 (1869) 225; id. Astrag. Turk. (1880) 295; O. et B. Fedtsch. Konsp. fl. Turk. 2, (1909) 237; Kryl. Fl. Zap. Sib. 7 (1933) 1702; Gontsch., M. Pop. and Boriss. in Fl. SSSR, 12 (1946) 769; Fl. Kazakhst. 5 (1961) 290; Opred. rast. Sr. Azii [Key to Plants of Mid. Asia] 6 (1981) 271; S.B. Ho in Bull. Bot. Research, 3, 1 (1983) 68; C.Y. Yang in Claves pl. Xinjiang, 3 (1985) 149; Liou f. in Fl. desert Sin. 2 (1987) 277.

—**Ic.**: Bong. et Mey. l.c. tab. 4; Fl. desert Sin. 2, tab. 97, fig. 15–21.

Described from East. Kazakhstan (sand along Irtysh). Type in St.-Petersburg (LE).

On hummocky sand.

IIA. Junggar: ***Cis-Alt.*** ("Altay [Shara-suma]"—S.B. Ho l.c.; C.Y. Yang l.c.; Liou f. l.c.), ***Zaisan*** (Chernyi Irtysh river, left bank, Mai-Kann area, hummocky sand, June 7; same locality, Dzhelkaidar, hummocky sand, June 9—1914, Schischk.; "in Irtysh river vicinity: Burchum, Zimunai"—S.B. Ho l.c.; C.Y. Yang l.c.; Liou f. l.c.).

General distribution: Fore Balkh. (Zaisan basin).

173. **A. iliensis** Bunge in Bull. Soc. Natur. Moscou, 32, 2 (1866) 20; id. Gen. Astrag. Sp. Geront. 1 (1868) 129 and 2 (1869) 227; id. Astrag. Turk. (1880) 292; Gontsch., M. Pop. and Boriss. in Fl. SSSR, 12 (1946) 778; Fl. Kazakhst. 5 (1961) 295; Opred. rast. Sr. Azii [Key to Plants of Mid. Asia] 6 (1981) 271; C.Y. Yang in Claves pl. Xinjiang, 3 (1985) 149; Liou f. in Fl. desert Sin. 2 (1987) 276.—*A. iliensis* var. *macrostephanus* S.B. Ho in Bull. Bot. Research, 3, 1 (1983) 68.

—**Ic.**: Fl. Kazakhst. 5, Plate 38, fig. 6; Fl. desert Sin. 2, tab. 97, fig. 8–14; S.B. Ho l.c., tab. 20, fig. 1–9.

Described from East. Kazakhstan (Ili river valley). Type in St.-Petersburg (LE).

On hummocky sand in plain.

IIA. Junggar: ***Dzhark.*** (Iliisk, April 17; Ili river bank, Suidun, June 1; Suidun district; June 1877; east of Talki river in Suidun district, May 7; between Suidun and Ili river, May 7; Suidun, May 8–1878, A. Reg.; Ili valley, right bank, 7–8 km south-east of Suidun town along road to Santokhodze border post, hummocky sand, Aug. 31, 1957—Yun. and I-f. Yuan'; "Ili Kazak Zizhizhou, Huocheng Xian, Sandohezi, 510 m, No. 10619, typus—var. *macrostephanus* S.B. Ho [PE]"—S.B. Ho l.c.; "Khuochen in Inin district [Kul'dzha]"—C.Y. Yang l.c.; Liou f. l.c.).

General distribution: Fore Balkh. (on Ili river), Jung.-Tarb. (Jung. Ala Tau; Dzharkent town vicinity); Mid. Asia (Kyzyl-Kum).

Note. Liou's report (Liou fil.) from Junggar basin region, in our view, appears incorrect. We noticed here intermediate forms between *A. iliensis* Bunge and *A. gebleri* Fisch. ex Bong. et Mey.

174. **A. brachypus** Schrenk. in Fisch. et Mey Enum. pl. nov. 1 (1841) 79; Ledeb. Fl. Ross. 1, 3 (1843) 610; Bunge Gen. Astrag. Sp. Geront. 1 (1868) 129 and 2 (1869) 227; id. Astrag. Turk. (1880) 292; Gontsch.,

M. Pop. and Boriss. in Fl. SSSR, 12 (1946) 774; Fl. Kirgiz. 7 (1957) 331; Fl. Kazakhst. 5 (1961) 294; Bait. Astrag. Tyan'-Shanya (1977) 87; Opred. rast. Sr. Azii [Key to Plants of Mid. Asia] 6 (1981) 271.—*A. halodendron* Bunge in Bull. Soc. Natur. Moscou, 39, 2 (1866) 21; id. Gen. Astrag. Sp. Geront. 1 (1868) 130 and 2 (1869) 227.

—**Ic.:** Fl. Kazakhst. 5, Plate 38, fig. 5.

Described from East. Kazakhstan (Fore Balkhash). Type in St.-Petersburg (LE).

On hummocky, dune, semifixed sand, plains and foothills.

IIA. Junggar: *Dzhark:* (Khoyur-Sumun, along Ili river bank, May 26, 1877—A. Reg.).

General distribution: Aralo-Casp., Fore Balkh., Nor. Tien Shan.

175. **A. hotanensis** S.B. Ho in Bull. Bot. Research, 3, 1 (1983) 68, tab. 21, fig. 1–8.

Described from Sinkiang (Khotan river basin). Type in Beijing (PE).

Along river banks.

IB. Kashgar: *South.* (Hetian He (Khotan river), Maza Shan, alt. 1100 m, in ripa fluminis, May 22, 1959, No. 9636, leg. Xinjiang Compl. Exped.—typus !).

General distribution: endemic.

Section 10 (54). **Ammodytes** (Stev.) Bunge

176. **A. ammodytes** Pall. Astrag. (1800) 7; DC. Astrag. (1802) 88; Ledeb. Fl. Alt. 3 (1831) 327, Fl. Ross. 1 (1842) 658; Bunge Gen. Astrag. Sp. Geront. 1 (1868) 109 and 2 (1869) 189; id. Astrag. Turk. (1880) 278; id. in Acta Horti Petrop. 7 (1880) 374; O. et B. Fedtsch. Konsp. fl. Turk. 2 (1909) 228; Kryl. Fl. Zap. Sib. 7 (1933) 1679; Gontsch. in Fl. SSSR, 12 (1946) 528; Fl. Kazakhst. 5 (1961) 209; Opred. rast. Sr. Azii [Key to Plants of Mid. Asia] 6 (1981) 255; Sanczir in Grub. Opred. rast. Mong. [Key to Plants of Mongolia] (1982) 162; Ulzij. in Tr. Inst. bot. AN MNR, 8 (1982) 27; S.B. Ho in Bull. Bot. Research, 3, 1 (1983) 46; C.Y. Yang in Claves pl. Xinjiang, 3 (1985) 157; Liou fil. in Fl. desert. Sin. 2 (1987) 285.

—**Ic.:** Pall. l.c. tab. 5; Fl. SSSR, 12, Plate 35, fig. 3; Fl. Kazakhst. 5, Plate 27, fig. 5.

Described from West. Siberia (from Irtysh river). Type in London (BM).

On hummocky sand.

IA. Mongolia: *Depr. Lakes* (Barun Turuun somon, Altai-els sand, on dune slope, July 2, 1977—Sanczir, Karam. et al. [UBA]; "Borig-Del, Khalbagany els, Nariin-gol sand"—Sanczir l.c.), *Khesi* ("Yuimyn', Tszyutsyuan'"—S.B. Ho l.c., Liou fil. l.c.).

IIA. Junggar: *Jung. Gobi* (80 km east of Altay somon, sand troughs among knolls, May 23, 1967—Shagdarsuren, Dovchin [UBA]; west. extremity of Argalante hillocky area 67 km south-east of Altay somon centre in Bodonchiin-gol, along road to former Khairkhan somon, sandy desert, Aug. 19, 1979—Grub. et al.; hummocky area south of Argalant-ula mountain, sand, July 27, 1984—Dariima, Kam.; south. slope of Sertengiin-Khubch mountain near junction with Khaldzan-ula hills, July 27; sand on south. trail of Khaldzan-ula mountains, No. 773, July 30; hummocky area south of Argalan-ula mountains, sand, July 31—1984, Kam. and Dariima; "Fukhai, Irtysh"—S.B. Ho l.c., C.Y. Yang l.c., Liou f. l.c.), ***Zaisan*** ("Burchum, Zimunai"—Liou f. l.c., C.Y. Yang l.c.).

General distribution: Aralo-Casp., Fore balkh.; West. Sib. (Irt.: in south).

Section 11 (55). **Cystium** Bunge

177. **A. skorniakovii** B. Fedtsch. in Acta Horti Petrop. 24 (1905) 227; Lipsky in Acta Horti Petrop. 26 (1907) 171; O. et B. Fedtsch. Konsp. fl. Turk. 2 (1909) 229; Fl. Tadzhik. 5 (1937) 430; Gontsch. and Boriss. in Fl. SSSR, 12 (1946) 561; Fl. Kirgiz. 7 (1957) 299; Fl. Kazakhst. 5 (1961) 225; Ikonn. Opred. rast. Pam. [Key to Plants of Pamir] (1963) 168; Bait. Astrag. Tyan'-Shanya (1977) 67; Nasir et Ali, Fl. West Pakist. No. 100 (1977) 207; Opred. rast. Sr. Azii [Key to Plants of Mid. Asia] 6 (1981) 252; Fl. Tadzhik. 6 (1981) 262.—*A. skorniakovii* B. Fedtsch. var. *wuqiaensis* S.B. Ho in Bull. Bot. Research, 3, 1 (1983) 49.

—**Ic.:** Fl. SSSR, 12, Plate 37, fig. 2; S.B. Ho l.c., tab. 5, fig. 1–6.

Described from Sinkiang (Jung. Ala Tau, Arasan). Type in St.-Petersburg (LE).

In hill steppes, rocky and rubbly as well as meadows, rarely melkozem slopes of mountains, along river valleys, banks of lakes.

IIA. Junggar: ***Jung. Ala Tau*** (Arason, 7000–11,000 ft, May 8, 1880 Fet., typus !).

IIIC. Pamir ("Wuqia Xian ad Yusitashi, in declivitatibus, alt. 3200 m, July 29, 1978, No. 1765, leg. Exped. Xinjiang Inst. Bot. Bor.-Occ.—typus var. *wuqiaensis* S.B. Ho").

General distribution: Nor. and Cen. Tien Shan, East. Pamir; Mid. Asia (Pamiro-Alay, Kopet Dag).

178. **A. physocarpus** Ledeb. Fl. Alt. 3 (1831) 335; Kryl. Fl. Zap. Sib. 7 (1933) 1684; Gontsch. and Boriss. in Fl. SSSR, 12 (1946) 588; Fl. Kazakhst. 5 (1961) 223; Opred. rast. Sr. Azii [Key to Plants of Mid. Asia] 6 (1981) 252.—*A. physodes* auct. non L.: Ledeb. Fl. Ross. 1, 3 (1843) 659, p.p.; Bunge Gen. Astrag. Sp. Geront. 1 (1868) 114 and 2 (1869) 197, p.p.; id. Astrag. Turk. (1880) 278; O. et B. Fedtsch. Konsp. fl. Turk. 2 (1909) 228, p.p.; Gontsch. and Boriss. in Fl. SSSR, 12 (1946) 559, p.p.; Fl. Kazakhst. 5 (1961) 223, quoad pl. ex Turgai.

—**Ic.:** Fl. Kazakhst. 5, Plate 39, fig. 4.

Described from Altay. Type in St.-Petersburg (LE).

Along steppes, commonly in arid, mostly solonetzic soils in plains and along gorges.

IA. Mongolia: ***Mong. Alt.*** (upper Tsagan-gol river, 1870—Kalning).

IIA. Junggar: ***Jung. Gobi*** (in mountains west of Turkyul', in sandy soil, June 15; vicinity of Adak village along Tugurik river, desert, June 17–1877, Pot.).

General distribution: Aralo-Casp., Fore Balkh.; West. Sib. (Altay, south).

***A. kurdaicus** Saposhn. ex Sumn. in Animadv. Syst. Herb., Univ. Tomsk, 9–10 (1936) 7; Gontsch. and Boriss. in Fl. SSSR, 12 (1946) 560; Fl. Kirgiz. 7 (1957) 299; Fl. Kazakhst. 5 (1961) 225; Bait. Astrag. Tyan'-Shanya (1977) 67; Opred. rast. Sr. Azii [Key to Plants of Mid. Asia] 6 (1981) 252.—*A. pseudophysodes* Gontsch. in Not. Syst. (Leningrad) 9 (1946) 138.

—**Ic.:** Fl. Kazakhst. 5, Plate 29, fig. 5.

Described from Kirghiz. Type in St.-Petersburg (LE).

On rocky and rubbly slopes of mountains.

Common in areas adjoining Jung. Ala Tau, Nor. and Cen. Tien Shan and may be found in nor. Sinkiang.

General distribution: Fore Balkh., Jung.-Tarb. (Jung. Ala Tau), Nor. and Cen. Tien Shan; Mid. Asia (Kopet Dag, Pamiro-Alay).

Section 12 (56). **Paracystium** Gontsch.

179. **A. lasiophyllus** Ledeb. Fl. Ross. 1, 3 (1843) 627; Gontsch. and Boriss. in Fl. SSSR, 12 (1946) 563; Fl. Kazakhst. 5 (1961) 226; Bait. Astrag. Tyan'-Shanya (1977) 68; Opred. rast. Sr. Azii [Key to Plants of Mid. Asia] 6 (1981) 253; S.B. Ho in Bull. Bot. Research, 3, 1 (1983) 50; C.Y. Yang in Claves pl. Xinjiang, 3 (1985) 158; Liou f. in Fl. desert Sin. 2 (1987) 286.—*A. pallasi* Fisch. Cat. Hort. Gorenk. (1812) 71, non Spreng (1807); Ledeb. Fl. Ross. 1, 3 (1843) 659; Bunge Gen. Astrag. Sp. Geront. 1 (1868) 114 and 2 (1869) 194; id. Astrag. Turk. (1880) 278; id. in Acta Horti Petrop. 7 (1880) 375; O. et B. Fedtsch. Konsp. fl. Turk. 2 (1909) 229.

—**Ic.:** Fl. SSSR, 12, Plate 37, fig. 1; Fl. Kazakhst. 5, Plate 30, fig. 3.

Described from Europ. Russia (Inders lake). Type in St.-Petersburg (LE).

In wormwood and saltwort-wormwood deserts, hummocky sand, along banks of rivers and lakes, rocky slopes, outcrops of Tertiary clays, in plains and foothills.

IIIA. Junggar: ***Dzhark.*** (around "Inin [Kul'dzha]"—S.B. Ho l.c., C.Y. Yang l.c., Liou f. l.c.), ***Jung. Gobi*** (in Urungu river valley, on pebble beds, April 22; Tsagan-Tunge area, on sand, May 14—1879, Przew.; in der Umgebung von Urumtschi, No. 1346, Aug. 26–29, 1908—Merzb.; "Urumchi, Fukhai etc."—S.B. Ho l.c., C.Y. Yang l.c., Liou f. l.c.), ***Zaisan*** (valley of Ch. Irtysh river, Mai-Kapchakai area east of Zaisan, clayey soil, June 1, 1903—Gr.-Grzh.).

General distribution: Aralo-Casp., Fore Balkh., Jung.-Tarb. (Jung. Ala Tau), Nor. and Cen. Tien Shan; Mid. Asia (Pamiro-Alay).

Section 13 (57). **Leucophysa** Bunge

180. **A. candidissimus** Ledeb. Fl. Alt. 3 (1831) 309; id. Fl. Ross. 1, 3 (1843) 623; Bunge Gen. Astrag. Sp. Geront. 1 (1868) 113 and 2 (1869) 193; id. Astrag. Turk. (1880) 270; O. et B. Fedtsch. Konsp. fl. Turk. 2 (1909) 224; Kryl. Fl. Zap. Sib. 7 (1933) 1683, excl. var. *pauciflorus* Kryl. et Serg.; Gontsch. in Fl. SSSR, 12 (1946) 554; p.p.; Fl. Kazakhst. 5 (1961) 222, p.p. Opred. rast. Sr. Azii [Key to Plants of Mid. Asia] 6 (1981) 254; S.B. Ho in Bull. Bot. Research, 3, 1 (1983) 49; C.Y. Yang in Claves pl. Xinjiang, 3 (1985) 157; Liou f. in Fl. desert Sin. 2 (1987) 279.

—**Ic.:** Pl. Fl. Ross. 3 (1831) tab. 237; Fl. Kazakhst. 5, Plate 30, fig. 1.

Described from East. Kazakhstan (Zaisan basin). Type in St.-Petersburg (LE). Map 2.

On sand dunes, poorly fixed hummocky sand.

IIA. Junggar: ***Zaisan*** (Alkabek, sand, Aug. 6, 1909—B. Fedtsch.; "Khabakhe [Kaba river], Burchum"—S.B. Ho l.c., Liou f. l.c.; "Zimunai"—C.Y. Yang l.c.).

General distribution: endemic in Zaisan basin.

181. **A. steinbergianus** Sumn. in Animadv. Syst. Herb. Univ. Tomsk, 2–3 (1934) 3; Gontsch. in Fl. SSSR, 12 (1946) 557; Fl. Kazakhst. 5 (1961) 222; Opred. rast. Sr. Azii [Key to Plants of Mid. Asia] 6 (1981) 255; S.B. Ho in Bull. Bot. Research, 3, 1 (1983) 49; C.Y. Yang in Claves pl. Xinjiang, 3 (1985) 158; Liou f. in Fl. desert Sin. 2 (1987) 280.

—**Ic.:** Fl. desert Sin. 2, tab. 98, fig. 16–20.

Described from Sinkiang. Type in Tomsk (TK). Map 3.

On hummocky sand, more rarely on sandy-pebbly formations.

IIA. Junggar: ***Zaisan*** (Ch. Irtysh river, left bank, Mai-Kain area, hummocky sand, June 7; same locality, Dzhelkaidar area, sand, June 8 and 9, typus !; same locality, above Kaba river, sandy-pebbly steppe, June 10; same locality, left bank westward facing Cherektas mountain, sandy-pebbly steppe, June 11; between Burchum and Kaba rivers, Kiikpai well, Karoi area, hummocky sand, June 15—1914, Schischk.; "Khabakhe [Kaba river]"—S.B. Ho l.c., Liou f. l.c.; "Zhimukhe, Burchum"—C.Y. Yang l.c.; "Bezhakhai"—Liou f. l.c.).

General distribution: endemic in Zaisan basin.

182. **A. urunguensis** Ulzij. in Byul. Mosk. obshch. ispyt. prir., otd. biol. 95, 2 (1990) 75.—*A. candidissimus* auct. non Ledeb.: F. Nemeth in Studia Bot. Hungarica, 12 (1989) 47, 45.

Described from Sinkiang (Jung. Gobi). Type in St.-Petersburg (LE). Map 8.

On coastal sand and along banks of rivers and lakes.

IIA. Junggar: ***Jung. Gobi*** (in Urungu river basin, vicinity of Bulun-Tokhoi basin, on sand and fields, Aug. 19, 1876—Potanin, typus !; south-east. bank of Ulyungur lake, in Ch. Irtysh valley, Aug. 15; east. bank of Ulyungur lake, Salburty hill, Aug. 16—1876, Pot.; same locality, along old coastal embankment, July 9; left bank of Urungu river, nor. fringe of Dzostyn sand, July 11—1959, Yun. and I-f. Yuan'; right bank of Ch. Irtysh, above Kran river estuary, sand, June 26, 1908—Sap.; Altay somon, sand near Ulan-Udzuryn-khuduk spring, Aug. 11, 1978, Ogureeva; "Bulgan river in the vicinity of Bulgan somon—July 2, 1983—F. Nemeth"—F. Nemeth l.c.).

General distribution: endemic.

183. **A. toksunensis** S.B. Ho in Bull. Bot. Research, 3, 1 (1983) 50, tab. 6, fig. 1–10.

Described from Sinkiang (Turfan, basin). Type in Lanzhou (LZDI). Map 6.

IB. Kashgar: ***East.*** (Toksun Xian, prope stationem in pratis, May 1, 1959, No. 60, Leg. Inst. Psamn. Lanzh. Ac. Sin.—typus !, ib. Hongshankou, Baiyanghe, in flumine sicco, May 20, 1959, No. 95, leg. id.—LZDI).

General distribution: endemic.

Section 14 (58). **Euodmus** Bunge

184. **A. uliginosus** L. Sp. pl. (1753) 757; Pall. Astrag. (1800) 31; Bunge Gen. Astrag. Sp. Geront. 1 (1868) 96 and 2 (1869) 168; id. Astrag. Turk. (1880) 262; O. et B. Fedtsch. Konsp. fl. Turk. 2 (1909) 219; Kryl. Fl. Zap. Sib. 7 (1933) 1670; Kitag. Lin. Fl. Mansh. (1939) 282; Boriss in Fl. SSSR, 12 (1946) 435; Fl. Kazakhst. 5 (1961) 195; Fl. Pl. herb. Chinae Bor.-Or. 5 (1976) 100; Fl. Intramong. 3 (1977) 209 and 2 ed. 3 (1989) 278; Opred. rast. Sr. Azii [Key to Plants of Mid. Asia] 6 (1981) 256; S.B. Ho in Bull. Bot. Research, 3, 1 (1983) 39.

—**Ic.:** Pall. l.c. tab. 16; Fl. Intramong. 3 (1977) tab. 95, fig. 8–14 and 3 (1989) tab. 108, fig. 1–6.

Described from Siberia. Type in London (LINN).

In wet sites along banks of rivers and lakes.

IA. Mongolia: ***East. Mong.*** ("Khulunbuir, Shilin-gol"—Fl. Intramong. l.c.).

IIA. Junggar: ***Tien Shan*** (? Turkestania, July 1879—A. Reg.), ? ***Tarb., Zaisan*** (Songoria chinensis, location and date not reported)—Dr. Kuhlewein.

General distribution: West. Sib. (Altay, south), East. Sib. (Sayans, Daur.), Nor. Mong. (besides Hentey), Far East, China (Altay ?, Dunbei), Korean peninsula, Japan.

185. **A. peduncularis** Royle, Ill. Bot. Himal. (1839) 199; Bunge Gen. Astrag. Sp. Geront. 1 (1868) 96 and 2 (1869) 168; Baker in Hook. f. Fl. Brit. Ind. 2 (1876) 136; Gontsch. in Fl. Tadzhik. 5 (1937) 408; Gontsch. and Boriss. in Fl. SSSR, 12 (1946) 438; Fl. Kirgiz. 7 (1957) 280; Fl. Kazakhst. 5 (1961) 195; Bait. Astrag. Tyan'-Shanya (1977) 58; Fl. Tadzhik. 6 (1981) 236; Opred. rast. Sr. Azii [Key to Plants of Mid. Asia] 6 (1981) 256; S.B. Ho in Bull. Bot. Research, 3, 1 (1983) 40; Li et Ni in Fl. Xizang, 2 (1985) 809.

—**Ic.:** Fl. Tadzhik. 5, Plate 46 and 6, Plate 38, fig. 8–14; Fl. SSSR, 12, Plate 30, fig. 2.

Described from Himalayas. Type in London (K).

On rocky-rubbly slopes, along banks of rivers, in moist sites and pebble beds in upper hill belt.

IIIB. Tibet: ***Weitzan*** ("Tsin'zhan mountain [Tangla mountain range], Gouyan"—S.B. Ho l.c.), ***South.*** ("Chzhada"—Li et Ni l.c.).

General distribution: Mid. Asia (Pamiro-Alay), Himalayas (West., Kashmir).

186. **A. odoratus** Lam. Encycl. 1 (1789) 311; Boiss. Fl. Or. 2 (1872) 423; Bunge Gen. Astrag. Sp. Geront. 1 (1868) 96 and 2 (1869) 168; id. Astrag. Turk. (1880) 261; O. et B. Fedtsch. Konsp. fl. Turk. 2 (1909) 219; Gontsch. and Boriss. in Fl. SSSR, 12 (1946) 441; Fl. Kazakhst. 5 (1961) 196; Bait. Astrag. Tyan'-Shanya (1977) 59; Opred. rast. Sr. Azii [Key to Plants of Mid. Asia] 6 (1981) 257.

Described from Near East (Levant—east coast of Mediterranean). Type in Paris (P).

On meadow slopes and among shrubs in foothills.

IIA. Junggar: ***Tarb.***

General distribution: Jung.-Tarb.; Caucasus, Balk.-Asia Minor, Fore Asia.

Note. Repeatedly indicated for Jung. Ala Tau but did not find reliable material.

Section 15 (59). **Gobicus** Ulzij.

187. **A. gobicus** Hanelt et Davazamc in Feddes Repert. 72, 2–3 (1965) 41; Grub. in Novosti sist. vyssh. rast. 9 (1972) 278; Sanczir in Grub., Opred. rast. Mong. [Key to Plants of Mongolia] (1982) 160; Ulzij. in Tr. Inst. bot. AN MNR, 8 (1982) 29; Grub. in Novosti sist. vyssh. rast. 21 (1984) 206.

—**Ic.:** Feddes Repert. 70, 2–3, fig. 3; Grub., Opred. rast. Mong. [Key to Plants of Mongolia] (1982) Plate 82, fig. 377.

Described from Mongolia (West. Gobi). Type in Gatersleben (GAT), isotype in Ulan Bator (UBA).

In deserts, oases in solonchaks.

IA. Mongolia: ***West Gobi*** (Talyn-Bilgekh-bulak 15–20 km east of Tsagan-Bogdo, solonchak meadow and solonchak, No. 14118 [LE], 14120, 14128, 14130 [UBA], July 31, 1943—Yun.; Bilgekh-bulak 45 km east of Tsagan-Bogdo mountain range, solonchaks in oasis, No. 1075, 1962, Hanelt et al.—typus ! [UBA, GAT]).

General distribution: endemic.

188. **A. leansanicus** Ulbr. in Bot. Jahrb. 36 (Beibl. 82) (1905) 62; Simps. in Not. Bot. Gard. Edinb. 8 (1915) 261; Peter-Stib. in Acta Horti Gotoburg, 12 (1937–38) 62; Wang and Tang, Ill. treatm. princip. pl. China, Legum. (1955) 387; S.B. Ho in Bull. Bot. Research, 3, 1 (1983) 43; K.T. Fu in Fl. Intramong. 3 (1977) 207 and 2 ed. 3 (1989) 276.—*A. stevenianus* auct. non DC.: Ulbr. in l.c. (1905) 63.

—**Ic.:** Wang and Tang l.c. fig. 374; Fl. Intramong. (1989) tab. 107, fig. 6–10.

Described from Nor.-West. China (Gansu). Type (?).

IA. Mongolia: ***Alash. Gobi*** (Ninsya, No. 12379, June 20, 1958—Y.-kh. Lyu [LZDI] "Ulan-bukhyn-elis sand"—K.T. Fu (1989) l.c.; "Chzhunvei"—Liou f. l.c.), ***Khesi*** (Gansu — No. 2214, June 9, 1931—T.-n. Liou [PE]; 1700 m, No. 4297, June 12, 1936—T.P. Wang [PE]; 2200 m, No. 13006, July 7, 1942 [PE]; No. 1315, 1958 [PE]).

IA. Kashgar: ***East.*** (Toksun, No. 7229, June 10, 1958, A.R. Lee).

General distribution: China (Nor.: Shan'si, Nor.-West.: Shen'si, Gansu).

189. **A. hamiensis** S.B. Ho in Bull. Bot. Research, 3, 1 (1983) 43; Liou f. in Fl. desert Sin. 2 (1987) 271.—*A. centrali-gobicus* Z.Y. Chu et Y.Z. Zhao in Acta Sci. Natur. Univ. Intramong. 4, 4 (1983) 447.—*A. banzragczii* Ulzij. in Bull. Soc. Natur. Moscou, ser. Biol. 92, 5 (1987) 111.

—**Ic.:** S.B. Ho l.c. tab. 2, fig. 1–9; Fl. desert Sin. 2, tab. 96, fig. 21–25; Z.Y. Chu et Y.Z. Zhao l.c. tab. 1, fig. 1–8.

Described from Sinkiang (Khami). Type in Wugong [NWBI]. Plate IV, fig. 4, Map 1.

In oases and deserts on saline soils and solonchaks.

IA. Mongolia: ***Alash. Gobi*** (prope Ejinqi oppidum, salsuginosus soils, No. 003, Sep. 15, 1982, Z.-y. Chu et Wen Du-su [HIMU]), ***Khesi*** (Gansu, Dunhuang Xian, Nanhu, in viaticus, No. 23, May 29, 1959—leg. Inst. Psamm. Lanzh. Ac. Sin. [LZDI]).

IB. Kashgar: ***East.*** (Xinjian, Hami, Liaodunzhan, in gobica, No. 16, May 23, 1978, leg. Exped. Xinjiang Inst. Bot. Bor.-Occ., typus !).

IIA. Junggar: ***Jung. Gobi*** (Burgastyn-bulag oasis, July 19, 1986—Rotschild [MW]; Uench somon, old Guchen road, around Eren-tologoi-ula from south, puffed solonchak, No. 5963, Sep. 13, 1948—Grub.).

General distribution: endemic.

Section 16 (60). **Ammotrophus** Bunge

190. **A. albicans** Bong. Verzeichn. Saisang-nor Pfl. (1841) 21; id. in Mém. Ac. Sci. St.-Petersb. 6 ser. 4 (1845) 177; Ledeb. Fl. Ross. 1, 3 (1842) 610; Bunge Gen. Astrag. Sp. Geront. 1 (1868) 112 and 2 (1869) 192; id. Astrag. Turk. (1880) 270; O. et B. Fedtsch. Konsp. fl. Turk. 2 (1909) 224; Kryl. Fl. Zap. Sib. 7 (1933) 1683; Gontsch. in Fl. SSSR, 12 (1946) 550; Fl. Kazakhst. 5 (1961) 220; Opred. rast. Sr. Azii [Key to Plants of Mid. Asia] 6 (1981) 261; Gub. in Byul. Mosk. obshch. ispyt. prir., otd. biol. 87, 1 (1982) 127; Sanczir in Grub., Opred. rast. Mong. [Key to Plants of Mongolia] (1982) 279.

—**Ic.:** Bong. 1841, l.c.; tab. 2; id. 1845, l.c. tab. 2.

Described from East. Kazakhstan (Zaisan basin). Type in St.-Petersburg (LE). Map 2.

On sand and pebble beds, along banks of lakes and slopes of hillocks.

IIA. Junggar: ***Jung. Gobi*** (Bodonchiin-gol river 15–20 km south of Altay somon, on sand, 1964—Danert, Davazamc et al. [UBA, GAT]; Bodonchiin-gol river floodplain in lower courses, 15 km south-west of Altay settlement, 1200 m, Aug. 1, 1979, Gub. [MW, LE]; "Bodoncin-gol. Aue, unterlauf. des Bodoncin-gol 30 km uterhalb. Altaj-sum., 1240 m, 1982—Jager").

General distribution: Fore Balkh.

Section 17 (61). **Pseudoammotrophus** Gontsch.

191. **A. saratagius** Bunge Astrag. Turk. (1880) 269; O. et B. Fedtsch. Konsp. fl. Turk. 2 (1909) 224; Fl. Tadzhik. 5 (1937) 420; Gontsch. in Fl. SSSR, 12 (1946) 553; Fl. Kirgiz. 7 (1957) 298; Opred. rast. Sr. Azii [Key to Plants of Mid. Asia] 6 (1981) 261; Fl. Tadzhik. 6 (1981) 257.—*A. saratagius* var. *minutiflorus* S.B. Ho in Bull. Bot. Research, 3, 1 (1983) 48.

—**Ic.:** Fl. Tadzhik. 5 (1937) Plate 48 and 6 (1981) Plate 42, fig. 7–13; S.B. Ho l.c. tab. 4, fig. 1–10.

Described from Mid. Asia. Type in St.-Petersburg (LE).

On rocky slopes of mountains and talus, in upper mountain belt.

IB. Kashgar: *West.* ("Wuqia Xian, Yusitaschi, in declivitate, alt. 3020 m, No. 1692, July 18, 1978, Exped. Xinjiang Inst. Bot. Bor.-Occ., typus ! var. *minutiflorus* S.B. Ho"—S.B. Ho l.c.).

General distribution: Mid. Asia (Pamiro-Alay).

***A. djilgensis** Franch. in Bull. Mus. Hist. Natur. Paris, 2 (1896) 344; Lipsky in Acta Horti Petrop. 26 (1907) 253, emend.: O. et B. Fedtsch. Konsp. fl. Turk. 2 (1909) 221; Fl. Tadzhik. 5 (1937) 413; Gontsch. in Fl. SSSR, 12 (1946) 508; Bait. Astrag. Tyan'-Shanya (1977) 63; Opred. rast. Sr. Azii [Key to Plants of Mid. Asia] 6 (1981) 260; Fl. Tadzhik. 6 (1981) 247.

Described from Pamir. Type in St.-Petersburg (LE).

On rocky and rubbly slopes of mountains, moraine, rock screes and near glaciers, in upper mountain belt.

Reports possible from **IIIC. Pamir** (Sinkiang).

General distribution: East. Pamir; Mid. Asia (Pamiro-Alay).

Note. This species will most likely be found in Sinkiang region.

***A. tranzschelii** Boriss. in Tr. Tadzhik. bazy AN SSSR, 2 (1936) 167; Fl. Tadzhik. 5 (1937) 413; Gontsch. in Fl. SSSR, 12 (1946) 508; Fl. Kirgiz. 7 (1957) 290; Fl. Tadzhik. 6 (1981) 246; Opred. rast. Sr. Azii [Key to Plants of Mid. Asia] 6 (1981) 260.

Described from Pamir (Transalay mountain range). Type in St.-Petersburg (LE).

On rocky and rubbly slopes of mountains.

General distribution: East. Pamir; Mid. Asia (East. Pamiro-Alay).

Note. Quite possibly, this species will be found in Chinese East. Pamir.

Section 18 (62). **Onobrychium** Bunge

192. **A. onobrychis** L. Sp. pl. (1753) 760; Pall. Astrag. (1800) 27; DC. Astrag. (1802) 9; Ledeb. Fl. Alt. 3 (1831) 302; id. Fl. Ross. 1, 3 (1842) 108; Boiss. Fl. Or. 2 (18) 438; Bunge Gen. Astrag. Sp. Geront. 1 (1868) 103 and 2 (1869) 183; id. Astrag. Turk. (1880) 265; id. in Acta Horti Petrop. 7 (1880) 374; O. et B. Fedtsch. Konsp. fl. Turk. 2 (1909) 221; Kryl. Fl. Zap. Sib. 7 (1933) 1676; Boriss. in Fl. SSSR, 12 (1946) 484; Fl. Kazakhst. 5 (1961) 204; Bait. Astrag. Tyan'-Shanya (1977) 62; Opred. rast. Sr. Azii [Key to Plants of Mid. Asia] 6 (1981) 258; C.Y. Yang in Claves pl. Xinjiang, 3 (1985) 147; Ulzij. and Gub. in Byull. Mosk. obshch. ispyt. prir., otd. biol. 92, 5 (1988) 113.

—**Ic.:** Fl. Kazakhst. 5, Plate 27, Fig. 1.

Described from Austria. Types in London (LINN).

On loamy and rocky-sandy soils in river valleys.

IA. Mongolia: ***Depr. Lakes*** (in Tes river floodplain, Tokhoi on left bank of Nariin-gol river, bed portion, July 1968—Tserendash).

IIA. Junggar: ***Cis-Alt.*** ("Altay"—C.Y. Yang l.c.), ***Tarb.*** ("Dachen" [Chuguchak town] —C.Y. Yang l.c.), ***Tien Shan*** ("Ili"—C.Y. Yang l.c.).

General distribution: Aralo-Casp., Jung.-Tarb. (Tarbagatai); Europe, Balk.-Asia Minor, Caucasus, West. Sib.

193. **A. viridiflavus** Ulzij. in Bull. Soc. Natur. Moscou, ser. biol. 95, 2 (1990) 78.

Described from Nor. Mongolia (Mong.-Daur). Type in St.-Petersburg (LE), isotype in Ulan Bator (UBA).

On arid slopes in montane-steppe and forest-steppe belts.

IA. Mongolia: ***Cen. Khalkha*** (arid valley on left bank of Toly river, Altan-Obo area, Aug. 5, 1925—Gus.).

General distribution: Nor. Mong. (Fore Hubs., Hent., Hang., Mong.-Daur).

Note. Evidently, the site of collection lay in the northern part of Central Khalkha within Central Asia.

194. **A. inopinatus** Boriss. in Not. Syst. (Leningrad) 10 (1946) 51; idem in Fl. SSSR, 12 (1946) 511; idem in Fl. Zabaik. 6 (1954) 594; Grub. Konsp. fl. MNR (1955) 184; M. Pop. Fl. Sr. Sib. 1 (1957) 333; Ulzij. Opred. rast. okrestn. Ulan-Batora [Key to Plants in the Vicinity of Ulan Bator] (1972) 174; Fl. Tsentr. Sib. 2 (1979) 600; Fl. pl. herb. Chinae bor.-or. 5 (1975) 100; Sanczir in Grub., Opred. rast. Mong. [Key to Plants of Mongolia] (1982) 159, p. max. p.; Ulzij. in Tr. Inst. bot. AN MNR, 8

(1982) 28; Ulzij. and Gub. in Byul. Mosk. obshch. ispyt. prir., otd. biol. 92, 5 (1987) 117.—*A. adsurgens* auct. non Pall.: S.B. Ho in Bull. Bot. Research, 3, 1 (1983) 44, p. min. p.

—**Ic.:** Fl. Zabaik. 6, fig. 304.

Described from East. Siberia (Yakutia). Type in St.-Petersburg (LE). Plate V, fig. 5.

On steppe slopes, in larch and pine forests and their borders, meadow-covered slopes, rocks, solonetzic banks of rivers and floodplain meadows, sandy steppes and chee grass thickets.

IA. Mongolia: ***Mong. Alt.*** (Khara-Adzarga mountain range, Khair-khan-Duru river vicinity, larch forest, Aug. 26, 1930—Pob.; 70 km west of Bayan-Undur settlement, July 14, 1979—Gub.), ***Cen. Khalkha*** (near Ugei-nor lake, in loamy steppes, July 14, 1924—Pavl.; Ubur-Dzhargalanta river between its sources and Agit mountain, meadow steppe, Aug. 11, 1925—Krasch. and Zam.; vicinity of Ikhe-Tukhum-nor lake, Dund-Targan-tala, road to Mishik-gun, June 1926—Polynov and Lebedev; same locality, Mishik-gun ledge terrace, June 1926—Zam.; Choiren, July 22, 1928—Tug.; Khukhshin-Orkhon and Orkhon interfluvine region 8–10 km east of Erdeni-Dzu, steppe, July 7, 1947; Khuren-del-ula pass, montane steppe, June 26, 1949—Yun.; upland south-west of Undzhul, 1500–1600 m, forb steppe, June 26, 1974—Golubkova and Tsogt; same locality, June 21, 1974—Dariima), ***East. Mong.*** (Dariganga, Shiliin-Bogdo-Ula), July 12 [MW]; 35 km nor.-west of Numurgiin border post, July 20 [MW]—1985, Gub.), ***Gobi-Alt.*** (south. Ikhe-Bogod-ula macro slope, on water in gorge, 2900 m, Aug. 4, 1973; same locality, steppe, 2950 m, Aug. 4, 1979—Isach. and Rachk.).

General distribution: East. Sib., Far East, Nor. Mong., China (Dunbei).

195. **A. laspurensis** Ali in Phyton, 11 (1966) 139; id. in Nasir. Fl. West Pakist. No. 100, Papilionac. (1977) 205; S.B. Ho in Bull. Bot. Research, 3, 1 (1983) 46.

—**Ic.:** Fl. West Pakist. No. 100, tab. 26, A–E.

Described from Pakistan (Chitral). Type ?

On slopes in high mountains.

IIIC. Pamir: ("Tashkurgan"—S.B. Ho l.c.).

General distribution: Himalayas (west.: Chitral, Laspur).

196. **A. potaninii** Ulzij. in Bull. Soc. Natur. Moscou, ser. biol. 95, 2 (1990) 77.

Described from Mongolia (Mong. Alt.). Type in St.-Petersburg (LE).

On arid montane steppes and in mountain passes.

IA. Mongolia: ***Mong. Alt.*** (in pass between Tatal and Saksa, July 8, 1877—Potanin, typus !; steppe between Mankhanei-Shanzga-bulak and Khobur-bulak springs, June 30, 1894; on left bank of Shara-usu river around Bombatu urton, July 13, 1895; Terkhi river valley somewhat before Bombatu-Bel'chir area, June 16, 1896—Klem.; Khasagtu-Khairkhan mountain range, east. extremity, on Gobi-Altay road—Daribi, lateral creek valley from springlet to nor.-west of Chandmani-ula, June 20; Botkhon-gola gorge near estuary, 1950 m, under rocks, June 21; Buyantu river basin, Delyun area near Bukhu-Tumur cemetery, solonchak meadow, July 1; upper Buyantu river, in hills nor. of Chigertei lake, after passes, 2500 m, solonetzic steppe, July 5; Kobdo and Sagsai-gol interfluvine area, Dabatuin-daba pass on Tsengel somon—Ulan-Khusu road, 2251 m, montane steppe, July 12—1971, Grub., Ulzij. et al.; Uenchi river basin, Nariin-gol valley 9 km before Ikhe-Uland-daba pass on road to Must somon, 2350 m, valley trail, steppe, Aug. 13, 1979—Grub. et al.).

General distribution: endemic.

197. **A. austrosibiricus** B. Schischk. in Kryl. Fl. Sib. Occid. 7 (1933) 1678; Boriss. in Fl. SSSR, 12 (1946) 510; id. in Fl. Zabaik. 6 (1954) 36; Grub. Konsp. fl. MNR (1955) 183; M. Pop. Fl. Sr. Sib. 1 (1957) 333; Fl. Kazakhst. 5 (1961) 208; Fl. Tsentr. Sib. (1979) 598; Sanczir in Grub. Opred. rast. Mong. [Key to Plants of Mongolia] (1982) 159; Ulzij. in Tr. Inst. bot. AN MNR, 8 (1982) 28; S.B. Ho in Bull. Bot. Research, 3, 1 (1983) 45; C.Y. Yang in Claves pl. Xinjiang, 3 (1985) 147.—*A. semibilocularis* Fisch. ex Bunge Gen. Astrag. Sp. Geront. 1 (1868) 103 and 2 (1869) 183, non DC. (1802); Pavl. in Byull. Mosk. obshch. ispyt. prir., otd. biol. 38, 1–2 (1929) 92.

Described from Altay (Riddersk). Type in Tomsk (TK). Plate V, fig. 6.

On exposed, more frequently rocky and rubbly slopes, sometimes pebbly sand banks of rivers and sparse forests.

IA. Monogolia: ***Khobd.*** (Kharkhira river valley, on rocks, July 10, 1879—Pot.), ***Mong. Alt.*** (Saksai river, arid ravine, July 31, 1909—Sap.; lower course of Turgen-gola river (left bank tributary of Bulgan), arid meadow, July 1947—Yun., Botkhon-gola gorge, near mouth of spring on right bank, 1950 m, under rocks, June 27, 1971—Grub., Ulzij. et al., Ulyastain-gola river basin, south. slope of Shadzgain-nuru mountain range, 2100 m, *Cobrasia* meadow, June 27, 1973—Golubkova and Tsogt; Uenchiin-gola river basin, Arshantyn-gol river valley 3 km from estuary, in gorge, 2500–2600 m, larch forest, Aug. 14, 1979—Grub. et al.; east. part of Khara-Adzargyn-nuru mountain range, July 7; 10 km south-west of Bugat somon, Ulyastain-gol river gorge, on pebble beds, July 5 (Bulgan-gol river basin, July 9, 1984—Kam. and Dariima), ***Cen. Khalkha*** (Ara-Undzhul-ula 35 km nor. of Undzhul somon, June 25, 1974—Dariima), ***Gobi-Alt.*** (Baga Bogdo, in canyon bottoms, 6000 ft, No. 267, 1925—Chaney; upper belt of spurs of Ikhe-Bogdo mountain range, June 29, 1926—Kozlova; Ikhe-Bogdo, south. macro slope, steppe, Aug. 4; same locality, 2700 m, on rocky beili (mountain trails), Aug. 6—1973, Isach. and Rachk.).

IIA. Junggar: ***Cis-Alt.*** ("nor. part of Sinkiang: Altay"—S.B. Ho l.c., C.Y. Yang l.c.), ***Tarb.*** ("Saur"—C.Y. Yang l.c.), ***Zaisan*** ("Burchum, Khabakhe"—C.Y. Yang l.c.).

General distribution: West. Sib. (Altay, south), East. Sib. (Sayans), Nor. Mong. (Fore Hubs., Hang.), China (Altay).

198. **A. adsurgens** Pall. Astrag. (1800) 40; Bunge Gen. Astrag. Sp. Geront. 1 (1868) 103 and 2 (1869) 184; Trautv. in Acta Horti Petrop. 1 (1872) 176; Forbes et Hemsl. in J. Linn. Soc. Bot. 23 (1887) 164; Pavl. in Byull. Mosk. obshch. ispyt. prir., otd. biol. 38, 1–2 (1929) 92; Peter-Stib. in Acta Horti Gotoburg, 12 (1938) 63; Kitag. Lin. Fl. Mansh. (1939) 279; R.C. Ching in Contrib. U.S. Nat. Herb. 28 (1941) 634; Boriss. in Fl. SSSR, 12 (1946) 509; idem in Fl. Zabaik. 6 (1954) 598; Grub. Konsp. fl. MNR (1955) 182; Wang and Tang in Ill. treatm. princip. pl. China, Legum. (1955) 387; M. Pop. Fl. Sr. Sib. 1 (1957) 333; Fl. Krasnoyar. kr. 6 (1960)

36; Ulzij. Opred. rast. okrestn. Ulan-Batora [Key to Plants in the Vicinity of Ulan Bator] (1972) 174; Fl. Tsentr. Sib. 2 (1979) 597; Fl. pl. Herb. Chinae bor.-or. 5 (1976) 100; K.T. Fu et Cheng f. in Fl. Intramong. 3 (1977) 211 and 2 ed. 3 (1989) 280; Sanczir in Grub., Opred. rast. Mong. [Key to Plants of Mongolia] (1982) 159; Ulzij. in Tr. Inst. bot. AN MNR, 8 (1982) 28; S.B. Ho in Bull. Bot. Research, 3, 1 (1983) 45, pro max. p. Opred. rast. Tuv. ASSR [Key to Plants of Tuva Autonomous Soviet Socialist Republic] (1984) 149.—C.Y. Yang in Claves pl. Xinjiang, 3 (1985) 148; Fl. Xizang, 2 (1985) 808, Liou fil. in Fl. desert Sin. 2 (1987) 282.—*A. prostratus* Fisch. ex Turcz. Fl. baic.-dahur. 1 (1842–45) 319.—*A. longispicatus* Ulbr. in Bot. Jahrb. 36, Beibl. 82 (1905) 61.—*A. oostachys* Peter-Stib. l.c. (1937–38) 64.

—**Ic.:** Pall. 1800, l.c. tab. 31; Wang and Tang l.c. fig. 373; M. Pop. 1957, l.c. Plate 57, fig. 3; Fl. pl. herb. Chinae bor.-or. 5, tab. 41, fig. 11–20; Fl. Intramong. 3 (1977) tab. 107, fig. 1–9 and 2 ed. 3 (1989) tab. 109, fig. 1–9.

Described from East. Siberia (Selenga river). Type in London (BM). Plate V, fig. 2.

On steppe slopes, forests and their borders, scrubs, steppified and foodplain meadows, chee grass thickets, solonetzic sand and coastal pebble beds, abandoned farms, fallow lands and hummocky thin sand.

IA. Mongolia: ***Khobd.*** (Achit-nuur lake, on coastal sand, Aug. 8, 1963 [UBA]; nor-west. bank of Ureg-nur lake, Aug. 17, 1967—Ulzij. et al. [UBA]; interfluvine zone of Bukhu-Muren and Khub-usu-gol rivers 7–8 km east-nor.-east of Bukhu-Muren somon centre, solonetzic meadow, July 15, 1971—*Grub.*, Ulzij. et al.), ***Mong. Alt.*** (in Datu-daban pass [in Khan-Taishir mountains], Aug. 17, 1874—Klem.; Dundu-Tsenkir river, plantations, Aug. 15, 1930—Bar.; Dundu-Seren-gol river bank, on pebble bed, Nov. 30; Bombatu-Khairkhan hills, plateau between Elo and Khapchik rivers, birch groves, Oct. 10, 1930—Pob.; Bulgan river valley beyond Bulgan somon centre, meadow, July–Aug. 1947—Tarasov; Khan-Taishir mountain range, south. slope, upper Shine-usu river nor. of Khalyun somon, steppe, June 19, 1971—Grub., Ulzij. et al.), ***Cen. Khalkha*** (common allover region), ***East. Mong., Depr. Lakes*** (Shuryk river, on sandy soil, July 20, 1877; near Torkh-ula mountain on Kobdo river, July 24, 1879—Pot.; Ulyasutai to Kosh-Agach, June 15—July 15, 1880, Pevtsov; around dried up irrigation canal 10 versts (1 verst=1.067 km) from Ubsa-nur lake, July 3, 1892—Kryl.; Kobdo town, weed in kitchen garden, July 1, 1898—Klem.; Dzergin river valley, solonchaks, Aug. 18, 1930—Bar.; Khobdosk state farm in lower courses of Buyantu-gol river, July–Aug. 1941—Kondratenko; bridge over Khobdo river on Khobdo-Ulangom road, floodplain—Aug. 23, 1944; Badryn-gol area 30–35 km south of Tugik-sume, on fallow lands, Aug. 11, 1945—Yun.; island on Dzapkhyn-gol river 75 km before shurgin-gol river estuary, Aug. 9, 1950, Collector ? bank of Shurgin-gol river near Khobdo town, Aug. 10, 1968—Ulzij. et al.; 8 km nor.-west of Sagil somon centre, July 13, 1977—Sanczir et al.; nor.-east. bank of Khara-Us-nur lake, Sep. 3, 1978 [MW]; 12 km nor. of Tes settlement in Tesiin-gol river floodplain, Aug. 26, 1979 [MW]—Gub.), ***Val. Lakes*** (Tuin-gol river bank, Sep. 4, 1886—Pot.; on left bank of Tuin-gol river, on sand, July 10; not far from Orok-nur lake, on sand, July 13; on right bank of Tatsa-gol river, among jewelvine, July 20—1893, Klem.; Orok-nor, Outer Mongolia, in gullies of gravelly ridges at 3800 ft, No. 292; Tsagan-Nor, shallow depressions between covered dunes at 4100 ft, No. 347–1925, Chaney; Orok-nur lake, solonetzic sand, Aug. 6, 1626—Tug.; Ongiin-gol river valley 40–45 km south of Khushu-khid, meadow, July 18, 1943— Yun.; Ongiin-gol river near Khushu-khid monastery, solonchak meadow, July 14, 1948— Grub.; along Ongiin-gol river, July 21, 1973—Golubkova and Tsogt; 170 km south of Erdene-Dalai settlement, Ongiin-gol river valley, July 10, 1979—Gub. [MW], ***Gobi-Alt.*** (in Tsagan-gol river valley, Aug. 4, 1894—Klem.; on way to Urgu from Alashan, Urten-gol river valley, July 22, 1909—Czet.), ***East. Gobi*** (5 km east of Choiren-ula, valley of steppe brook, solonetzic meadow, Aug. 22, 1940—Yun.; Bulgan somon, in a farmstead irrigated section of experimental plantation, Aug. 13, 1962—Lavr., Yun. and Dashnyam; same locality, around spring close to somon, July 20; same locality, under shadow of a tree at somon centre, June 20—1970, Sanczir [UBA]; "Baotou, Ulantsab et al."—K.T. Fu et Cheng l.c.), ***Alash. Gobi*** ("Ulan-Oukhyn-els sand"—Liou fil. l.c.), ***Ordos, Khesi*** ("Gansu: Khesi corridor"—Liou fil. l.c.).

IB. Kashgar: ***East., Takla-Makan*** ("Tarim basin"—Liou fl.).

IC. Qaidam: ***Plain*** ("Qaidam basin"—Liou f. l.c.).

IIIA. Qinghai: ***Nanshan*** (25 km south of Kulan, east. extremity of Nanshan moutain range, gently inclined slopes of low mountains, 2450 m, montane steppe, Aug. 12, 1958; 24 km south of Xining town, slopes of hillocks, steppe, 2650 m, Aug. 4; Kukunor lake, meadow on east bank, 3200 m, Aug. 5—Petr.).

General distribution: West. Sib. (Tuva), East. Sib. (Sayans, Daur.), Far East, Nor. Mong.; China (Dunbei, North, North-West, South-West).

Note. 1. Highly polymorphous species. Within its distribution range are known some varieties which differ in the sizes of inflorescence, flowers and leaflets as well as in the form of leaflets and other characteristics.

2. C.Y. Yang (l.c.) does not cite the actual location of the collection in Sinkiang territory. Judging from herbarium collections, preserved in the Komarov Botanical Institute of the Russian Academy of Sciences, the typical form of this species does not probably enter Sinkiang territory.

Section 19 (63). **Craccina** (Stev.) Bunge

199. **A. discolor** Bunge ex Maxim. in Bull. Ac. Sci. St.-Petersb. 24 (1878) 33; Peter-Stib. in Acta Horti Gotoburg, 12 (1937–38) 61; Wang et Tang, Ill. treatm. princip. pl. China, Legum. (1955) 387; K.T. Fu et Cheng in Fl. Intramong. 3 (1977) 209 and 2 ed. 3 (1989) 276; S.B. Ho in Bull. Bot. Research, 3, 1 (1983) 40; Liou F. in Fl. desert. Sin. 2 (1987) 274.—*A. ulaschanensis* Franch. in Nouv. Arch. Mus. Paris, ser. 2, 5 (1883) 239; id. Pl. David, 1 (1884) 87; Peter-Stib. in Acta Horti Gotoburg, 12 (1937–38) 61.—*A. biondianus* Ulbr. in Bot. Jahrb. 36, Beibl. 82 (1905) 62.

—**Ic.:** Fl. Intramong. (1977) tab. 106, fig. 9–16 and 2 ed. 3 (1989) tab. 107, fig. 1–5.

Described from Inner Mongolia (Alash. Gobi). Type in St.-Petersburg (LE). Plate VI, fig. 4. Map 1.

In steppes and deserts, on flat summits of loessial hillocks, sandy sites, clayey-sandy precipices, coastal sand, in mountain gorges.

IA. Mongolia: ***East. Mong.*** (mont. Muni-ulf, 1871—Przew.; Datsinshan', at foot of hill, 2100 m, No. 204—Ts.-u Yan [HIMC]; "Khukh-khot" K.T. Fu et Cheng l.c., ***East. Gobi***

("Ulantsab: Suuzhi, Baotou"—K.T. Fu et Cheng l.c., Liou f. l.c.), ***Alash. Gobi*** (Alashan, small forest in gorge, No. 167, June 30, 1873—Przew., typus !; Khelan'shan' toward south, montane gorge, 2150 m, No. 235, July 31, 1963—Yu-ch. Ma [HIMC]; "Holan-shan mountains, No. 1109, Ching"—Peter-Stib. l.c.; "Alashan mountain range"—K.T. Fu et Cheng l.c., Liou f. l.c.), ***Ordos*** (Echzhin-khoro, along deep ravines on precipices, Aug. 18; Kuity-gol river valley, on coastal sand, Aug. 19; Chichirgan river valley, on sandy soil, Aug. 19—1884, Pot.; Ordos, June 1871, No. 168—Przew.; "Ikechzhao, Echzhin-khoro"—K.T. Fu et Cheng l.c., Liou f. l.c.), ***Khesi*** (south of Dadzhin [Dajin] town, in desert, Aug. 21, 1880—Przew.; "Gansu: Gaolin'"—Liou f. l.c.).

General distribution: China (North: Hebei, nor. Shansi; North-West: Shensi, Nin'sya).

200. **A. argutensis** Bunge Gen. Astrag. Sp. Geront. 1 (1868) 98 and 2 (1869) 170; Kryl. Fl. Zap. Sib. 7 (1933) 1675; Gontsch. and Boriss. in Fl. SSSR, 12 (1946) 457; Grub. Konsp. fl. MNR (1955) 183; Sanczir in Grub. Opred. rast. Mong. [Key to Plants of Mongolia] (1982) 160; Ulzij. in Tr. Inst. bot. AN MNR, 8 (1982) 26; Grub. Novosti sist. vyssh. rast 21 (1984) 213.

—**Ic.:** Grub. Opred. rast. Mong [Key to Plants of Mongolia] (1982) Plate 83, fig. 384.

Described from Altay (Argut river). Type in St.-Petersburg (LE). Plate V, fig. 3. Map 2.

In montane steppes.

IA. Mongolia: ***Khobd.*** (Tsagan-Shibetu mountains, nor. bank of Ureg-nur lake, July 17, 1967—Ulzij. et al. [UBA]), ***Mong. Alt.*** (beyond Tshenty pass, on hill slope around Dandzhur-nor lake, July 1, 1898—Klem.; Delyun river valley, rocky ridge, July 13, 1906, Saksai river, arid ravine of west. mountain range, July 31, 1909—Sap.; Tolbo-nur lake, gravelly steppe, Aug. 5, 1930—Bar.).

General distribution: West. Sib. (Altay).

201. **A. variabilis** Bunge ex Maxim. in Bull. Ac. Sci. St.-Petersb. 24 (1878) 33; Pavl. in Byul. Mosk. obshch. ispyt. prir., otd. biol. 38, 1–2 (1929) 93; Peter-Stib. in Acta Horti Gotoburg, 12 (1937–38) 62; Grub. Konsp. fl. MNR (1955) 187; Fu in Fl. Intramong. 3 (1977) 213 and 2 ed. 3 (1989) 281; Sanczir in Grub. Opred. rast. Mong. [Key to Plants of Mongolia] (1982) 161; Ulzij. in Tr. Inst. bot. AN MNR, 8 (1982) 21; S.B. Ho in Bull. Bot. Research, 3, 1 (1983) 41; Grub. in Novosti sist. vyssh. rast. 21 (1984) 214; C.Y. Yang in Claves pl. Xinjiang, 3 (1985) 148; Gub. et al. in Byul. Mosk. obshch. ispyt. prir., otd. biol. 92, 1 (1987) 120.—*A. loczii* Kanitz, A novencani (1891) 17.—*A. discolor* auct. non Bunge: Grub. Konsp. fl. MNR (1955) pr. Gub. n. pl. e mont. Adzhi-Bogdo.

—**Ic.:** Fl. Intramong. 3 (1977) tab. 106, fig. 1–8 and 3 (1989) tab. 109, fig. 7–12; Grub. Opred. rast. Mong. [Key to Plants of Mongolia] (1982) Plate 85, fig. 390.

Described from Inner Mongolia (Alash. Gobi). Type in St.-Petersburg (LE). Plate VI, fig. 1, Map 5.

On rubbly mountain trails, solonetzic sand, floors of gullies and fringes of toirims.

IA. Mongolia: *Mong. Alt.* (Bulgan river valley 35 km before Bulgan settlement—Aug. 12, 1982), ***Val. Lakes*** (between Ul'zuitu-nor lake and Zadagai-usu spring, on steppe—Klem.; steppe between Tuin- and Tatsy-gol rivers, Sep. 13, 1924—Pavl; 4 km south of Ba-Tsagan somon desert in lower part of mountain trail, June 24, 1974—Rachk. and Volk.; 35–40 km east of Beger settlement, Aug. 8, 1983 [MW]; same locality, No. 8942, Aug. 11, 1984 [MW]—Gub.), ***Gobi Alt.*** (south. slope of pass through Tostu mountain range, Aug. 16; in valley between Tostu and Nemegtu mountain ranges, Aug. 19; between Legin-gol river and Ubtyn-daban pass, Aug. 29—1889, Pot.; trail of Tszolin hill, Sep. 8, 1931—Ik.-Gal.; Bayan-Tukhum area, trail of Bain-Tsagan mountain range, Aug. 31, 1938—Luk'yanov; Khurm in somon, rocky mountain slopes and valley floor, June–July 1939—Surmazhab; road from Khobdo somon to Dalan-Dzadgad near intersection with road to Bayan-Dzag, steppe, July 27; Tsagan-derisu-khural 10 km nor.-west of Noyan somon, hillocky area, sep. 15—1951, Kal.; Tostu mountain range, rocky granite hillocky area, July 16, 1973—Isach. and Rachk.; same locality 45 km west of Tost somon, montane steppe on nor. slope, Aug. 4, 1976—Rachk. and Damba; Dzhinst-ula mountain range, Altain-tsagan-khalga gorge, Sep. 7, 1979 [UBA]; same locality, Shombon mountain, Sep. 5, 1980 [UBA]—Sanczir, east. part of Tost-ula mountain range 18 km from Gruvan-Tes somon, Aug. 9, 1984—Kam. and Dariima), ***East. Gobi*** (Galbyn-Gobi, on road to Burgastai from Khara-Morite, May 15, 1909—Napalkov and Czet.; Galbyn-Gobi, south of Galba hillocky area, Barun-Khuren-khuduk area, Sep. 25, 1940—Yun.; Bulgan somon, in Baaran region 2 km nor.-west of source, Sep. 14, 1953—Dashnyam; Galbyn-Gobi, in the region of Bugutur-Khubur-khuduk collective, July 31; Tsagan-Obo hillock near Bayan-Munkh-khida ruins, Aug. 6, 1970, Grub., Ulzij. et al.; 22 km nor. of Altan-shire somon, steppe, July 8, 1 km south of Ikhe-Dzhargalante, steppe on plain, July 15—1971, Isach. and Rachk.; Galbyn-Gobi 55 km south-south-east of Khan-Bogdo somon, desert, June 26, 1972—Guricheva and Rachk. [UBA]; "Ulaantsab, Bayan-nur, Chzhakhor (West. Part)"—K.T. Fu et Cheng l.c., Liou f. l.c.), ***West. Gobi*** (Khubchiin-nuru mountain range, Tukhmyin-khundei ravine, Dzolen Bogdo [Adzhi-Bogdo], south. mountain trail, saxaul desert, Aug. 9—1947, Yun.; Dzulganai-gol 110 km west of Gurvan-Tes settlement, July 13, 1970—Gub.; south. mountain trail of Adzhi-Bogdo mountain range, on Altay somon—Tseel somon road 19 km from former, mountain trail, 1380 m, Aug. 24, 1979—Grub. et al.; foothills of Adzhi-Bogdo mountain range 60 km nor. of Altay settlement near Dzolen-Sudzhiin-bulak spring, Sep. 8, 1983—Gub. [MW]; hillocky area of south. extremity of Khubchiin-nuru mountain range, Tukhumyin-khundei gorge, Aug. 2, 1982—Kam. and Dariima [UBA]), ***Alash. Gobi*** (valley of nor. bend of Huang He river, near Mandaltyn-bulak collective, on rocky foothills of marginal mountain range, No. 34, May 23, 1872—Przew., typus !; south. Alashan, Tengeri sand, in west up to Serik-Dolon lake, Alashan desert, Shrugul-khuduk well, No. 47, June 16, 1873—paratypus !; south. Alashan mountain range, on sand, Aug. 25, 1880—Przew.; Alashan mountain range, Tszosto gorge, on all slopes, May 15, 1908—Czet.; Bortszon-gobi area near Khailyas-khuduk, April 24; same locality, Bulgan-khural, south of Barun-Tsokhë mountain, hillocky plain, desert, April 26–1941, Yun.; Khugshu-Üla mountain, nor.-west. trail, Suchzhi-khuduk well, desert of pebble bed, Aug. 10, 1948—Grub.; hillocky plain between Khaltszan-ula and Dubnig-Ula hills, Sep. 9, 1950—Lavr. and Kal.; 10 km west of Chzhunvei town, friable sand on Huang He river terrace, July 1; Alashan, Bayan-Khot town, 35 km south of Tsilantai lake, sand-covered pebbly submontane plain, July 9; same locality, 15 km west of Chzhunvei town, sandy-pebbly terrace, Huang He river, July 25—1957; Alashan, Bayan-Khoto, Divusumu 70 km south-east of Bain-Ula hills, along rocky gorges, June 11; same locality, Nalin-sukhaitu 8 km south-east of Bain-Ula mountain, arid rocky slopes and gorge in nor. part, June 13; same locality, Nalin-sukhaitu settlement 20 km south-west of Bain-Ula mountain, hillocky area, June 13; Bayan-Khoto 12 km south-west of Taodaokhe near Syrkhe weel, ridge of wind-blown bedrocks, June 15; Uvei, Maochantszin' well and settlement, south. fringe of Tengeri sand, along depressions between dunes, June 23; Bayan-Khoto, Yaburaiyan'chi settlement 13 km west-nor.-west, south. fringe of Yaburai mountain, rocky-rubbly slopes, June 30; same locality, Yaburaiyanchi 75 km nor.-east of south. submontane sandy-pebbly plain of Yaburai mountain 18 km west of Chzhan'e town, June 30; high terrace of Huang He river, July 13—1958, Petr.; 25 km south-west of Tsagan-Deris border post, July 6 [MW]; Tsagan-Tolgoi-khuduk area, July 9 [MW]; 8 km east of Shuulin border post, Aug. 4—1981 [MW], Gub.; "Bayan-nur, Alashan"—K.T. Fu et Cheng l.c., Liou f. l.c.), ***Ordos*** ("Ikhe-Dzou"—Liou f. l.c.), ***Khesi*** (vicinity of shakhe village, 1498 m, June 4; vicinity of Fuiitin town, June 5—1886, Pot.; 7 km west of Gaotai town along road from Yuimyn', on sand, Oct. 8, 1958; 23 km from Yunchuan' town toward east, on nor. Nanshan foothills, June 28; 30 km south-east of Min'tsin town, vicinity of Suvushan' village, high terrace on fringe of oasis, July 3, 1959—Petr.; "Khesi corridor"—Liou f. l.c.).

IB. Kashgar: ***South.*** (Kerii mountain range, 2500 m, Kamysh-bulak gorge, on ploughed land, May 18, 1885—Przew.; nor. foothills of Russky mountain range, Oi-yailak area, about 2130 m, June 18; same locality, 1829–2134 m, rocky and sandy steppe, June 18, 1890, Rob.), ***East.*** (Bagrashkul' lake region, 10 km from Bortu in Khomote, in arid valley, No. 6927, Aug. 2, 1958—A.R. Lee (1958); "Khami"—C.Y. Yang l.c.).

—**IC.: Qaidam:** ***Plain*** ("Qaidam basin"—Liou f. l.c.).

IIA. Junggar: ***Jung. Gobi*** (Junggar Gobi, 20 km west of Dzag post, Aug. 2, 1979—Gub. [MW]; "Tsitai"—C.Y. Yang l.c.).

IIIA. Qinghai: ***Nanshan*** (Humboldt mountain range, nor. slope, vicinity of Kuu-usu river, clayey mound, 2743–3353 m, May 14, 1894—Rob.), ***Amdo*** (along arid clayey banks of Huang He river, in Guidui town vicinity, Aug. 1, 1880—Przew.).

General distribution: endemic.

202. **A. brachybotrys** Bunge in Ind. Sem. Horti Dorpat. (1839) 7; Ledeb. Fl. Ross. 1 (1842) 615; Bunge Gen. Astrag. Sp. Geront. 1 (1868) 98 and 2 (1869) 169; Kryl. Fl. Zap. Sib. 7 (1933) 1673; Gontsch. and Boriss. in Fl. SSSR, 12 (1946) 457; Grub. Konsp. fl. MNR (195) 183; Gub. in Byul. Mosk. obshch. ispyt. prir., otd. biol. 87, 1 (1982) 127; Sanczir in Grub., Opred. rast. Mong. [Key to Plants of Mongolia] (1982) 161, p. max. p.; Ulzij. in Tr. Inst. bot. AN MNR (1982) 26; Grub. in Novosti sist. vyssh. rast. 21 (1984) 213; Ulzij. and Gub. in Byul. Mosk. obshch. ispyt. prir., otd. biol. 92, 5 (1988) 116.—*A. miniatus* auct. non Bunge: Sanczir in Grub., Opred. rast. Mong. [Key to Plants of Mongolia] (1982) p. min. p.

Described from East. Altay. Type in St.-Petersburg (LE). Plate VI, fig. 3. Map. 7.

In mountain and desert steppes, arid rubbly and rocky slopes, in gullies.

IA. Mongolia: ***Khobd.*** (Khatu river, along its exit from gorge, on dry pebbly bed, June 17, 1879—Pot.; Khobdo somon, Ubsanur ajmaq, 51 km south-west of Urkhain-surin, along floor of dry pebble bed, Aug. 1, 1977—Sanczir, Karam. et al. [UBA]), ***Mong. Alt.*** (Adzhi Bogdo mountain range, Dzusylan gorge, June 29; Saksa river valley, July 7; Tsitsirin-gol river, on arid pebble bed, July 10—1877, Pot.; on mountain range cliffs running between Taishir-ula and Burkhan-ula, July 18, 1894; between Ikhys-nur and Tonkil-nur, on bank of arid bed, July 24, 1897; montane slope in Botkhon gorge, July 18, 1898—Klem.; Kak-kul' lake between Tsagan-gol and Kobdo, arid rubbly ravine, June 22, 1906—Sap.; Ulan-Ergiin-gol valley at centre of Must somon, Mu-ulan-tologoi granite hillock, woody-rocky slope and rocks, Aug. 12; Adzhi-Bogdo mountain range, south. macro slope, Ikhe-gol river, gorge, left flank, 2200–2300 m, steppe, Aug. 22—1979, Grub., Muldashev et al.;

20 km west of Bayan-Undur settlement, July 14, 1979; foothill of Gichgeniin-nuru mountain range, 75 km south-west of Bayan-Undur settlement, Aug. 22, 1982; 70 km south of Tonkhil settlement, July 9, 1984—Gub.; Uliastain-gol river gorge 10 km south-west of Bugat somon, along pebble beds, July 5; Alag-Khairkhan-ula mountains 12 km south-west of Bugyn-daba pass, high plain, July 5—1984, Dariima and Kam.), ***Depr. Lakes*** (island on Dzankhyn-gol river, 75 km before Shurugiin-gol river estuary [Shireegiin-gol] Aug. 9, 1950—collector ?, east. fringe of Shargain-Gobi, on Altay-Sharga somon road 19 km from ajmaq centre, gently inclined trail, steppe, Aug. 9, 1979—Grub. et al.), ***Val. Lakes*** (80 km nor.-east-east of Altay town, along left bank of Dzabkhyn river near Gulin settlement, July 6, 1984—Gub. [MW]), ***Gobi Alt.*** (Ikhe-Bogdo mountain range, foothill and lower belt of mountains, Aug. 18, 1926—Tug.; same locality, south, trail, lower third, steppe, July 20; Nemegetu-nuru mountain range, west extremity, summit of Khara-Obo mountain, large west. gully in its midportion, Aug. 7; Tostu-nuru mountain range, main summit of Sharga-Morite, 2300–2565 m, on summit and along nor.-west. slope, Aug. 15—1948, Grub.; central portion of Gurban-Saikhan mountain range along road to Khushu-khural monastery, steppe slopes, July 19, 1950— Kal.; Ikhe-Bogdo-ula, on rocky trail, 2300 m, steppe, Aug. 6, 1973—Isach. and Rachk.; Shine-Dzhinst-ula 15 km south of Shine-Dzhiist settlement, July 9 [MW], Gub.), ***East. Gobi*** (Ara-Khashchyatyi well, at Delger-Khangai foothill, July 21, 1924—Pakhomov; Avrakh mountains near Avrakh-khuduk well, on rocky slopes, Aug. 21, 1925—Glag.).

IIA. Junggar: ***Jung. Gobi*** (east. macro slope of Baitag-Bogdo mountain range, Bulun-Khargaityn-gol river basin, July 28, 1979—Gub. [MW]; nor. extremity of Maikhan-ulan mountain 28 km south-west of Bugat somon, Aug. 1; west. spurs of Khuvchiin-nuru mountain 8 km south-west of Maikhan-Ulan moutains, Aug. 1—1984, Kam. and Dariima).

General distribution: West. Sib. (Alt. south-east.: Chui steppe).

Note. We consider Tost-nuru plant as distinct subsp.: subsp. *tosticus* Ulzij. subsp. nov. The plant differs sharply from the type in the following characteristics: leaflets oblong, elliptical or lanceolate, 3–10 mm long, (2.5) 3 mm broad; calyx 4 mm long with 1 mm long teeth; wings 10 mm long, bilobed at tip; pods linear, up to 12–13 mm long, about 2 mm broad, not curved. Type: Tostu-nuru mountain range, main summit of Sharga-Morite, 2300–2565 m, at summit and along nor.-west slope, No. 5360, Aug. 15, 1948, Grub.

203. **A. miniatus** Bunge Gen. Astrag. Sp. Geront. 1 (1868) 98 and 2 (1869) 169; Pavl. in Byul. Mosk. obshch. ispyt. prir., otd. biol. 38, 1–2 (1929) 92; Gontsch. and Boriss. in Fl. SSSR, 12 (1946) 458; Boriss. in Fl. Zabaik. 6 (1954) 592; Grub. Konsp. fl. MNR (1955) 185; M. Pop. Fl. Sr. Sib. 1 (1957) 333; Fl. pl. herb. Chinae bor.-or. 5 (1976) 98; Fu et Cheng f. in Fl. Intramong. 3 (1977) 209 and 2 ed 3 (1989) 273; Fl. Tsentr. Sib. 2 (1979) 602; Sanczir in Grub., Opred. rast. Mong. [Key to Plants of Mongolia] (1982) 161; Ulzij. in Tr. Inst. bot. AN MNR, 8 (1982) 26; S.B. Ho in Bull. Bot. Research, 3, 1 (1983) 41; Liou f. in Fl. desert Sin. 2 (1987) 270.—*A. ervoides* Turcz. Fl. baic.-dahur.1 (1842–45) 328; Ledeb. Fl. Ross. 1 (1842) 617, non A. Gray.—*A. brachybotrys* auct. non Bunge: Sanczir in Grub., Opred. rast. Mong. [Key to Plants of Mongolia] (1982) 161, p. min. p.

—**Ic.:** Fl. pl. herb. Chinae bor.-or. 5 (1976) tab. 43, fig. 10–17; Fl. Intramong. 3 (1977) tab. 96, fig. 1–7 and 2 ed. 3 (1989) tab. 105, fig. 6–10.

Described from East. Siberia (Dauria). Type in St.-Petersburg (LE). Plate VI, fig. 2. Map 8.

On rubbly and rocky steppe slopes of mountains, in mountain trails, rocks, pebble bed terraces and along solonetzic banks of rivers.

IA. Mongolia: ***Cen. Khalkha*** (Choiryn-ula, 1940—Sanzha and Damdin; Tsavchiryn-gol area 45 km south-west of Man't station, solonchak, July 2, 1970—Banzragch et al.; 70 km south-east of Undurkhan town, saline lake, Khaya-Ulan-nur, slope of main bank, chee grass thicket, June 20; same locality, on lake terrace, June 20—1971, Dashnyam, Isach. et al.; Dzhargalanta river basin, midcourse of Ubur-Dzhargalanta river, near Dol'che-gegen monastery, rubbly slopes, Aug. 10; same locality, steppe of third terrace, Aug. 22; same locality, arid ravine among plateau-like elevations, Aug. 25–26—1925, Krasch. and Zam.; same locality, vicinity of Ikhe-Tukhum-nor lake, second terrace; same locality, Sairyn-khuduk, Mishik-gun, June 1926—Zam.). ***East. Mong.*** (in locis subarenosis Mongoliae chinensis, 1831—N. Kuzhetsov); Mongolia chinensis, Borochodshirtu, in arenosis, June 29, 1842—Tatarinow; Mongolia chinensis, 1841—Kirilow; Choi-ling—June 14 [?]; Bulun-Cholu, June 15—Fischer; Sutszy station on caravan course, Aug. 1, 1989—Zab.; Kulun-buirnorsk plain, Singerkhe, June 7; same locality, steppe south of Kerulen river, June 10—1899, Pot. and Sold.; in Bain-gol river valley, Sep. 2, 1928—Shastin; 47 km south of Khar-nur lake, summit of hillocks, Aug. 3; same locality, Bayan-bulak region, 12 km west of Khavirga, slopes of hillocks, Aug. 12—1954; 14 km nor. of Enger-Shanda, steppe, May 27 [UBA]; 1 km nor. of Enger-Shanda, along periphery of Tukhumyin-Gobi, Aug. 27—1957, Dashnyam [UBA]; East. Sunit, on mountain slope, June 12, 1959—D. Ivanov; Dariganga somon, Dar'-Obo cones, June 19, 1967—Gombozhav [UBA]; 20 km east of Matad settlement, Matadyn-tuur area, June 22, 1987—Budantsev, Ganbold et al.; Kerulen river valley, 60 km nor. of Choi-balsan, July 21; bank of Khukh-nur lake, July 27—1987, Gub., Dariima et al.; "Khulunbuir, Shilin-gol"—K.T. Fu et Cheng l.c. Liou f. l.c.), ***Val. Lakes*** (vicinity of Tsakhir-bulak springlet, on cliffs, July 19, 1894—Klem.; rocky slope of bank along Tatsyn-gol river, Sep. 14, 1924—Pavl.; valley of Tatsyn-gol river, July 20, 1926—Kozlova; nor. bank of Tsagan-nur, terrace above lake, Aug. 17, 1949—Kal.), ***Gobi-Alt.*** (Gurban-Saikhan, open slopes, 6500–7400 ft, No. 127, 1925—Chaney; Gurban-Saikhan mountain range, pass between Dzun- and Dundu-saikhan, Dundu-Saikhan trail in midportion of steppe, July 22; trail on west. extremity of Dzun-Saikhan mountain range, near road from Dalan-Dzadgad to Bayan-Dalai somon, arid steppe, July 22—1943; Dzun-Saikhan mountain range, middle and lower belts, July 19—1945, Yun.; Artsa-Bogdo mountain range, nor. macro slope, steppe, July 4, 1973—Isach. and Rachk.), ***East. Gobi*** (on way to Urgu from Alashan, on road from Duten-Taza area to Bulygin-urto area, June 5; same locality, on road to Khara-Tologoi from Mandalyn-Gobi area, July 8—1909, Napalkov and Czet.; Delger-Khangai, mountain slopes, July 20; Baga-Ude, gully in Khara-ula Mountains, Aug. 16; steppe in basalts, 70 km south of Choiren, Aug. 26—1926, Lis.; Delger-Khangai hills, upper section of slope, Aug. 1, 1931—Ik.-Gal.; 16 km nor.-east of Sain-shanda on road to Baishintu, steppified desert, June 29, 1940—Shubin; Bayan-Munkh somon 20–25 km south-west of old somon camp site, desert steppe. June 7, 1941—Tsatsenkin; Ikhe-Erien somon, depression eastward of Bayan-Tsogt mountains on road to Bayan-Zhargalan from somon, May 29; 0.5 km east of Bayan-Zhargalan somon, desert steppe along ravines between knolls, May 30—1941; 12 km nor.-nor.-east of Dalan-Dzadgad along road to Ulan-Bator, lowland, June 8—1949, Yun.; Ongiin-gol river near Khushu-Khid monastery, saline meadow, July 14, 1948—Grub.; Dalan-Zhargalan somon centre, Aug. 6, 1965—Zhamsran and Badrakh [UBA]; south-east of Sain-Shanda 20 km from Khairkhan area, 1120 m, Aug. 4; Tsagan-Obo knoll near Bayan-Munkh-khida ruins, gully, Aug. 6—1970, Grub., Ulzij. et al.; 90 km east of Sain-Shanda town, bank of Ikh-Ulan-nur lake, July 5, 1982; Altan-Shire somon, 30 km nor.-west of Delgerkhan settlement, July 4, 1985—Gub.; "Bayan-nur: Urot"—K.T. Fu et Cheng l.c.).

General distribution: East. Sib. (Daur. South-east: Barun- and Dzun-Torei, Abagatui), Nor. Mong. (Hang. south, Mong.-Daur.), China (Dunbei).

204. **A. sulcatus** L. Sp. pl. (1753) 756; DC. Prodr. 2 (1825) 284; Ledeb. Fl. Alt. 3 (1831) 302; id. Fl. Ross. 1, 3 (1843) 619; Bunge Gen. Astrag. Sp. Geront. 1 (1868) 21 and 2 (1869) 23; O. et B. Fedtsch. Konsp. fl. Turk. 2 (1909) 199; Pavl. in Byul. Mosk. obshch. ispyt. prir., otd. biol. 38, 1–2 (1929) 90; Kryl. Fl. Zap. Sib. 7 (1933) 1647; Gontsch. and Boriss. in Fl. SSSR, 12 (1946) 451; Boriss. in Fl. Zabaik. 6 (1954) 594; Grub. Konsp. fl. MNR (1955) 187; M. Pop. Fl. Sr. Sib. 1 (1957) 332; Fl. Krasnoyar. kr. 6 (1960) 36; Fl. Kazakhst. 5 (1961) 199; excl. pl. e Tarbagataj et Alatau Dshungaricae; Fl. Tsentr. Sib. 2 (1979) 605; Bait. Astrag. Tyan'-Shanya (1977) 60; Opred. rast. Sr. Azii [Key to Plants of Mid. Asia] 6 (1981) 275; Sanczir in Grub., Opred. rast. Mong. [Key to Plants of Mongolia] (1982) 161; Ulzij. in Tr. Inst. bot. AN MNR, 8 (1982) 27; S.B. Ho in Bull. Bot. Research, 3, 1 (1983) 41; C.Y. Yang in Claves pl. Xinjiang, 3 (1985) 156. —*A. leptostachys* Pall. Astrag. (1800) 50.

—**Ic.:** Pall. (1800) l.c.: tab. 40 (sub nom. *A. leptostachys* Pall.); Fl. Kazakhst. 5, Plate 26, fig. 1; C.Y. Yang l.c. tab. 7, fig. 3.

Described from "Siberia". Type in London (LINN). Plate VI, fig. 5.

On solonetzic coastal and floodplain meadows, pebble beds along river banks, lakes and irrigation canals, along flanks and floors of gullies in mountain trails, forest borders.

IA. Mongolia: ***Mong. Alt.*** (Bulgan river floodplain at confluence into it of Uliastai-gol river from left, forb meadow, July 20, 1947—Yun.; 70 km west-nor.-west of Altay somon, Ikh-Alag-ula, moist rock fissures, Aug. 25, 1973—Isach. and Rachk.; 60 km nor.-west of Altay settlement, near Bitin-bulak spring in Nogon-daban hills, Sep. 6, 1983—Gub. [MW]), ***Depr. Lakes*** (Ulangom area, June 26; Ubsa lake facing Baga-nor., on coastal pebble bed, Sep. 22, 1879, Pot.; around irrigation canal 10 versts (1 verst = 1.067 km) from Ubsa lake, July 3, 1892—Kryl.), ***Val. Lakes*** (west. fringe of Beger lake basin, Tsagan-Dugyu, near irrigation canal, July 11, 1877—Pot.; not far from Orok-nor lake, on sand, July 13, 1893; on bank of Tsakhir-bulak springlet, July 18; on moist bank of Khunkhyr river, July 12—1894, Klem.; arid short-grass meadows on bank of Tuin-gol river, Sep. 2, 1924—Pavl.; west. extremity of Beger-nur basin along road to Khalyun, gorge in Gobi formations along gully, Aug. 23, 1943—Yun.).

IIA. Junggar: ***Cis.-Alt.*** ("Altay"—Liou f. l.c.), ***Tien Shan*** (Khaidyk-gol river, Tubogorin-nor area, 1219 m, on ploughed land, Aug. 17, 1893—Rol.; Urumchi region, pass between Tien Shan and Bogdo-Ola, Davanchin gorge, along brook, Sep. 4, 1926—Pop.), ***Jung. Gobi*** ("Urumchi"—S.B. Ho l.c., C.Y. Yang l.c.), ***Zaisan*** ("Khabakhe" [Kaba river]—S.B. Ho l.c.; "Burchum"—C.Y. Yang l.c.).

IIIA. Qinghai: ***Nanshan*** (lower boundary of alpine belt of Nanshan mountain range, up along Dankhe bank, on sand and rocks, 2438 m, July 5; same locality, July 8—Przew.).

General distribution: Aralo-Casp., Fore Balkh.; Europe (Cen., East.), Balk.-Asia Minor, West. Sib. (Irt.), East. Sib. (Sayans).

205. **A. consanguineus** Bong. et Mey. in Mém. Ac. Sci.-Petersb. (Sci. Phys.-Math.) 6, 6 (1841) 178; Kryl. Fl. Zap. Sib. 7 (1933) 1672; Gontsch. and Boriss. in Fl. SSSR, 12 (1946) 452; Fl. Kazakhst. 5 (1961) 199, quoad

pl. e Tarbagataj et Alatau Dshungaricae; Opred. rast. Sr. Azii [Key to Plants of Mid. Asia] 6 (1981) 275; C.Y. Yang in Claves pl. Xinjiang, 3 (1985) 156.

Described from East. Kazakhstan (Zaisan basin). Type in St.-Petersburg (LE).

On solonetzic soils, sandy banks of saline lakes.

IB. Kashgar: ***East.*** (Alagao in Toksun, about 500 m, No. 7287, June 16, 1958—A.R. Lee).

IIA. Junggar: ***Tarb.*** ("Dachen"—C.Y. Yang l.c.), ***Zaisan*** ("Burchum, Zimunia"—C.Y. Yang l.c.).

General distribution: Fore Balkh., Jung.-Tarb.

Note. Toksun plant differs from type *A. consanguineus* in longer (11 mm long) and broader (up to 2 mm) pods and from *A. sulcatus* in rounded (undivided) tip of wings.

Section 20 (64). **Proselius** (Stev.) Bunge

206. **A. platyphyllus** Kar. et Kir. in Bull. Soc. Natur. Moscou, 15 (1842) 345; Bunge Gen. Astrag. Sp. Geront. 1 (1868) 121 and 2 (1969) 215; id. Astrag. Turk. (1880) 280; id. in Acta Horti Petrop. 7 (1880) 376; Lipsky in Acta Horti Petrop. 26 (1907) 263; O. et B. Fedtsch. Konsp. fl. Turk. 2 (1909) 229; Kryl. Fl. Zap. Sib. 7 (1933) 1686; Gontsch. Fl. Tadzhik. 5 (1937) 431; Boriss. in Fl. SSSR, 12 (1946) 638; Fl. Kirgiz. 7 (1957) 313; Fl. Kazakhst. 5 (1961) 238; Bait. Astrag. Tyan'-Shanya (1977) 72; Opred. rast. Sr. Azii [Key to Plants of Mid. Asia] 6 (1981) 216; Fl. Tadzhik. 6 (1981) 275; S.B. Ho in Bull. Bot. Research, 3, 1 (1983) 62; C.Y. Yang in Claves pl. Xinjiang, 3 (1985) 149.

—Ic.: Fl. SSSR, 12, Plate 41, fig. 1; Fl. Kazakhst. 5, Plate 29, fig. 1.

Described from East. Kazakhstan (Jung. Ala Tau). Type in St.-Petersburg (LE).

On rocky and rubbly slopes in middle and upper mountain belts.

IB. Kashgar: ***West.*** ("Uchi"—C.Y. Yang l.c.).

IIA. Junggar: ***Tarb.*** ("Dachen"—C.Y. Yang l.c.), ***Tien Shan*** (Kokkamyr, nor.-east. Kul'dzha, 1829–2134 m, July; between Kyzemchek and Sairam, 2134–2743 m, July 29; Kyzemchek, July 29—1878; between Piluchi and gorge, 914–1219 m, April 22—1879, A. Reg.; Burkhan-tau, June 5, 1878—Fet.), ***Dzhark.*** ("vicinity of Khuachen"—S.B. Ho l.c.), ***Jung. Gobi*** (Beidashan, in larch forest, No. 413, Sep. 28, 1957—Shen; Sary-bulak along Suidun river, 1219–1829 m, April 24; Srednii Khorgos, south-west. Kul'dzha, 914–1524 m, April 15–1878, A. Reg.).

General distribution: Jung.-Tarb., Nor. and Cen. Tien Shan, East. Pamir; Mid. Asia (Pamiro-Alay).

Note. Beidashan plant differs from type in semibilocular, trigonous-oblong-ovate pods.

Section 21 (65). **Helmia** Bunge

207. **A. helmii** Fisch. in DC. Prodr. 2 (1825) 301; Ledeb. Fl. Ross. 1 (1842) 613; Kryl. Fl. Zap. Sib. 7 (1933) 1682; Gontsch. and M. Pop. in Fl. SSSR, 12 (1946) 548; Fl. Kazakhst. 5 (1961) 218 p.p.; Opred. rast. Sr. Azii [Key to Plants of Mid. Asia] 6 (1981) 229.

—**Ic.:** Fl. Kazakhst. 5 (1961) Plate 29, fig. 2.

Described from South. Urals. Type in Geneva [G].

On steppe slopes of mountains.

IB. Kashgar: *Nor.* (Uch-Turfan, Airi gorge, along submontane plains, June 2, 1908—Divn.).

IIA. Junggar: *Tien Shan* (turfed slope exposed southward, valley of Chendokhoze river, 1800 m, May 27, 1954—Moiseenko).

General distribution: Fore Balkh. (Ulu Tau mountains); Europe (south-east.), West. Sib. (Irt.).

Note. In its characteristics, Uch-Turfan plant exactly matches with this species but is distinctly separated from the main distribution range. Var. *kaschgaricus* Ulzij.— Foliola 3–4 (5), pinnatae (non 4–7 pinnatae), 5–8 mm longae, 2–3 mm latae. Flores sulphures.

208. **A. heptapotamicus** Sumn. in Animadv. Syst. Herb. Univ. Tomsk. 5–6 (1933) 7; Gontsch. and M. Pop. in Fl. SSSR, 12 (1946) 547; Fl. Kirgiz. 7 (1957) 297; Fl. Kazakhst. 5 (1961) 217; Bait. Astrag. Tyan'-Shanya (1977) 66; Opred. rast. Sr. Azii [Key to Plants of Mid. Asia] 6 (1981) 230; S.B. Ho in Bull. Bot. Research, 3, 1 (1983) 47; C.Y. Yang in Claves pl. Xinjiang, 3 (1985) 157.—*A. polakovii* M. Pop. in Not. Syst. (Leningrad) 10 (1947) 6; Gontsch. and M. Pop. in Fl. SSSR, 12 (1946) 547; Fl. Kazakhst. 5 (1961) 217.

—**Ic.:** Fl. Kazakhst. 5, Plate 31, fig. 2.

Described from East. Kazakhstan (Jung. Ala Tau). Type in St.-Petersburg (LE).

In steppe and deserted rocky and clayey slopes, along river valleys.

IB. Kashgar: *Nor.* (Muzart river valley 7–8 km beyond its emergence into Baisk basin, steppe belt, along rubbly slopes, Sep. 7; same locality, Oi-Terek area, 1 km downstream, old lateral moraine, steppified desert, 2350 m, Sep. 11—1958, Yun. and I-f. Yuan').

IIA. Junggar: ***Tarb.*** ("Dachen"—C.Y. Yang, l.c.), ***Tien Shan*** (Sairam lake, 1219 m, June 21; same locality, No. 190, July; same locality, Talkibash, July 19—1877, A. Reg.; "south. bank of Sairam lake"—S.B. Ho l.c.; "Ili"—C.Y. Yang l.c.).

General distribution: Fore Balkh., Jung.-Tarb., Cen. Tien Shan.

Note. The plant from Muzart river valley differs from type in (2) 3–5 mm long leaflets and linear-oblong pods 16 mm long, 4.5–5 mm broad, on 1–1.5 mm long stalk.

209. **A. tuvinicus** Timoch. in Sist. i geogr. rast. Sib. [Taxonomy and Geography of Siberian Plants] (1978) 8; Opred. rast. Tuv. ASSR [Key to Plants of Tuva Autonomous Soviet Socialist Republic] (1984) 146; Ulzij. and Gub. in Byul. Mosk. obshch. ispyt. prir., otd. biol. 92, 5 (1987) 113.

Described from Tuva. Type in Novosibirsk (NS).

In steppes, on rubbly and rocky slopes.

IA. Mongolia: ***Mong. Alt.*** (south-east. part: Bugat somon, Maikhan-Ulaan mountains, near Tsagan-bulak spring, July 31, 1984—Kam. and Dariima), ***Depr. Lakes*** ?

IIA. Junggar: ***Jung. Gobi*** (Khaldzan-ula mountain range, 50 km east-south-east of Altay somon, Sep. 2, 1983—Gub.).

General distribution: East. Sib. (steppe Tuva).

210. **A. depauperatus** Ledeb. Fl. Alt. 3 (1831) 314; id. Fl. Ross. 1 (1842) 612; Kryl. Fl. Zap. Sib. 7 (1933) 1681; Gontsch. and M. Pop. in Fl. SSSR, 12 (1946) 546; Fl. Krasnoyar. kr. 6 (1960) 37; Fl. Kazakhst. 5 (1961) 216; Sanczir in Grub. Opred. rast. Mong. [Key to Plants of Mongolia] (1982) 163; Opred. rast. Tuv. ASSR [Key to Plants of Tuva Autonomous Soviet Socialist Republic] (1984) 146; C.Y. Yang in Claves pl. Xinjiang, 3 (1985) 157; Ulzij. and Gub. in Byul. Mosk. obshch. ispyt. prir., otd. biol. 92, 5 (1987) 116; F. Nemeth in Studia Bot. Hungarica, 21 (1989) 47 and 45.—*A. eriolobus* Bunge in Mém. Sav. Etrang. Ac. Sci. Petersb. 2 (1835) 591.

Described from Altay. Type in St.-Petersburg (LE).

In solonetzic desert and arid steppes, on rubbly and rocky slopes of mountains and hills, riverine pebble beds.

IA. Mongolia: ***Khobd.*** (Turgen' river 30 km nor.-west of Ulangom town, in floodplain, Aug. 31, 1984—Gub.), ***Mong. Alt.*** (Uliastain-gol river, at its emergence into Bulgan-gol river valley, floodplain, on pebble bed, Aug. 16; Adzhi-Bogdo mountain range, south. macro slope, Ikhe-gol river, gorge, left bank, 2200–2300 m, steppe, Aug. 22—1979, Grub. et al.; valley of Nariin-gol river, middle and lower courses, July 16, 1984—Kam. and Dariima; "in Muikh-Khairkhan settlement region, 3000 m, Aug. 9; 20 km south-west of Mankhan settlement, foothill, Aug. 10—1986, Nemeth"—F. Nemeth l.c.).

IIA. Junggar: ***Cis-Alt.*** ("Altay"—C.Y. Yang l.c.), ***Tarb.*** ("Dachen"—C.Y. Yang l.c.), ***Zaisan*** ("Burchum"—C.Y. Yang l.c.).

General distribution: West. Sib. (Alt., Tuva), East. Sib. (Sayans), Nor. Mong. (Hang., cen.).

211. **A. kasachstanicus** Golosk. in Not. Syst. (Leningrad) 18 (1957) 111; Fl. Kazakhst. 5 (1961) 219; Ulzij. in Tr. Inst. bot. AN MNR, 8 (1982) 34; Ulzij. and Gub. Byul. Mosk. obshch. ispyt. prir., otd. biol. 92, 5 (1987) 113.—*A. laguroides* auct. non Pall.: Sanczir in Grub. Opred. rast. Mong. [Key to Plants of Mongolia] (1982) 161, p. min. p.—*A. sabuletorum* Ledeb.: Sanczir, ibid., 161, p. min. p.

—**Ic.:** Fl. Kazakhst. 5, Plate 29, fig. 3.

Described from West. Kazakhstan (Kzylzhar mountains). Type in St.-Petersburg (LE).

On rocky slopes of desert-steppe hillocky area.

IA. Mongolia: ***Mong. Alt.*** (east. slopes toward Tonkhilnur basin, hilly-desert steppe, Aug. 13, 1945—Yun.; Ushgiin-Barun-khoolai valley 6 km nor. of pass on Tonkhil somon—Tsetseg-nur road, slope of spur, steppe, Aug. 11, 1984—Gub. [MW]).

IB. Kashgar: *Nor.* (10 km nor. of Baichen, 2000 m, No. 8219, Sep. 6, 1958—A.R. Lee).

IIA. Junggar: *Jung. Ala Tau* (Toli town region, steppe, No. 2953, Aug. 4, 1957—Shen).

General distribution: West. Sib. (Altay, Irtysh).

Section 22 (66). **Pseuderioceras** Ulzij.

212. **A. rudolfii** Ulzij. in Bull. Soc. Natur. Moscou, ser. biol. 95, 2 (1990) 80.

Described from Mongolia (Mong. Altay). Type in St.-Petersburg (LE), isotype in Ulan Bator (UBA). Map 9.

On arid montane steppe and desert-steppe slopes of mountains.

IA. Mongolia: *Mong. Alt.* (Bulgan river basin, Deed-Nariin-gol 1 km from estuary, 1550–1600 m, rocky slope, desert steppe, Aug. 17; same locality, 1520 m, trail of left bank, rubbly desert, Aug. 17, 1979, Grub. et al.; Narin-gol river valley, tributary of Bulgan river, July 16, 1984—Kam. and Dariima, typus ! (holo—LE, iso—UBA); Shadzgain-nuru mountain range, south. slope, Khoit-Dzhargalant-gol river basin, Bayan-sala gorge, July 27, 1984—Kam. and Dariima).

IIA. Junggar: *Jung. Gobi* (Khabeir village nor. of Ertai, in hill gorge, No. 10357, June 3, 1959—A.R. Lee (1958)).

General distribution: endemic.

213. **A. granitovii** Sancz. ex Ulzij. in Bull. Soc. Natur. Moscou, ser. biol. 95, 1 (1990) 81; Sanczir in Grub. Opred. rast. Mong. [Key to Plants of Mongolia] (1982) 160 (descr. ross. in claves); Ulzij. in Tr. Inst. bot. AN MNR, 8 (1982) 29; Grub. in Novosti sist. vyssh. rast. 21 (1984) 207; Ulzij. and Gub. in Byul. Mosk. obshch. ispyt. prir., otd. biol. 92, 5 (1987) 116; F. Nemeth in Studia Bot. Hungarica, 21 (1989) 47 and 45.

Described from Mongolia (Jung. Gobi). Type in Ulan Bator [UBA]. Map 9.

On steppe rubbly-rocky slopes of mountains.

IA. Mongolia: *Mong. Alt.* (14–15 km south of Tamchi-Nur lake, July 17, 1947—Yun.; hillocky area 30 km south-west of Bugat somon centre, No. 7119, Rachk. and Volk.; Alag-Khairkhan-ula mountain 12 km south-west of Bugyn-daba pass, high plain, July 5; nor. extremity of Maikhan-Ulan hill 28 km south-west of Bugat somon, Aug. 1—1984, Kam. and Dariima; 70 km south of Tonkhil settlement, July 9, 1984—Gub. [MW]; "lowland and valley around Uenchi settlement on road to Uenchi from Ongon, rocky hillock, Aug. 1, 1981—Nemeth"—F. Nemeth l.c.).

IIA. Junggar: *Jung. Gobi* (nor. macro slope of Khabtag-ula hill 80 km south of Altay somon centre, Aug. 21, 1984—Buyan-Orshikh (UBA)—typus !; south. extremity of Khubchiin-nuru mountain, Aug. 1, 1984—Kam. and Dariima).

General distribution: endemic.

Note. We could not examine the plant collected by F. Nemeth from Uenchi somon. It probably belongs to *A. rudolfii* Ulzij.

Section 23 (67). **Erioceras** Bunge

214. **A. neo-popovii** Golosk. in Fl. Kazakhst. 5 (1961) 491 and 213, incl. var. *leiolobus* Golosk.; Bait. Astrag. Tyan'-Shanya (1977) 65; Opred. rast. Sr. Azii [Key to Plants of Mid. Asia] 5 (1981) 233.

Described from East. Kazakhstan (Jung. Ala Tau). Type in Alma Ata (AA), isotype in St.-Petersburg (LE).

On rocky slopes and mountain trails.

IIA. Junggar: ***Jung. Ala Tau:*** will undoubtedly be found in Junggar Ala Tau.

General distribution: endemic.

Note. The report of this species on the southern slope of Junggar Ala Tau mountain range in People's Republic of China is highly possible. We have therefore included it in the floristic composition of Central Asia.

*__A. infractus__ Sumn. in Animadv. Syst. Herb. Univ. Tomsk, 9–10 (1936) 4; Gontsch. and Boriss. in Fl. SSSR, 12 (1946) 539; Fl. Kirgiz. 7 (1957) 295; Fl. Kazakhst. 5 (1961) 213; Bait. Astrag. Tyan'-Shanya (1977) 65; Opred. rast. Sr. Azii [Key to Plants of Mid. Asia] 6 (1981) 233.

Described from Kirghiz (Kirgiz. Ala Tau). Type in Tomsk (TK).

On riverine pebble beds.

IIA. Junggar: *Tien Shan* (?).

General distribution: Nor. Tien Shan (Kirgiz. Ala Tau), East. Pamir (Transili Ala Tau) endemic.

215. **A. petraeus** Kar. et Kir. in Bull. Soc. Natur. Moscou, 15 (1842) 333; Bunge Gen. Astrag. Sp. Geront. 1 (1868) 126 and 2 (1869) 221; id. Astrag. Turk. (1880) 286; id. in Acta Horti Petrop. 7 (1880) 376; O. et B. Fedtsch. Konsp. fl. Turk. 2 (1909) 232; Gontsch. and Boriss. in Fl. SSSR, 12 (1946) 532; Fl. Kirgiz. 7 (1957) 292; Fl. Kazakhst. 5 (1961) 210; Bait. Astrag. Tyan'-Shanya (1977) 64; Opred. rast. Sr. Azii [Key to Plants of Mid. Asia] 6 (1981) 231; S.B. Ho in Bull. Bot. Research, 3, 1 (1983) 46; C.Y. Yang in Claves pl. Xinjiang, 3 (1985) 161.—*A. xylorrhizus* Bunge Astrag. Turk. (1880) 267; O. et B. Fedtsch. Konsp. fl. Turk. 2 (1909) 222. —*A. irkeschtami* B. Fedtsch. in Not. Syst. (Leningrad) 8 (1940) 168.

—**Ic.:** Fl. Kazakhst. 5, Plate 28, fig. 2.

Described from East. Kazakhstan (Jung. Ala Tau). Type in Moscow (MW), isotype in St.-Petersburg (LE). Plate V, fig. 4.

On rocky, rocky-rubbly arid slopes, clay exposures, rocky terraces of rivers, in lower and middle belts of mountains.

IB. Kashgar: ***Nor.*** (15 km south-west of Kzyl-bulak settlement on road to Avat, pass through ridgy upland, steppified desert, Sep. 13, 1958—Yun. and I-f. Yuan'; Aksu region, at crossing on Talak-gol river, 2350 m, No. 8901, Sep. 25, 1958—A.R. Lee. "Un-Sui [Wensu], Aksu, Baichen [Bai]"—S.B. Ho l.c.), ***West.*** (upper course of Kizil-su river beyond Kashgar, between Sim-khane customhouse and Egin, July 1, 1929—Pop.; 8 km east of Ken-su mine on road to Irkeshtam from Kashgar, desert, 2200 m, June 17; same locality, 30 km east of Ulugchat settlement on road to Kashgar from Irkeshtam, intermontane valley, steppified desert, June 18—1959, Yun. and I-f. Yuan').

IIA. Junggar: *Tien Shan* (nor. Borborogusun, 1524 m, April 24; Borborogusun, 1829 m, April 27; Piluchi, 2134–2438 m, April 17; Dzhin river, tributary of Tsagan-Usu, 975 m, June 8—1879, A. Reg.; "Davachin"—C.Y. Yang l.c.). ***Jung. Gobi*** ("Chingil river"—C.Y. Yang l.c.).

General distribution: Jung.-Tarb., Nor. and Cen. Tien Shan; Mid. Asia (Pamiro-Alay).

Note. Yang's reference (l.c.) to the occurrence of this species in Chingil' river area in the northern part of Junggar Gobi is highly improbable. Judging from the site of report, this may, in all probability, be *A. rudolfii* Ulzij.

216. **A. arcuatus** Kar. et Kir. in Bull. Soc. Natur. Moscou, 14 (1841) 407; Ledeb. Fl. Ross. 1, 3 (1843) 631; Bunge Gen. Astrag. Sp. Geront. 1 (1868) 110 and 2 (1869) 190, excl. pl. Lehman.; id. Astrag. Turk. (1880) 266, excl. pl. Lehman.; O. et B. Fedtsch. Konsp. fl. Turk. 2 (1909) 222; Kryl. Fl. Zap. Sib. 7 (1933) 1680; Gontsch. and Boriss. in Fl. SSSR, 12 (1946) 533; Fl. Kazakhst. 5 (1961) 210; Bait. Astrag. Tyan'-Shanya (1977) 64; Opred. rast. Sr. Azii [Key to Plants of Mid. Asia] 6 (1981) 232; C.Y. Yang in Claves pl. Xinjiang, 3 (1985) 161.—*A. subarcuatus* auct. non M. Pop.: S.B. Ho in Bull. Bot. Research, 3, 1 (1983) 47.

—**Ic.:** Fl. Kazakhst. 5. Plate 38, fig. 3.

Described from West. Siberia (Irtysh river, between Omsk and Semipalatinsk). Type in Moscow (MW).

On clayey-rocky slopes, pebble beds, sandy-rubbly plateau in arid steppes and hamadas, on arid river beds.

IIA. Junggar: ***Tarb.*** (?), ***Jung. Ala Tau*** (?), ***Zaisan*** ("Burchum"—C.Y. Yang l.c., "Khabakhe [Kaba river]"—S.B. Ho l.c.).

General distribution: Aralo-Casp., Fore Balkh., Jung.-Tarb.

217. **A. kaschgaricus** M. Pop. ex Ulzij.

Described from Sinkiang. Type in St.-Petersburg (LE). Map 2.

On rocky, rubbly arid slopes, aeolian soils, rocks and clays, along brooks.

IB. Kashgar: ***Nor.*** (Ui-tal river gorge, on aeolian soil and rocks, 2743 m, June 1; Kara-Teke, on clay with pebbles along brooks, 1524–2438 m, June 7—1889, Rob.-typus !; declivitas australis jugi montium Tianschan vor Abad, May 30; Oberstes Dschanart Tal bis hinauf zum Pass, July 14–17—1903, Merzb.).

General distribution: endemic.

***A. innominatus** Boriss. in Not. Syst. (Leningrad) 7 (1937) 230; Gontsch. and Boriss. in Fl. SSSR, 12 (1946) 544; Ikonn. Opred. rast. Pam. [Key to Plants of Pamir] (1963) 169; Fl. Tadzhik. 6 (1981) 252; Opred. rast. Sr. Azii [Key to Plants of Mid. Asia] 6 (1981) 234.

—**Ic.:** Boriss. l.c. fig. 10.

Described from Pamir. Type in St.-Petersburg (LE).

Along arid valleys and slopes, on debris cones and pebble beds, in belts of alpine deserts and cryophilic barren cushions.

IIIC. Pamir ?

General distribution: endemic in East. Pamir.

Note. Reported from Kyzyl-Rabat region and many other sites adjoining Tajik East. Pamir. Its report is likely in Chinese East. Pamir.

*A. **alitschuri** O. Fedtsch. in Acta Horti Petrop. 23 (1904) 108; Lipsky in Acta Horti Petrop. 26 (1907) 262; O. et B. Fedtsch. Konsp. fl. Turk. 2 (1909) 233; Boriss. in Fl. Tadzhik. 5 (1937) 415; Gontsch. and Boriss. in Fl. SSSR, 12 (1946) 543; Ikonn. Opred. rast. Pam. [Key to Plants of Pamir] (1963) 165; Nasir et Ali, Fl. West Pakist. No. 100 (1977) 210; Fl. Tadzhik. 6 (1981) 251; Opred. rast. Sr. Azii [Key to Plants of Mid. Asia] 6 (1981) 234.

Described from East. Pamir. Type in St.-Petersburg (LE).

On rocky-rubbly and melkozem slopes of mountains, arid moraines, in steppes and alpine deserts, along banks of lakes at 3300–4300 m.

Report possible from:

IIIC. Pamir ? (reported from adjoining East. Pamir territory: Kashka-Kara-Su; Kuisa area; Alichur river valley; Kara-Dyumer lake and others).

General distribution: East. Pamir, Pakistan.

*A. **arganaticus** Bunge ex Regel et Herd. in Bull. Soc. Natur. Moscou, 39, 3 (1866) 23, incl. var. *campylanthus* Bunge; id. Gen. Astrag. Sp. Geront. 1 (1868) 110 and 2 (1869) 190; id. Astrag. Turk. (1880) 266; Lipsky in Acta Horti Petrop. 26 (1907) 255; O. et B. Fedtsch. Konsp. fl. Turk. 2 (1909) 222; Gontsch. and Boriss. in Fl. SSSR, 12 (1946) 541; Fl. Kazakhst. 5 (1961) 214; Bait. Astrag. Tyan'-Shanya (1977) 66; Opred. rast. Sr. Azii [Key to Plants of Mid. Asia] 6 (1981) 233.

Described from East. Kazakhstan (Arganaty mountains). Type in St.-Petersburg (LE).

On rocky slopes of low mountains, rocky montane trails, more rarely on pebble beds and sand along banks of desert rivers.

Reported from Altan-Emel' region adjoining Sinkiang territory and its report is likely in Jung. Ala Tau?, Balkh.-Alak. ?

General distribution: Fore Balkh. (Arganaty hills), Jung.-Tarb. (Jung. Ala Tau).

Section 24 (68). **Chomutoviana** B. Fedtsch. emend Sancz.

218. **A. wensuensis** S.B. Ho in Bull. Bot. Research, 3, 1 (1983) 60. —**Ic.:** S.B. Ho l.c.: tab. 15, fig. 1–10.

Described from Sinkiang (Kashgar). Type in Beijing (PE).

On sand in river valleys.

IB. Kashgar: *Nor.* (Wensu Xian, Po-Cheng-Zi, Kuleikedali, 2100 m, May 13, 1978, No. 78412; leg. Chen Shao Yu—typus ! (PE), Baicheng Xian (Bai), Korgan, in valle rivuli, 2000 m, Sep. 6, 1958, No. 8219, leg. A.R. Lee et J.N. Zhu; ib. Muzati He, Tubiliqi, in valle rivuli sabulosis, 2400 m, May 28, 1978, No. 780131, leg. Exped. Toksun).

General distribution: endemic.

219. **A. saichanensis** Sancz. in J. Bot. (Leningrad) 59, 3 (1974) 366, Sanczir in Grub., Opred. rast. Mong. [Key to Plants of Mongolia] (1982)

162; Ulzij. in Tr. Inst. bot. AN MNR, 8 (1982) 33; Grub. in Novosti sist. vyssh. rast. 21 (1984) 207, p.p.

—**Ic.:** Grub., Opred. rast. Mong. [Key to Plants of Mongolia] (1982). Plate 84, fig. 385.

Described from Mongolia (Gobi Altay). Type in Ulan Bator (UBA), isotype in St.-Petersburg (LE).

On rubbly montane steppes, mountain trails and ridges.

IA. Mongolia: ***Mong. Alt.*** (2 km south-east of Tamchi somon on road to Tamchi-daban, intermontane valley, slope of ridge, July 16, 1947—Yun.; 20 km south-west of Bugat somon, Bugat-daba pass, steppe, Sep. 2, 1973—Isach. and Rachk.; Uertiin-khuren-ula mountains 20 km north-east of Bugat somon and 5 km from pass, 2543 m, July 5, 1984—Kam. and Dariima), ***Gobi-Alt.*** (Barun-Saikhan mountain range, Bayan-Dalai-khotos area, in intermontane valley along summits of hillocks, desert steppe, No. 65, Aug. 4, 1971—Sanczir, typus !; Artsa-Bogdo, summit of mountain range, 2250 m, steppe, July 5, 1973—Isach. and Rachk.).

General distribution: endemic.

Note. Plant from Nemegetu-nuru mountain range (on main summit, 2747 m, on southern rocky slope, No. 5489, Aug. 8, 1948—Grub.) was wrongly identified by Ch. Sanczir as *A. saichanensis* Sancz. and included by him in "Opred. sosud. rast. Mongolii" [Key to Vascular Plants of Mongolia] of V.I. Grubov: in fact, it is *Oxytropis* sp.

220. **A. chomutovii** B. Fedtsch. in Bull. Herb. Boiss. 2, 7, 11 (1899) 826; O. et B. Fedtsch. Konsp. fl. Turk. 2 (1909) 228; Fl. Tadzhik. 5 (1937) 429; Gontsch. in Fl. SSSR, 12 (1946) 593, excl. syn *A. enaphae* B. Fedtsch. et N. Basil.; Fl. Kirgiz. 7 (1957) 311, p.p.; Ikonn. Opred. rast. Pam. [Key to Plants of Pamir] (1963) 162; Bait. Astrag. Tyan'-Shanya (1977) 71; Fl. Tadzhik. 6 (1981) 269; Opred. rast. Sr. Azii [Key to Plants of Mid. Asia] 6 (1981) 229; S.B. Ho in Bull. Bot. Research, 3, 1 (1983) 60; C.Y. Yang in Claves pl. Xinjiang, 3 (1985) 160.

—**Ic.:** Fl. SSSR, 12, Plate 35, fig. 2; Fl. Tadzhik. 6 (1981) Plate 44, fig. 19–24.

Described from Pamir. Type in St.-Petersburg (LE).

On rocky and rubbly slopes, trails, pebble beds, debris cones in alpine deserts, at 3000–4000 m.

IB. Kashgar: *Nor.* (south. slope of Ui-tal gorge, on pebble bed along brook, June 1, 1889—Rob.).

IIA. Junggar: ***Tien Shan*** (declivites australis jugi montium Tianschan. Aufsteig von Schauhle zum Karabura Pass, June 22, 1903—Merzb.; "west. part of East. Tien Shan"—S.B. Ho l.c.).

IIIC. Pamir (Muz-Tag-Ata foothill, along rock screes, July 20, 1909—Divn.; 42 km south of Bulgan-kul' upward along Sarykol valley, on road to Tashkurgan from Kashgar, alpine desert steppe, 3900 m, June 12, 1959—Yun. and I-f. Yuan'; "Tashkurgan"—C.Y. Yang l.c.).

General distribution: Cen. Tien Shan, East. Pamir.

*__A. tekessicus__ Bajt. in Not. Syst. (Alma Ata) 6 (1969) 33; Bait. Astrag. Tyan'-Shanya (1977) 71; Opred. rast. Sr. Azii [Key to Plants of Mid. Asia] 6 (1981) 229.—*A. chomutovii* auct. non B. Fedtsch.: B. Nikit. in Fl. Kirgiz. 7 (1957) 311, p.p.

Described from Kirghizstan (Tersk Ala Tau). Type in Alma Ata (AA).

On limestone, rubbly-melkozem and clayey slopes in upper belt of hills.

Report likely from:

IIA. Junggar: ***Tien Shan.***

General distribution: Cen. Tien Shan; Mid. Asia (Transalay mountain range).

221. **A. caudiculosus** Kom. in Feddes Repert. 13 (1915) 230.

Described from Sinkiang (South. Kashgar). Type in St.-Petersburg (LE). Map. 9.

IB. Kashgar: ***West.*** (Kunlun, nor. slope, 22 km beyond Pusa on Tibet highway to Kyude and Ak-këz-daban, wormwood desert, May 31; same locality, Ak-këz-daban pass, 3280 m, wormwood desert along nor.-east. slope around pass, May 31—1959, Yun. and I-f. Yuan'), ***South.*** (nor. slope of Russky mountain range, 2438–2743 m, second half of March and April, 1885; southward road from Cherchen to Achan oasis, 2800 m, May 9; Kerii mountain range, Ui-Bulak river, May 19, typus !, 1885—Przew.; Kyuk-egil', July 9; Nura river, 2743 m, July 23—1885, Przew.).

IIIB. Tibet: ***Chang Tang*** (nor. slope of Russky mountain range, Bain-bulak area, on Aksu river, in meadows along gorges, 3810 m, July 1; same locality, upper Aksu river, 3353–3658 m, July 2; same locality, Karasai village, 3048 m, on aeolian soil, July 8—1890, Rob.; nor. slope, Keria river basin, 4 km south of Polur settlement, 3000 m, montane desert along ridge, May 11; 3–4 km south of Polur, aeolian ridges, wormwood steppified desert, 2600–2800 m, May 11—1959, Yun. and I-f. Yuan').

General distribution: endemic.

222. **A. roborowskyi** Ulzij. Novosti sist. vyssh. rast. 33 (2001) 138.

Described from Qinghai (Nanshan). Type in St.-Petersburg (LE). Map 7.

In arid montane steppes and along clayey banks of rivers at 3300–4300 m.

IIIA. Qinghai: ***Nanshan*** (Humboldt mountain range, nor. slope, Ulan-bulak spring, 3505 m [11500 ft], on clay, June 17; same locality, Ulan-daban area, 3353–3658 m [11000–12000 ft], arid steppe, and Ritter mountain range, Baga-Khaitym river, June 23—1894, Rob., typus !; Ritter mountain range, east. continuation of Ikhe-daban, along arid steppe, 3658 m, June 27, 1894—Rob.).

IIIB. Tibet: ***Weitzan*** (Dzhagyn-gol river, 4267 m., on clayey and clayey-sandy cliffs on both banks of river, July 4, 1900—Lad.).

General distribution: endemic.

223. **A. divnogorskajae** Ulzij., Novosti sist. vyssh. rast. 33 (2001). 140.

Described from Sinkiang (Pamir). Type in St.-Petersburg (LE). Map 7.

On arid, rubbly and clayey slopes of desert-steppe belt of mountains.

IB. Kashgar: ***Nor.*** (Muzart river valley 7–8 km beyond its exit from gorge in Baisk basin, steppe belt, along rubble slopes, Sep. 7; same locality, 2–3 km before Sazlik area along road to Oi-Terek, along lateral debris cone, among rocks, Sep. 9; same locality, Oi-Terek area, 1 km downstream, lateral old moraine, 2350 m, steppified desert, sep. 11—1958, Yun. and I-f. Yuan'), ***West.*** (Sarykol' mountain range, Bostan-Terek locality, July 11, 1929 —Pop.; King-tau mountain range, nor. Slope 1 km nor. of Kosh-Kulak settlement, foothill, steppe belt, June 10; same locality, 2 km nor. of Kosh-Kulak settlement, steppe belt, 2450 m, gorge in hillocks, along hill trail, June 10—1959, Yun. and I-f. Yuan').

IIIC. Pamir (Taret pass near Pasrabat, along clayey-rocky slopes, June 19–20; Ulug-tuz gorge in Charlym river basin, along arid clayey slopes, No. 311, June 29—1909, Divn., typus !).

General distribution: endemic.

224. **A. arnoldii** Hemsl. et Pearson in J. Linn. Soc. Bot. London, 35, (1902) 172; S.B. Ho in Bull. Bot. Research, 3, 1 (1983) 61; P.C. Li et Ni in Fl. Xizang, 2 (1985) 805.—*A. culcitiformis* P.C. Li et Ni in Acta Phytotax. sin. 17 (1979) 106.

—**Ic.:** Fl. Xizang, 2, tab. 259, fig. 1–9.

Described from Tibet (Chang Tang). Type in London (LINN).

In alpine meadows, along river banks and alpine rocky slopes at 4500–5100 m.

IIIA. Qinghai: ***Nanshan*** (West. "Qinghai"—S.B. Ho l.c.; "South-East. Qinghai"—Fl. Xizang l.c.).

IIIB. Tibet: ***Chang Tang*** (nor. Tibet, 1884—Przew.; nor. slope of Russky mountain range, upper course of Aksu river, 3658 m [12000 ft], along pebbles on brooks, July 1, 1890—Rob.; without locality, 17500 ft, Deasy and Pike (1896) No. 800, 810—typus !, 17500 ft, Thorold (1896) No. 12a, 37; Ban'ge, 5100 m, No. 9499, June 23; same locality, 5100 m, No. 9687, Aug. 2—1976, Qinghai-Tibet expedition [PE]—typus *A. culcitiformis* P.C. Li et Ni, "Tibetan upland"—S.B. Ho l.c.; "Ban'ge, Shuankhu, Getszi, Zhitu"—Fl. Xizang l.c.), ***South.*** ("Pulan'"—Fl. Xizang l.c.).

General distribution: endemic.

225. **A. monticola** P.C. Li et Ni in Acta Phytotax. sin 17, 2 (1979) 105; S.B. Ho in Bull. Bot. Research, 3, 1 (1983) 61; Fl. Xizang, 2 (1985) 807.

—**Ic.:** P.C. Li et Ni (1979) l.c. tab. 3, fig. 1–9; Fl. Xizang, 2 (1985) tab. 260, fig. 1–9.

Described from Tibet (Zhongba). Type in Beijing (PE).

On rocky and rubbly slopes and alpine meadows at 4200–5000 m.

IIIB. Tibet: ***South*** (Zhongba, alt. 4700 m, Aug. 17, 1975, Chinghai-Tibetan Complex Exp., No. 6767—typus ! (PE); "Chzhunba"—P.C. Li et Ni (1985) l.c.).

IIIC. Pamir (Ulug-Rabat pass, on road to Tashkurgan from Kashgar, near Muztag-Ata peak, 4200 m, alpine wormwood steppe, June 12, 1959—Yun. and I-f. Yuan').

General distribution: Himalayas (east.).

Section 25 (69). **Corethrum** Bunge

226. **A. nematodes** Bunge ex Boiss. Fl. Or. 2 (1872) 425; Bunge in Acta Horti Petrop. 3 (1874) 105; id. Astrag. Turk. (1880) 273; O. et B. Fedtsch. Konsp. fl. Turk. 2 (1909) 225; Fl. Tadzhik. 5 (1937) 424; Gontsch. and Boriss. in Fl. SSSR, 12 (1946) 467; Fl. Kirgiz. 7 (1957) 290; Fl. Kazakhst. 5 (1961) 203; Fl. Tadzhik. 6 (1981) 245; Opred. rast. Sr. Azii [Key to Plants of Mid. Asia] 6 (1981) 278; S.B. Ho in Bull. Bot. Research, 3, 1 (1983) 41; C.Y. Yang in Claves pl. Xinjiang, 3 (1985) 155.

—**Ic.:** Fl. SSSR, 12, Plate 32, fig. 2; Fl. Kazakhst. 5, Plate 26, fig. 2; Fl. Tadzhik. (1981) Plate 40, fig. 20–25.

Described from Mid. Asia (Mogoltau hills). Type in St.-Petersburg (LE).

On rubbly-rocky slopes, pebble beds, in rock fissures, on plains up to lower mountain belt at 500–2000 m.

IB. Kashgar: ***Nor.*** ("Artush, Chemo"—S.B. Ho l.c.; "South. foothill of Tien Shan"—C.Y. Yang l.c.), ***West.*** ("Uchi [Ulugchat]"—S.B. Ho l.c.).

General distribution: Mid. Asia (West. Tien Shan).

227. **A. kronenburgii** B. Fedtsch. ex Kneuck. in Allg. Bot. Zeitsch. 11, 10 (1905) 171; O. et B. Fedtsch. Konsp. fl. Turk. 2 (1909) 225; Gontsch. and Boriss. in Fl. SSSR, 12 (1946) 464; Fl. Kirgiz. 7 (1957) 289; Fl. Kazakhst. 5 (1961) 202; Bait. Astrag. Tyan'-Shanya (1977) 61; Opred. Rast. Sr. Azii [Key to Plants of Mid. Asia] 6 (1981) 278.—*A. kujukensis* B. Fedtsch. in Acta Horti Petrop. 24 (1905) 225; Lipsky in Acta Horti Petrop. 26 (1907) 225.—*A. kronenburgii* var. *chaidamuensis* S.B. Ho in Bull. Bot. Research, 3, 1 (1983) 42.

—**Ic.:** Fl. Kazakhst. 5, Plate 26, fig. 5.

Described from Mid. Asia (Alay mountain range). Type in St.-Petersburg (LE).

On rocky and rubbly slopes of mountains, in scrubs, lower mountain belt.

IA. Mongolia: ***Khesi*** ("Dunhuang ad Aksay, Aug. 2, 1958, No. 380, leg. Inst. Psamm. Lanzh. Ac. Sin."—S.B. Ho l.c.).

IC. Qaidam: ***Plain*** ("Haixi Mongolzu Zangzu Kazakzu Zizhizhou, Delingha, in alluviis, alt. 3290 m, July 21, 1959, No. 805, leg. Exped. Gansu et Qinghai Ac. Sin.—typus var. *chaidamuensis* S.B. Ho ([NWBI], non vidi); ib. Dachaidam, Baligou, in fissuris rupium ad limen, alt. 3700 m, July 15, 1959, No. 307, leg. id."—S.B. Ho l.c.).

General distribution: Nor. Tien Shan; Mid. Asia (Pamiro-Alay).

Note. We had no possibility to examine the type of above variety. It probably belongs to *A. hesiensis* Ulzij. and not *A. kronenburgii*.

228. **A. dschangartensis** Sumn. in Animadv. Herb. Univ. Tomsk, 1–2 (1935) 5; Gontsch. and Boriss. in Fl. SSSR, 12 (1946) 466; Fl. Kirgiz. 7 (1957) 289; Bait. Astrag. Tyan'-Shanya (1977) 62; Opred. rast. Sr. Azii

[Key to Plants of Mid. Asia] 6 (1981) 278; S.B. Ho in Bull. Bot. Research, 3, 1 (1983) 42; C.Y. Yang in Claves pl. Xinjiang, 3 (1985) 155.

Described from Kirghizstan (Cen. Tien Shan). Type in St.-Petersburg (LE).

On rocky slopes and coastal pebble beds.

IB. Kashgar: ***Nor.*** ("Aksu"—S.B. Ho l.c.), ***West.*** ("Akto, Echen, Kargalyk"—S.B. Ho l.c.), ***South.*** ("Yutyan town [Keriya]"—S.B. Ho l.c.).

IIA. Junggar: ***Tarb.*** ("Dzhamur"—C.Y. Yang l.c.).

General distribution: Cen. Tien Shan (valley of Dzhangart, Sarydzhas, Kaindy, Irtash rivers).

229. **A. semenovii** Bunge in Bull. Soc. Natur. Moscou, 39, 3 (1866) 22; id. Gen. Astrag. Sp. Geront. 1 (1868) 98 and 2 (1869) 171; id. Astrag. Turk. (1880) 272; Lipsky in Acta Horti Petrop. 26 (1907) 270; O. et B. Fedtsch. Konsp. fl. Turk. 2 (1909) 225, quoad pl. e Maj-Tube; Gontsch. and Boriss. in Fl. SSSR, 12 (1946) 465; Fl. Kazakhst. 5 (1961) 203; Bait. Astrag. Tyan'-Shanya (1977) 61; Opred. rast. Sr. Azii [Key to Plants of Mid. Asia] 6 (1981) 278; C.Y. Yang in Claves pl. Xinjiang, 3 (1985) 155; Golosk. Fl. Jung. Ala Tau (1984) 73.

—**Ic.:** Fl. Kazakhst. 5, Plate 26, fig. 3.

Described from East. Kazakhstan (Ili river valley). Type in St.-Petersburg (LE).

IIA. Junggar: ***Jung. Ala Tau*** (?) ***Tien Shan*** (?), ***Dzhark.*** ("Ili river valley"—C.Y. Yang l.c.).

General distribution: Jung.-Tarb. (Jung. Ala Tau), Nor. Tien Shan (Ketmen'-Tau).

*__A. schachdarinus__ Lipsky in Acta Horti Petrop. 26, 2 (1907) 181 and 271 (emend.): O. et B. Fedtsch. Konsp. fl. Turk. 2 (1909) 225; Fl. Tadzhik. 5 (1937) 425; Gontsch. and Boriss. in Fl. SSSR, 12 (1946) 466; Podlech et Deml in Mitt. Bot. Staatssamml. München ? 13 (1977) 442; Ikonn. Opred. rast. Badakhsh. [Key to Plants of Badakhshan] (1979) 230; Fl. Tadzhik. 6 (1981) 244; Opred. rast. Sr. Azii [Key to Plants of Mid. Asia] 6 (1981) 208.

—**Ic.:** Fl. Tadzhik. 5 (1937) Plate 49 and 6 (1981) Plate 40, fig. 13–19.

Described from Mid. Asia (Badakhshan). Type in St.-Petersburg (LE).

On rocky and rubbly-melkozem slopes, riverine pebble beds, on sand among boulders, in upper belt of mountains, at 1800–4200 m.

Reports possible from:

IIIC. Pamir (reported from Tajikistan regions adjoining Pamir: Tanymas and Kaindy river).

General distribution: Mid. Asia (Pamiro-Alay).

*A. **terektensis** Fisjun. in Fl. Kazakhst. 5 (1961) 491 and 201; Bait. Astrag. Tyan'-Shanya (1977) 60; Opred. rast. Sr. Azii [Key to Plants of Mid. Asia] 6 (1981) 277; Golosk. Fl. Dzhung. Alat. (1984) 73.

Described from East. Kazakhstan (Jung. Ala Tau). Type in Alma-Ata (AA).

On rubbly slopes.

Reports possible from:

IIA. Junggar: *Jung. Ala Tau* ? (reported so far only from a single site along Terekt river in Kazakhstan.

General distribution: endemic.

230. **A. pseudoscoparius** Gontsch. in Not. Syst. (Leningrad) 9 (1946) 134; Gontsch. and Boriss. in Fl. SSSR, 12 (1946) 462; Fl. Kirgiz. 7 (1957) 285; Opred. rast. Sr. Azii [Key to Plants of Mid. Asia] 6 (1981) 277; Fl. Tadzhik. 6 (1981) 241; S.B. Ho in Bull. Bot. Research, 3, 1 (1983) 42; C.Y. Yang in Claves pl. Xinjiang, 3 (1985) 156; Liou f. in Fl. desert Sin. 2 (1987) 270.

—**Ic.:** Fl. Tadzhik. 6, Plate 40, fig. 1–6.

Described from Mid. Asia (Pamiro-Alay). Type in St.-Petersburg (LE).

On rubbly and rocky slopes of mountains, on rocks, along river valleys in middle mountain belt, up to 4700 m.

IIA. Junggar: *Jung. Gobi* (nor. trail of East. Tien Shan 3 km east of bridge on Yantszikhai, on Manas-Shikho road, along gully, July 7, 1957—Yun. and I-f. Yuan'; "Savan: Shichan', Emo-shan' near Urumchi town"—S.B. Ho l.c.).

IIIA. Qinghai: *Amdo* ("Balekun"—Liou fil. l.c.).

General distribution: Mid. Asia (Pam.-Alay).

Note. The possibility of finding this species in Amdo territory (upper Huang He river, Balekun) appears, in our view, improbable.

231. **A. scoparius** Schrenk in Fisch. et Mey. Enum. pl. nov. 1 (1841) 82; Ledeb. Fl. Ross. 1, 3 (1843) 625; Bunge Gen. Astrag. Sp. Geront. 1 (1868) 98 and 2 (1869) 171; id. Astrag. Turk. (1880) 273; O. et B. Fedtsch. Konsp. fl. Turk. 2 (1909) 225, Gontsch. and Boriss. in Fl. SSSR, 12 (1946) 461; Grub. in Bot. mater. (Leningrad) 19 (1959) 544; Fl. Kazakhst. 5 (1961) 200; Bait. Astrag. Tyan'-Shanya (1977) 60; Opred. rast. Sr. Azii [Key to Plants of Mid. Asia] 6 (1981) 277; S.B. Ho in Bull. Bot. Research, 3, 1 (1983) 43; Golosk. Fl. Dzhung. Alat. (1984) 73; C.Y. Yang in Claves pl. Xinjiang, 3 (1985) 155; Fl. desert Sin. 2 (1987) 285.

—**Ic.:** Fl. Kazakhst. 5, Plate 28, fig. 4.

Described from East. Kazakhstan (Jung. Ala Tau). Type in St.-Petersburg (LE). Plate IV, fig. 2.

On rocky and rubbly slopes in lower mountain belt.

IB. Kashgar: ***South.*** (Russky mountain range, nor. foothill, Bostan-tograk river gorge, 2134–2743 m, on pebble, June 10, 1890—Rob.).

IIA. Junggar: ***Dzhark.*** (Aktyube, in Kul'dzha vicinity, 914 m, May 13; Piluchi in Kul'dzha region, Aug. 1877, A. Reg.; "Gunlyu, Inin"—S.B. Ho l.c.), ***Jung. Gobi*** (Gobi, in Kuku-Syrkhe hills, May 21, 1879—Przew.; rocky steppe west of Turkyul', June 15, 1877—Pot.; left bank of Manas river, uninundated terrace, May 28, 1954—Moiseenko; "Manas"—C.Y. Yang l.c.).

General distribution: Jung.-Tarb., Cen. Tien Shan.

232. **A. hesiensis** Ulzij., Novosti sist vyssh. rast. 33 (2001) 142.

Described from nor.-west. Gansu (Khesi corridor). Type in St.-Petersburg (LE). Map 8.

IA. Mongolia: ***Khesi*** (Bayan-gol river [tributary of Lonsyr river], June; Lonsyr river around Liyuan' town, 1888 m, June 2; valley of Sha-khe river, 1498 m, June 4—1886, Pot.; nor. foothill strip of Nanshan mountain range, pebbles, 1524–1829 m [5000–6000 ft], May 14, 1894—Rob., typus !; vicinity of Tszyutsyuan' town, No. 421, May 19, 1957—Kuan; Ninyanlu settlement 40 km nor. of Yunchan town, moist meadow in valley, July 1, 1958—Petr.).

IB. Qaidam: ***Plain*** (Qaidam, 1884—Przew.).

IIIA. Qinghai: ***Nanshan*** (Nanshan mountain range, Dankhe river, along coastal pebble beds and sand, July 5; Kuku-usu [Dankhe river tributary], Serik area, on arid clay with sand, 3658 m, June 4; nor. slope of Humboldt mountain range, Mogyndy-Bysyn area, 2438 m, on clay, July 23–1895, Rob.; Aksai 5 km southward, high nor. foothills of Alpyntag mountain range, near foothills, Aug. 2, 1958—Petr.).

General distribution: endemic.

Section 26 (70). **Hololeuce** Bunge (***Chlorosphaerus*** Bunge)

233. **A. angustissimus** Bunge Gen. Astrag. Sp. Geront. 1 (1868) 135 and 2 (1869) 232; id. Astrag. Turk. (1880) 312; id. in Acta Horti Petrop. 7 (1880) 373; O. et B. Fedtsch. Konsp. fl. Turk. 2 (1909) 225; Gontsch. and Boriss. in Fl. SSSR, 12 (1946) 464; Fl. Kirgiz. 7 (1957) 286; Fl. Kazakhst. 5 (1961) 201; Bait. Astrag. Tyan'-Shanya (1977) 61; Opred. rast. Sr. Azii [Key to Plants of Mid. Asia] 6 (1981) 280.—*A. oxypetalus* Bunge Astrag. Turk. (1880) 273.

Ic.: Fl. Kazakhst. 5. Plate 26, fig. 4.

Described from South. Junggar. Type in St.-Petersburg (LE). Plate V, fig. 3.

On clayey and rocky slopes, along river banks, in foothills and lower mountain belt.

IIA. Junggar: ***Dzhark.*** (Almaty gorge, 1219–1524 m, April 26—1878; between Piluchi and gorge, 914–1219 m, April 22; Sarybulak near Suidun, 1219–1829 m, April 22, 1879—A. Reg.).

General distribution: Jung.-Tarb. (Jung. Ala Tau), Nor. and Cen. Tien Shan (Akche-Tash mountain range.

234. **A. kuldshensis** Bunge in Acta Horti Petrop. 7 (1880) 374.

Described from Sinkiang (Kul'dzha). Type in St.-Petersburg (LE). Plate V, fig. 1. Map 5.

Evidently grows on mountain slopes.

IIA. Junggar: ***Dzhark.*** (Kuldscha, No. 354, 1876—Golicke, typus !; Sarybulak river on Suidun river, 1219–1829 m [4000–6000 ft], April 24, 1878—A. Reg.).

General distribution: endemic.

Section 27 (71). **Pseudorosei** Ulzij.

235. **A. pseudoroseus** Ulzij., Novosti sist. vyssh. rast. 33 (2001) 135.

Described from Sinkiang (Zaisan basin). Type in St.-Petersburg (LE). Map 1.

In arid montane steppes.

IIA. Junggar: ***Zaisan*** (arid slopes between Kholustu and Chenkur [Burchum]—Sap., typus !).

General distribution: endemic.

Section 28 (72). **Mixotricha** Ulzij.

236. **A. megalanthus** DC. Astrag. (1802) 165; id. Prodr. 2 (1825) 288; Ledeb. Fl. Alt. 1 (1831) 627; Bunge Gen. Astrag. Sp. Geront. 1 (1868) 116 and 2 (1869) 198; id. Astrag. Turk. (1880) 277; Kryl. Fl. Zap. Sib. 7 (1933) 1692; Gontsch. and Boriss. in Fl. SSSR, 12 (1946) 577; Opred. rast. Sr. Azii [Key to Plants of Mid. Asia] 6 (1981) 225.

—**Ic.:** DC. (1825) l.c. tab. 20.

Described from "Russia". Type in Geneva (G).

In steppe, on rocky and rubbly steppe slopes of foothills and hillocky areas.

IA. Mongolia: ***Cen. Khalkha*** (several finds, on road to Khara-Tologoi area from Mandalyn-Gobi area, June 9, 1909, No. 89; Irdynyn-gol—Sypsul', June 13, 1909, Napalkov and Czet.), ***East Mong.*** (several finds, 15 km nor. of Mandal-Gobi, rocky smoothed troughs, in feather grass steppe, June 5, 1949—Yun.), ***East. Gobi*** (Luus somon, Khatu-Tugrik area 75 km south-west of Mandal-Gobi, feather grass steppe, June 9, 1951—Kal.).

IIA. Junggar: ***Zaisan*** (Bugotar river, Altay upland, between Burchum and Kran (Burchum basin), June 11, 1903—Gr.-Grzh.).

General distribution: Fore Balkh. (Zaisan basin); West. Sib. (Alt.).

Note. Cen. Khalkha plants belong to distinct subspecies *A. megalanthus* subsp. *chalchaensis* Ulzij.

237. **A. testiculatus** Pall. Astrag. (1800) 82; Ledeb. Fl. Ross. 1, 3 (1843) 655, excl. syn. *A. lactiflorus*: Bunge Gen. Astrag. Sp. Geront. 1 (1868) 116 and 2 (1869) 197, excl. syn. *A. lactiflorus*: id. Astrag. Turk. (1880) 277, excl. syn. *A. lactiflorus*, id. in Acta Horti Petrop. 7 (1880) 376; O. et B. Fedtsch. Konsp. fl. Turk. 2 (1909) 226; Kryl. Fl. Zap. Sib. 7 (1933) 1689; Gontsch. and Boriss. in Fl. SSSR, 12 (1946) 578; Fl. Kirgiz.

7 (1957) 307; Fl. Kazakhst. 5 (1961) 232; Fl. Tadzhik. 6 (1981) 265; Opred. rast. Sr. Azii [Key to Plants of Mid. Asia] 6 (1981) 226; Golosk. Fl. Dzhung. Alat. (1984) 73; C.Y. Yang in Claves pl. Xinjiang, 3 (1985) 160.

—**Ic.:** Fl. SSSR, 12, Plate 38, fig. 2; Fl. Kazakhst. 5, Plate 31, fig. 2, sub. *A. heptopotamico;* Fl. Tadzhik. 6, Plate 44, fig. 7–12.

Described from Caspian deserts. Type in London (BM).

On rocky slopes of knolls in plain, on rocky-rubbly slopes in hills, in steppes, fringes of spruce forests; ascends up to middle mountain belt 1800–3600 m.

IIA. Junggar: ***Cis-Alt.*** ("Altay"—C.Y. Yang l.c.), ***Tarb.*** ("Saur"—C.Y. Yang l.c.).

General distribution: Aralo-Casp., Fore Balkh., Jung.-Tarb., Nor. Tien Shan; Europe (east.), Caucasus, Mid. Asia, West. Sib. (Alt., south), East. Sib. (Sayans), China (Altay).

238. **A. lactiflorus** Ledeb. Ic. pl. fl. Ross. 2 (1830) 5; Opred. rast. Sr. Azii [Key to Plants of Mid. Asia] 6 (1981) 225.—*A. poliotes* Bunge Gen. Astrag. Sp. Geront. 1 (1868) 116 and 2 (1869) 197; id. Astrag. Turk. (1880) 276; Kryl. Fl. Zap. Sib. 7 (1933) 1691; Gontsch. and Boriss. in Fl. SSSR, 12 (1946) 579; C.Y. Yang in Claves pl. Xinjiang, 3 (1985) 160.

—**Ic.:** Ledeb. (1830) l.c. tab. 103.

Described from East. Kazakhstan (Altay foothills). Type in St.-Petersburg (LE).

IIA. Junggar: ***Cis-Alt.*** ("Altay"—C.Y. Yang l.c.), ***Tarb.*** ("Saur"—C.Y. Yang l.c.).

General distribution: Fore Balkh., Jung.-Tarb.; West. Sib. (Altay).

Section 29 (73). **Scabriseta** R. Kam.

239. **A. scabrisetus** Bong. in Bong. et Mey. Verzeichniss Saissan-Nor Pfl. (1841) 26; Ledeb. Fl. Ross. 1, 3 (1843) 657; Bunge Gen. Astrag. Sp. Geront. 1 (1868) 115 and 2 (1869) 195; id. Astrag. Turk. (1880) 275; id. in Acta Horti Petrop. (1880) 375; O. et B. Fedtsch. Konsp. fl. Turk. 2 (1909) 226; Kryl. Fl. Zap. Sib. 7 (1933) 1687; Gontsch. and Boriss. in Fl. SSSR, 12 (1946) 592; Fl. Kazakhst. 5 (1961) 237; Bait. Astrag. Tyan'-Shanya (1977) 71; Gub. in Byul. Mosk. obshch. ispyt. prir., otd. biol. 87, 1 (1982) 127; S.B. Ho in Bull. Bot. Research, 3, 1 (1983) 58; Golosk. Fl. Dzhung. Alat. (1984) 73; C.Y. Yang in Claves pl. Xinjiang, 3 (1985) 158; Fl. desert. Sin. 2 (1987) 285.—*A. scabrisetus* var. *caulescens* Kar. et Kir. in Bull. Soc. Natur. Moscou, 15 (1842) 342.—*A. geerwusuensis* H.C. Fu in Fl. Intramong. 2 ed., 3 (1989) 671 and 285.

—**Ic.:** Fl. SSSR, 12, Plate 38, fig. 1; Fl. Kazakhst. 5, Plate 31, fig. 4; Fl. desert Sin. 2, tab. 100, fig. 19–23; Fl. Intramong. 3 (1989) tab. 111, fig. 1–6 (sub. nom. *A. geerwusuensis* H.C. Fu).

Described from East. Kazakhstan (Zaisan basin). Type in St.-Petersburg (LE).

On sand, sandy-rocky and rocky slopes, arid solonchaks and clayey sites.

IA. Mongolia: ***West. Gobi*** (40 km south-west of Shara-Khulsin-bulak, near Dzamyn-Bilgekhu post, Aug. 4, 1978—Gub. [MW]), ***Alash. Gobi.*** ("Alashanyouqi, Geerwusu, June 10, 1983, leg. Lei Xi-fing, No. 83067—typus !, *A. geerwusuensis* H.C. Fu [HIMC]").

IB. Kashgar: ***Nor.*** (Kei intermontane basin in Kyzyl-Su river upper courses, desert, along gullies, Sep. 1, 1958—Yun. and I-f. Yuan'), ***East.*** ("Alag-ul mountain range"— Liou fil. l.c.).

IIA. Junggar: ***Cis-Alt.*** (Ch. Irtysh river valley, Koksun mountain range, Uzun-bulak river, June 4, 1903—Gr.-Grzh.; "Qinhe"—S.B. Ho l.c., C.Y. Yang l.c.), ***Tien Shan*** ("Ili"—C.Y. Yang l.c.), ***Jung. Gobi*** (in Urumchi region on slope, No. 591, June 7, 1957—Kuan; alongside highway from Urumchi to Turfan, desert, No. 6009, May 29, 1958—A.R. Lee; left bank of Urungu river, Sulyugou area, 75 km from Shatszge state farm (on Khobuk-gol), along road to Dinsyan' desert, July 12, 1959—Yun. and I-f. Yuan'; "Tsitai, Fukhai, Kuitun"—S.B. Ho l.c.; ***Zaisan*** ("Burchum, Zimunai"—C.Y. Yang l.c.).

General distribution: Aralo-Casp., Fore Balkh.

240. **A. grubovii** Sancz. in J. Bot. (Bot. zh.) 59, 3 (1974) 367; Sanczir in Grub., Opred. rast. Mong. [Key to Plants of Mongolia] (1982) 163; Ulzij. in Tr. Inst. bot. AN MNR (1983) 181; Grub. in Bot. zh. 59 (1974) 367; Ulzij. and Gub. in Byul. Mosk. obshch. ispyt. prir., otd. biol. 92, 5 (1987) 116; H.C. Fu in Fl. Intramong. 2 ed., 3 (1989) 289; p.p.; F. Nemeth in Studia Bot. Hungarica, 21 (1989) 47, 45.—*A. alaschanensis* H.C. Fu in Fl. Intramong. 3 (1977) 288 and 203; Ulzij. and Gub. in Byul. Mosk. obshch. ispyt. prir., otd. biol. 92, 5 (1987) 111; S.B. Ho in Bull. Bot. Research, 3, 1, (1983) 60; Liou fil. in Fl. desert Sin. 2 (1987) 287.—*A. scabrisetus* Bong. var. *multijugus* Hand.-Mazz. in Oesterr. Bot. Zeitschr. 88 (1939) 303.—*A. dengkouensis* H.C. Fu nom. nov. in Fl. Intramong. 2 ed., 3 (1989) 290.

—**Ic.:** Fl. Intramong. 2 ed. 3 (1989) tab. 112, fig. 7–12 and tab. 114, fig. 6–11 and Fl. Intramong. 3 (1977) tab. 102, fig. 1–6 (sub nom. *A. alaschanensis*—Ic. bona); S.B. Ho l.c. tab. 14, fig. 1–9.

Described from Mongolia (East. Gobi). Type in Ulan Bator (UBA), isotype in St.-Petersburg (LE). Plate VII, fig. 1. Map 4.

On sandy-rocky, sandy, sand-covered and loosely-rubbly slopes of trails of hillocks in deserts and desert steppes.

IA. Mongolia: ***Mong. Alt.*** (south-east.: Khan-Taishiri mountain range, Dzhamtyr-daban pass from Beger-nur basin to Khalyun, sandy floor of gully, June 17; same locality, south. slope, upper Shine-usu (nor. of Khaliun somon), 2380–2450 m, steppe, June 19—1971, Grub., Ulzij. and Dariima; Ulyastai-gol river gorge, 10 km south-west of Bugat somon, along pebble beds, July 5, 1984—Kam. and Dariima; 60 km south of Tonkhil settlement near Tamchi-daba pass, July 9, 1984—Gub. [MW]), ***Depr. Lakes*** (Buyantu river, near Tsagan-burgas, arid river bed, Sep. 6, 1930—Bar.; south. fringe of Khara-Usu-nura basin near road to Khobdo desert, June 27, 1971; right bank of Khungui river, 7 km east of Ikhe-Margats-ula on road to Urgamal-somon, steppe, Aug. 18, 1972—Grub., Ulzij.

et al.; Mongol-els sandy desert, 40 km nor. of Khukh-Morit settlement on left bank of Dzabkhyn river, Aug. 21, 1984—Gub.; "plain semidesert on hills in northern foreground of Khobd city, July 28, 1986"—F. Nemeth l.c.), ***Val. Lakes*** (on rocky talus, on right bank of Tuin-gol river, July 9, 1893—Klem.), ***Gobi-Alt.*** (Bayan-Tsagan mountain range, Chulutu area, rocky slopes in upper belt of hills, May 23, 1938—Luk'yanov; Barun-Saikhan mountain range, nor. trail, south of Bulgan somon, desert steppe, June 13, 1971—Sanczir [UBA], same locality, submontane plain and trail, desert steppe, June 25, 1971, Sanczir—typus ! [UBA]; Shine-Zhinst-ula, Altain-Tsagan-khaalga gorge, on flanks of gullies, Sep. 7, 1979, Sanczir [UBA]), ***East. Gobi*** (on way to Urgu from Alashan, along road to Bulagin-urto area from Duten-tal area, June 5, 1909—Czet.; 1 km east of Dalan-Dzadagad town, solonchaklike meadow along brook, May–July 1939—Surmazhab; 12 km nor.-nor.-east of Dalan-Zadagad along road to Ulan-Bator, solonchak meadows, June 8, 1949—Yun.; 22 km nor.-east of Bulgan somon to Bayan-dzagu, June 8, 1971—Borissova, Bespalova et al.; at centre of Bulgan somon, under shade of plantations, June 25; Bayan-Dzag depression, solonchak lowland, Aug. 8, 1971—Tseple and Sanczir [UBA]; 95 km south-east of Mandal-Gobi town, Khudiin-Khuren-obo mountain, on slope of knoll, July 3, 1972—Guricheva and Rachk.; hillocky massif south-south-east of Khan-Bogdo somon 10 km nor.-west of Bosgony-khuduk collective, in ravine, July 20, 1974—Rachkov and Volk.; "Ulantsab: Darkhan-umu-myangan"—H.C. Fu l.c.), ***West. Gobi*** (between Atas-Bogdo mountain range and Maikhan-bulak, saxaul desert, Aug. 16, 1943—Yun.; south. bend of road toward Chonoin-bom area, rocky hillocky area, among rocks along slopes of knolls and on sand at foothill, Aug. 18; 8 km nor.-west of Chonoin-bom on road to Ekhiin-gol, rocky slopes of knolls, Aug. 19—1948, Grub.; Atas-Bogdo-ula 7 km nor. of Del-ula, No. 78, Aug. 3, 1978—Ogureeva, ridgy hillock 6 km south-east of Engeriin-us spring, rocky trail, desert, Aug. 6; hillocky area north of Bulgan-Khoshuny-nuru mountain range 22 km nor.-west of Dzamyn-Bilgekh-bulak on border road, sandy plain between knolls, Aug. 27—1979, Grub. et al.; 118 km nor. of Ekhiin-gol, floor of gullies, Sep. 6, 1979—Sanczir [UBA]; 12 km east of Altay settlement, hillocky area south of Adzhi-Bogdo mountain range, July 15, 1984—Gub. [MW], ***Alash Gobi*** (Bordzon-Gobi area, nor. trail and marginal hillocky area Khalzan-ula, desert, along gullies, June 18, 1949—Yun.; 80 km nor.-east of Min'tsin' town, vicinity of Baituai Tengeri village, at boundary with Minchi oasis, windblown sand, June 5; 20 km nor. of Bayan-Khoto town, submontane plain, June 11—1958, Petr.; vicinity of Taudokhu lake, June 3, 1959 [HIMC]; sands of "Tengeri, Badamzhiren, Denkou, Bayan-nur, Ulantsab and others"—H.C. Fu l.c.), ***Ordos*** ("Ikhe-Chzhao: Khubchin-els, Muu-us-els"—H.C. Fu l.c.), ***Khesi*** ("Khesi corridor"—Liou fil. l.c.).

IIA. Junggar: *Jung. Gobi* (Altay somon, Takhiin-us, May 31, 1968—Dovchin [UBA]; Ikhe-Alag-ula mountain along road to Altay somon [Bayan-Obo] from former Khairkhan somon, 18 km from gorge beginning, Khatsavchiin-bulak spring, sandy-rubbly trail, Aug. 20, 1979—Grub. et al.; hillocky area south of the extreme end of Khubchiin-nuru mountain range, Tukhumyn-khundei gorge, Aug. 2, 1984—Kam. and Dariima).

General distribution: endemic.

Section 30 (74). **Trachycercis** Bunge

241. **A. pseudotesticulatus** Sancz. ex Ulzij. in Bull. Soc. Natur. Moscou, ser. biol. 95, 2 (1990) 82.—*A. pseudotesticulatus* Sancz. in Grub. Opred. rast. Mong. [Key to Plants of Mongolia] (1982) 162, descr. ross. in clave; Grub. in Novosti sist. vyssh. rast. 21 (1984) 207.

Described from Mongolia (Mong. Altay). Type in St.-Petersburg (LE), isotype in Ulan Bator (UBA). Map 4.

On arid rubbly slopes in montane-steppe belt.

IA. Mongolia: ***Mong. Alt.*** (montane slope on Dzurkhe river, one of the summits of Tsagan-gol, sparse larch forest, July 30, 1898—Klem.; Khudzhirt somon on Sairyn-gol river, on standing moraine, July 25, 1947—Yun.; upper Bulgan river, valley of Ulaagchin river, on road to Khudzhirt, left bank 1 km before Khudzhirtyn-gol river estuary, July 3, 1971—Grub., Ulzij. and Dariima, typus !; Bayan-gol river, nor.-west. slope of Indert hill, July 23, 1984—Buyan-Orshikh [UBA]).

IIA. Junggar: ***Cis-Alt.*** (10 km nor. of Kok-Togai [Fuyun'], trough of pass, July 15, 1959 —Yun. and I-f. Yuan').

General distribution: endemic.

242. **A. salsugineus** Kar. et Kir. in Byull. Soc. Natur. Moscou, 15 (1842) 941; Bunge Gen. Astrag. Sp. Geront. 1 (1868) 116 and 2 (1869) 197; id. Astrag. Turk. (1880) 276; O. et B. Fedtsch. Konsp. fl. Turk. 2 (1909) 226; Gontsch. and Boriss. in Fl. SSSR, 12 (1946) 582; Fl. Kazakhst. 5 (1961) 235; Bait. Astrag. Tyan'-Shanya (1977) 70; Opred. rast. Sr. Azii [Key to Plants of Mid. Asia] 6 (1981) 226.—*A. salsugineus* var. *multijugus* S.B. Ho in Bull. Bot. research, 3, 1 (1983) 52; H.C. Fu in Fl. Intramong. 2 ed., 3 (1989) 293.—*A. grubovii* Sancz. var. *angustifolia* H.C. Fu l.c. 671 and 289.

—**Ic.:** Fl. Intramong. 2 ed., 3 (1989) tab. 114, fig. 1–5 and tab. 112, fig. 13.

Described from East. Kazakhstan. Type in St.-Petersburg (LE).

On clayey, mostly solonetzic soils, sand along banks of brooks and lakes, near wells, in desert zone.

IA. Mongolia: ***East. Gobi*** ("Ulantsab: Darkhan-Mu-myangan"—H.C. Fu l.c.).

General distribution: Aralo-Casp., Fore Balkh.; Mid. Asia.

243. **A. junatovii** Sancz. in J. Bot. URSS (Bot. zh.) 59, 3 (1974) 368; Sanczir in Grub. Opred. rast. Mong. [Key to Plants of Mongolia] (1982) 163; Ulzij. in Tr. Inst. bot. AN MNR, 8 (1982) 35; Grub. in Novosti sist. vyssh. rast. 21 (1984) 207; Ulzij. and Gub. in Byul. Mask. obshch. ispyt. prir., otd. biol. 92, 5 (1987) 117.

—**Ic.:** Grub. Opred. rast. Mong. [Key to Plants of Mongolia], Plate 83, fig. 383.

Described from Mongolia (Gobi Altay). Type in Ulan Bator (UBA), isotype in St.-Petersburg (LE). Map 9.

In sandy and gravelly-clayey desert steppes and deserts on sandy-pebbly terraces and along flat bottoms of Gobi depressions.

IA. Mongolia: ***Gobi-Alt.*** (in sand dunes 25–30 km west of Bayan-Tukhum area, Sep. 1, 1931—Ik.-Gal.; 5 km west of Nomgon somon, sandy steppe, April 27, 1941—Yun.; nor. trail of Barun-Saikhan mountain range, red-coloured formations in Bulgan depression, desert steppe, June 13, 1971, Sanczir—typus !; Zhinst-ula mountain, 15 km south of Shine-zhinst settlement, July 4, 1979—Gub. [MW]; 10 km south of Bayan-Dalai somon, sand, July 29, 1988—F. Nemeth), ***East. Gobi*** (vicinity of Khoir-Ul'dzeitu, May 28, 1929—Kondrat'ev; Khan-Bogdo somon, Khoir-Uldzeitu area near Khutag-ula, desert steppe, June 25, 1930—Kuznetsov; 16 km nor.-east of Sain-Shanda town on road to Baishintu,

May 14, 1940—Shubin; slope of Kholbo-Obo hillock toward Uidzengin-toirim lowland, desert steppe, June 2; Mandal-Obo, 37 km south-west of Khul-Khairkhan mountain range, plain along left bank of Ongiin-gol, desert, May 9—1941, Yun.; Bayan-Dzak area, Gobi bed cliffs, Sep. 5, 1950—Lav. and Yun.; Khutag-Ula mountain range, July 10, 1982—Gub. [MW]), ***Alash. Gobi*** (Dyn-Yuan'-in, on sand, April 16; Alashan mountain range, Tsubur-gan-gola gorge, April 30—1908; Tengeri sand, Ulan-Sai area, in sand, No. 3; on way to Urgu from Alashan, Shara-burdu area, on sandy plain, May 5—1909; Czet.; Sultan-khoolai basin, Tyrmis-khuduk collective, on desert sand, April 14, 1926—Glag.; 6 km nor.-west of Boso-Khuduk well, thin sand and slopes of hillock covered with sand, June 14, Bortszon-Gobi, nor. slope of valley, thin sand, June 17—1949, Yun.; "nor. part of Bayan-nur"—H.C. Fu l.c.).

General distribution: endemic.

244. **A. pseudoscaberrimus** Wang et Tang ex S.B. Ho in Bull. Bot. Research, 3, 1 (1983) 57; Liou fil. in fl. desert Sin. 2 (1987) 288; Wang et Tang in Ill. treatm. princip. pl. China, Legum. (1955) 383, nom. nud.—*A. grubovii* auct. non Sancz.: Fl. Intramong. 2 ed. 3 (1989) 289, p. min. p.

—**Ic.:** S.B. Ho l.c., tab. 12, fig. 1–7; Fl. desert Sin. 2, tab. 101, fig. 15–21.

Described from Inner Mongolia (Alash. Gobi). Type in Beijing (PE). Map 4.

On high sandy-pebbly terraces and in gullies.

IA. Mongolia: ***Alash. Gobi*** (Wulanwusu, alt. 1500 m, May 26, 1931, No. 2085, leg. T. N. Liou—typus ! [PE], S.B. Ho l.c., non vidi; Tengeri sand, "Ulan-bukha and Badamzhireng-els sands"—Liou fil. l.c.), ***Ordos*** ("Muu-us sand"—Liou fil. l.c.), ***Khesi*** (vicinity of Tszyutsyuan' town, No. 423, May 19; same locality, Gaotai town, No. 409, June 18—1957, Kuan; 30 km south-east of Min'tsin town, vicinity of Suvushan' village, sandy-pebbly terrace, July 3; Yuimin' 55 km west of Tazyutsyuan', arid beds, Aug. 6—1958, Petr.).

IIA. Junggar: ***Jung. Gobi*** ("Junggar basin"—Liou fil. l.c.).

General distribution: endemic.

Note. Liou (Liou fil.) cites the distribution range of this species in Junggar. We could not find corresponding collections.

245. **A. scaberrimus** Bunge Enum. Pl. China Bor. (1833) 17; id. in Mém. Sav. Etrang. Ac. Sci. Petersb. 2 (1835) 91; id. Gen. Astrag. Sp. Geront. 1 (1868) 166 and 2 (1869) 197; Ledeb. Fl. Ross. 1 (1842) 649; Forbes and Hemsl. in J. Linn. Soc. Bot. 23 (1887) 166; Hand.-Mazz. Symb. Sin. 7 (1933) 558; Peter-Stib. in Acta Horti Gotoburg, 12 (1937–38) 66; Kitag. Lin. Fl. Mansh. (1939) 281; Gontsch. and Boriss. in Fl. SSSR, 12 (1946) 586; Boriss. in Fl. Zabaik. 6 (1954) 587; Grub. Konsp. fl. MNR (1955) 186; Wang and Tang in Ill. treatm. princip. pl. China, Legum. (1955) 382; M. Pop. Fl. Sr. Sib. 1 (1957) 335; Ic. Cormoph. Sin. 2 (1972) 417; Fl. Pl. herb. Chinae bor.-or. 5 (1976) 101; Fl. Intramong. 3 (1977) 208; Fl. Tsentr. Sib. 2 (1979) 604; Sanczir in Grub., Opred. rast. Mong. [Key to Plants of Mongolia] (1982) 163; Ulzij. in Tr. Inst. bot. AN MNR, 8 (1982) 34; S.B. Ho in Bull. Bot. Research, 3, 1 (1983) 52; Liou fil. in Fl. desert

Sin. 2 (1987) 288; H.C. Fu in Fl. Intramong. 3 (1989) 283.—*A. giraldianus* Ulbr. in Bot. Jahrb. 36, Beibl. 82 (1905) 64.—*A. harmsii* Ulbr. l.c. (1905) 63.

—**Ic.:** Wang and Tang (1955) l.c. fig. 368; Ic. Cormoph. Sin. 2, fig. 2563; Fl. Intramong. 3, tab. 103; fig. 8–15 and 2 ed., 3, 110, fig. 1–6; Grub. Opred. rast. Mong. [Key to Plants of Mongolia] (1982) Plate 85, fig. 391, Fl. desert Sin. (1987) tab. 101. fig. 8–14.

Described from East. Siberia (Transbaikal). Type in Paris (P). Plate VII, fig. 2.

On rubbly and rocky slopes of mountains in steppes, on rocks, along pebble beds on banks of saline lakes and on solonetzic steppes.

IA. Mongolia: ***Cen. Khalkha*** (not far from Khabyr-nor lake, on steppe, June 19, 1893; 4 versts (1 verst = 1.067 km) before Chin-Tologoi mountains near well, among pea shrubs, May 19, 1894; Bayan-khuduk well in Darkhan-ula, on slopes, Aug. 12, 1897—Klem.; vicinity of Ikhe-Tukhum-nur lake, Uber-Bulgain-ama trough, June 1926—Zam.; steppe near Khara-Nyutu [Khara-Nuden] urton, Sep. 4, 1926—Ik.-Gal. and Prokhanov; Dalan-Zhargalan somon, 507 km east of Choiren-ula, steppe, Aug. 22, 1940—Yun.; 70 km south-east of Undurkhan, Khaya-Ulan-nur lake, chee grass thickets, June 20, 1971—Dashnyam, Isach. et al.; Zorgol-Khairkhan-ula mountain, near foothill, June 9 [UBA]; Ara-Undzhul mountain, 30 km nor. of Undzhul somon, steppe, June 22; 7 km nor. of Undzhul somon, Senzhit-khuduk well, July 4—1974, Dariima [UBA]; 80 km south-south-east of Undurkhan town, Zaan-shire mountain, June 19, 1987—Budantsev, Ganbold et al.), ***East. Mong.*** (Muni-ula mountains, April–May 1872—Przew.; steppe between Bain-nur and Khuntu-nur lakes, June 21, 1899—Poch. and Sold.; nor.-east. fringe of Buir-nur lake, near its confluence with Khalkhin-gol river, sandy steppe, May 9; nor.-west. fringe of Zodol-Khan-ula hills, steppe, May 14; 10 km west of Yugodzyr, slopes of gentle ridges, steppe, May 14; nor.-west. fringe of Ongon-elesu sand, Derisin-khuduk, along basalt palteau cliff, May 17—1944, Yun.; nor.-west. extremity of Ongon-elesu sand, Derisin-khuduk, along basalt plateau cliff, May 17—1944, Yun.; Matad somon 70 km south-east of Choibalsan town, steppe plain, June 14; same locality, on road to Tamtsar, June 5—1954; 2 km nor. of Choibalsan somon centre, slopes of hillocks, May 26, 1958—Yun.; Manchuria station, Beishan' mountains, No. 818, June 23, 1951—Sh. Li. Dariganga somon, Khulgaryn-guu, Aug. 3, 1967—Gombozhav [UBA]; Ongon-Elis sand, near Khaya-khuduk well on Baishintu-Dariganga road, between sand ridges, Aug. 7, 1970—Grub., Ulzij. et al.; Gangyn-Tsagan-Obo mountain (1530 m) 23 km west of Dariganga, steppe near foothill, July 7, 1971—Dashnyam. Karam. et al.; 60 km south-east of Mun-khan settlement on road to Barun-Urt, June 12, 1980—Gub. [MW]; 25 km east of Matad settlement, Matadyn-tuur area, June 22; 10 km west of Buir-nur lake, July 20; Choibalsan town near fuelling point, July 21; coast of Khukh-nur lake, July 22—1987, Gub., Kam. et al.; "Shilin-gol, Ulan-khada, Khukh-khoto"—H.C. Fu l.c.), ***East. Gobi*** (Khutag-ula mountain range, on slope, 1300 m, July 10, 1982—Gub.; "Ulantsab, nor. part of Bayan-nur"—H.C. Fu l.c.), ***Alash. Gobi*** (Tsokto-kure temple, 1524 m, Sep. 25, 1901—Lad.); ***Ordos*** (on right bank of Huang He river facing Khekou, valley at Tsaidemin-Chzhao monastery, 966 m, Aug. 8, 1884—Przew.; "IKe-Chzhao"—H.C. Fu l.c.; Liou fil. l.c.), ***Khesi*** ("Gansu"—Liou fil. l.c.).

IIIA. Qinghai: ***Nanshan*** (Tsagan-daban pass, upper part of Bayan-gol river valley, tributary of Lonsyr river [Naiman-gol], 1888 m, June 1—1886, Pot.), ***Amdo*** (upper course of Huang He river, 2896–3353 m, May 8; valley of Churmyn river, 2743–2896 m, May 14—1880, Przew.; valley of Dzhanba river [Itel'-gol], June 1; San-chuan' river basin on left bank of Yellow river, April 2; San-chuan' on south. slopes of mountains, April 7; same locality, on arid loessial soil, April 8; valley of Dzhanba river, April 13 and 15; valley of

San-chaun' river and vicinity of valleys of Gyangyn, Dzhanba and other rivers, April, 15; valley of Badzhou-gol river, in Lanzhe-fu region, April 17; vicinity of Gumbum monastery, 2637 m, in Nan'-Chun'-kho river valley, May 2; Nurun-Dzhanba river, May 11—1885, Pot.).

General distribution: East. Sib. (Daur.), Nor. Mong. (Hent. south., Hang. nor.-east, Mong.-Daur), China (Dunbei, North, North-west).

246. **A. glomeratus** Ledeb. Fl. Alt. 3 (1931) 327; id. Fl. Ross. 1 (1842) 658; Bunge Gen. Astrag. Sp. Geront. 1 (1868) 116 and 2 (1869) 197; Kryl. Fl. Zap. Sib. 7 (1933) 1689; Gontsch. and Boriss. in Fl. SSSR, 12 (1946) 584; Fl. Kazakhst. 5 (1961) 236; C.Y. Yang in Claves pl. Xinjiang, 3 (1985) 159.

—**Ic.:** Ledeb. Icon. pl. fl. Ross. 3 (1843) tab. 299.

Described from East. Kazakhstan (Irtysh valley). Type in St.-Petersburg (LE).

Along exposed rubble slopes and trails in steppes.

IA. Mongolia: ***Mong. Alt.*** (57 km south-south-west of Bayan-Ulgii town, steppe along slope of hillock, July 28, 1977—Karam et al.), ***Gobi-Alt.*** (on sand dunes 25–30 km west of Bayan-Tukhum area, Sep. 1, 1931—Ik.-Gal.; in Dund-Saikhan mountains 35 km south-west of Dalan-Dzadagad, steppe, July 20, 1950—Kal.).

IIA. Junggar: ***Cis-Alt.*** ("Altay"—C.Y. Yang l.c.).

General distribution: West. Sib. (Alt., Irt.), Nor. Mong. (Hang. south).

247. **A. brevifolius** Ledeb. Fl. Alt. 3 (1831) 334; Bunge Gen. Astrag. Sp. Geront. 1 (1868) 115 and 2 (1869) 196; Kryl. Fl. Zap. Sib. 7 (1933) 1688; Gontsch. and Boriss. in Fl. SSSR, 12 (1946) 585; Grub. Konsp. fl. MNR (1955) 183; M. Pop. in Fl. Sr. Sib. 1 (1957) 355; Fl. Tsentr. Sib. 2 (1979) 599; Sanczir in Grub. Opred. rast. Mong. [Key to Plants of Mongolia] (1982) 163; Ulzij. in Tr. Inst. bot. AN MNR, 8 (1982) 34; Grub. in Novosti sist. vyssh. rast. 21 (1984) 213; Opred. rast. Tuv. ASSR [Key to Plants in Tuva Autonomous Soviet Socialist Republic] (1984) 145.—*A. galactites* auct. non Pall.: Sanczir in Grub. Opred. rast. Mong. [Key to Plants of Mongolia] (1982) 163.

—**Ic.:** Ledeb. Ic. pl. fl. Ross. 4, tab. 307.

Described from Altay (Chui river valley). Type in St.-Petersburg (LE).

On steppe rubbly and rocky slopes, on trails and in alpine arid steppes.

IA. Mongolia: ***Khobd.*** (Oigur river, June 28, 1905—Sap.; beyond Tashenta pass in the vicinity of Dandzhur-nur lake, July 1, 1898—Klem.), ***Mong. Alt.*** (Khar-nor, June 18, 1869—Malevskii; on way to Khobdo, June 18, 1870—Kalning; Khan. Taishiri mountain range, upper Shine-usu river [nor. of Khalyun somon], steppe, June 19, 1971—Grub., Ulzij. et al.; Tamchi somon 10 km nor. of Bidzhi-gola, foothill plain, desert, July 17; Bus-Khairkhan mountain range, upper part of trail, steppe, July 17; 14–15 km south of Tamchi-nur lake, steppe, July 17—1947, Yun.; 50 km south of Mankhan settlement, July 24, 1979—Grub. [MW]; Uertiin-Khuren-ula mountains 20 km nor.-east of Bugat somon and 5 km away from pass, 2543 m, July 5, 1984—Kam. and Dariima [UBA]), ***Cen. Khalkha*** (Sangiin-Dalai, south. watershed, July 14, 1926—Lis.; Khukhu-khoshu, rocky slope, July

24, 1926—Gus.; Choiren-ula, along trails of main outlier, steppe, May 28, 1941; Mandal somon, Sakhilte-ula, rocky slopes, May 20; Nilga somon, Burul'zhud-tala area, slopes of rather low hillocks, May 22—1944; 15 km nor. of Mandal Gobi, rocky ridges, steppe, June 5, 1949—Yun.; Sumber somon, 6 km south of Sain-khuduk well, arid steppe, July 2, 1970—Mirkin et al.; Zorgol-Khairkhan-ula, June 9, 1974—Darima; Undzhul somon, 1600 m, steppe, June 25, 1974—Golubkova, Tsogt et al.), ***Depr. Lakes*** (12 km south-east of Khobdo town on road to Ulan Bator, summit of pass, steppe, July 8, 1937—Luk'yanov; 42 km nor. of Daribi somon, sandy desert, Aug. 5, 1977—Sanczir et al.), ***Val. Lakes*** (between Ongiin-gol river and Tsagan-Tes-tala valleys, rocky slope, Aug. 21, 1926—Glag. [UBA]), ***Gobi-Alt.*** (Dzun-Saikhan mountain range, nor. slope, July 21, 1970—Grub., Ulzij. et al.; Dzun-Saikhan mountain range, Elyn-ama gorge, July 7, 1971—Sanczir; Ikhe-Bogdo mountain range, 2500 m, rocky trail, steppe, Aug. 6, 1973—Isach. and Rachk.), ***East. Gobi*** (Luus somon, Khatu-Tugrik area 75 km south-west of ajmaq centre, steppe on ploughed land, June 9, 1951—Kal.; west of Shara-Murun, Inner Mongolia, on dry plateau, No. 51, 1925—Chaney).

IIA. Junggar: ***Tien Shan*** (Barkul' highland, Uliastai village, June 2, 1879—Przew.), ***Jung. Gobi*** (in steppe valley nor. of Tien Shan, on sandy soil, June 12, 1877—Pot.; south. Altay, May 1–20, 1879—Przew.).

General distribution: West. Sib. (Altay), East. Sib. (Daur.: Borgoisk steppe).

248. **A. galactites** Pall. Astrag. (1800) 85; DC. Prodr. 2 (1825) 301; Turcz. in Bull. Soc. Natur. Moscou, 15 (1842) 775; Bunge Gen. Astrag. Sp. Geront. 1 (1868) 115 and 2 (1869) 185; Pavl. in Byul. Mosk. obshch. ispyt. prir., otd. biol. 38, 1–2 (1929) 92; Peter-Stib. in Acta Horti Gotoburg, 12 (1938) 66; Gontsch. and Boriss. in Fl. SSSR, 12 (1946) 585; Boriss. in Fl. Zabaik. 6 (1954) 586; Grub. Konsp. fl. MNR (1955) 184; Wang and Tang in Ill. treatm. princip. pl. China, Legum. (1955) 382; M. Pop. Fl. Sr. Sib. 1 (1957) 335; Ulzij. Opred. rast. okrestn. Ulan-Batora [Key to Plants in the Vicinity of Ulan Bator] (1972) 173; Fl. pl. herb. Chinae bor.-or. 5 (1976) 103; Fl. Intramong. 3 (1977) 203; Fl. Tsentr. Sib. 2 (1979) 600; Sanczir in Grub. Opred. rast. Mong. [Key to Plants of Mongolia] (1982) 163; Ulzij. in Tr. Inst. bot. AN MNR, 8 (1982) 35; S.B. Ho in Bull. Bot. Research, 3, 1 (1983) 57; Grub. in Novosti sist. vyssh. rast. 21 (1984) 213; Liou fil. in Fl. desert Sin. 2 (1987) 286; H.C. Fu in Fl. Intramong. 2 ed., 3 (1989) 287.—*A. otosemius* Kitag. in Rep. First. Sci. Exped. Mansh., Sect. 4, 4 (1936) 88; id. Lin. Fl. Mansh. (1939) 281.

—**Ic.:** Pall. (1800) l.c. tab. 69; Fl. Zabaik. 6, fig. 301; Wang and Tang l.c. fig. 367; Fl. Intramong. 3, tab. 103, fig. 1–7 and 2 ed., 3, tab. 112, fig. 1–6; Fl. desert Sin. 2, tab. 101, fig. 1–7.

Described from East. Siberia (Dauria). Type in St.-Petersburg (LE).

On steppe rubbly slopes and trails of mountains, in sandy steppes in intermontane lake valleys.

IA. Mongolia: ***Cen. Khalkha*** (in valley on right bank of Kukshin-Orkhon, June 18, 1894; valley on left bank of Toly river 50 versts (1 verst = 1.067 km) before Navan-Tseren-guna khure, on slope of sandy hillock, May 16, 1894; Boro-Khundei area, May 19, 1896; in Songinyn-bulan area, 20 versts west of Urga, on mountain slopes, June 7, 1897—Klem.; Choiren-ula, 1940—Sanzha and Damdin; Choiren-ula, arid steppe on granite eluvium, May 28, 1941; Bayan-Delger somon, 15 km nor.-nor.-west of Baishintu-sume, summit of ridge, steppe, May 18, 1944—Yun.; 42 km nor. of Undzhul somon centre, June 18–19 [UBA]; same locality, rocky slopes of hillock, June 25—1974, Dariima; 80 km south-east-east of Undurkhan town, Zaan-Tire hill, June 19, 1987—Budantsev, Ganbold et al.), ***East. Mong.*** (Angirtu lake in adjoining arid steppe, May 28; same locality, lake, on arid sandy soil, May 29; Shilin-khuduk well on steppe between Kulun and Buir lakes, June 11; on Buir-nor lake, on sandy soil, June 18—1899, Pot. and Sold.; Batu-khan mountain between Kerulen and Dolon-nor, 1870—Lomonossov; Gurban-Zagal somon, 12 km nor. of Val. Chingiskhan station 2 km from railroad, June 6; 70 km south-east of Choibalsan town, plain, June 14; Matad somon on road to Tamtsak, June 15; 75 km west of Tamtsak, steppe, Aug. 22—1954 [UBA]; 5 km from Enger-Shanda in north, inclined summit of hillock, June 1, 1955 [UBA]; Matad somon in Ulan-Tsyrik station area, plain, June 4; same locality, plain in Shorba lake region, steppe, June 5—1956, Dashnyam [UBA]; at Dariganga somon centre, Aug. 4, 1965—Gombozhav [UBA]; 60 km south-east of Munkh-Khan settlement on road to Barun-Urt town, June 12, 1980—Gub. [MW]; 25 km east of Matad settlement, Matadyn-tuur area, June 22, 1987—Kam., Gub. et al.).

General distribution: East. Sib. (Daur. south.), Nor. Mong. (Fore Hubs., Hent. South., Hang. east., Mong.-Daur.).

249. **A. parvicarinatus** S.B. Ho in Bull. Bot. Research, 3, 1 (1983) 55.

—**Ic.:** S.B. Ho l.c. tab. 10, fig. 1–9.

Described from Inner Mongolia (vicinity of Bayan-Khoto). Type in Ugon town [NWBI].

On sandy massif.

IA. Mongolia: ***Alash. Gobi*** ("Bayanhot-Shi, 1500 m, super arenas, May 31, 1959, No. 2552, leg. Y.C. Ho-typus !; Ningxia: Yinchuan, prope viam ferream, 1200 m, super arenas, No. 2137, May 14, 1959, leg. Y.C. Ho"—S.B. Ho l.c.).

General distribution: endemic.

250. **A. jiuquanensis** S.B. Ho in Bull. Bot. Research, 3, 1 (1983) 56.

—**Ic.:** S.B. Ho l.c. tab. 11, fig. 1–8.

Described from Gansu (Khesi). Type in Lanzhou (LZU).

On slopes of mountains.

IA. Mongolia: ***Khesi*** ("Jiuquan, in jugo motis, 3000 m, Aug. 11, 1977, No. 6659, leg. Wan. Q.R. et Feng Bi Yu—typus ! [LZU]")—non vidi.

General distribution: endemic.

251. **A. hypogaeus** Ledeb. Ic. pl. fl. Ross. 1 (1829) 23; id. Fl. Alt. 3 (1831) 329; id. Fl. Ross. 1 (1842) 657; Bunge Gen. Astrag. Sp. Geront. 1 (1868) 115 and 2 (1869) 195; id. Astrag. Turk. (1880) 275; id. in Acta Horti Petrop. 7 (1880) 375; O. et B. Fedtsch. Konsp. fl. Turk. 2 (1909) 226; Kryl. Fl. Zap. Sib. 7 (1933) 1687; Gontsch. and Boriss. in Fl. SSSR, 12 (1946) 580; Grub. Konsp. fl. MNR (1955) 184; Fl. Kazakhst. 5 (1961) 234; Opred. rast. sr. Azii [Key to Plants of Mid. Asia] 6 (1981) 226; Sanczir in Grub. Opred. rast. Mong. [Key to Plants of Mongolia] (1982) 163; Ulzij. in Tr. Inst. bot. AN MNR, 8 (1982) 35; Golosk. Fl. Dzhung. Alat. (1984) 73; C.Y. Yang in Claves pl. Xinjiang, 3 (1985) 159.

—**Ic.:** Ledeb. Ic. pl. fl. Ross. tab. 95; Fl. Kazakhst. 5, Plate 31, fig. 3.

Described from Altay. Type in St.-Petersburg (LE).

In steppes, on rubbly and rocky slopes of mountains, on talus and pebble terraces.

IA. Mongolia: ***Khobd.*** (on mountains east of Uryuk-nor, June 22, 1879—Pot.), ***Mong. Alt.*** (Adzhi-Bogdo mountain range, Dzhusylan, June 29, 1876—Pot.; between Dayan-gol and Ak-Korum lakes, June 27, 1903—Gr.-Grzh.; Tsagan-Kobu pass from Tsagan-gol to Kalgutty, steppe slopes, June 28, 1905—Sap.; Khara-Adzarga mountain range, valley of Shutyn-gol river, deep gorge, along pebble bed, Aug. 28, 1930—Pob.; valley of Tsakdult-gol river (tributary of Bodonchi river), Sep. 30, 1930—Bar.; Khadzhingiin-nuru southward of Tsast-Bogdo-ula, near Bel'chiriin-khuduk well, valley, meadow along raving floor, June 25, 1971—Grub., Ulzij. et al.; Uenchiin-gola basin, valley of Arshantyn-gola, right tributary of Khargaityn-gola 3 km from estuary, slope, steppe, Aug. 14, 1979—Grub. et al.; valley of Nariin-gol river, upper course and interfluvine altitude, July 13, 1984— Kam. and Dairima), ***Depr. Lakes*** (8 km west of Ulangom, along flanks of gullies, July 3, 1977—Sanczir, Karam et al. [UBA]; 3 km south of Ulangom, river bank around Chandman' mountain, coastal meadow, July 15, 1977—Karam., Sanczir et al.).

IIA. Junggar: ***Cis-Alt.*** ("Altay"—C.Y. Yang l.c.), Tarb. ("Saur."—C.Y. Yang l.c.).

General distribution: West. Sib. (Alt., Irt.), Nor. Mong. (Hang.: Khan-Khukhei mountain range).

252. **A. pseudohypogaeus** S.B. Ho in Bull. Bot. Research, 3, 1 (1983) 58.

—**Ic.:** ib. tab. 13, fig. 1–10.

Described from Sinkiang (Kashgar). Type in Ugon [NWBI].

On southern slopes of mountains.

IB. Kashgar: ***Nor.*** (Bai Baichang Xian, Koye Cuen, alt. 1590 m, declivitate heliotropica, Sep. 1, 1958, No. 8156, leg. A.R. Lee et J.N. Zhu—typus ! [NWBI])—S.B. Ho l.c.—non vidi).

General distribution: endemic.

253. **A. koburensis** Bunge Gen. Astrag. Sp. Geront. 1 (1868) 116 and 2 (1869) 196.

Described from Mongolia (East. Gobi). Type in St.-Petersburg (LE). Map 9.

In desert steppes.

IA. Mongolia: ***East. Gobi*** (Kobur [Kebur], May 23, 1857, Fischer—typus !; between Alashan and Urga, July–Aug. 1874—Przew.).

General distribution: endemic.

254. **A. ordosicus** H.C. Fu in Fl. Intramong. 2 ed., 3 (1989) 671 and 290.

—**Ic.:** ib. tab. 113, fig. 1–7.

Described from Inner Mongolia (Ordos). Type in Khukh-Khoto (HIMC).

In sandy deserts.

IA. Mongolia: ***Ordos*** (Yikezhaomeng, Etuokeqi, Haibowan, Aug. 24, 1974, No. 494. leg. Xu Zhi-jue—typus ! [HIMC]; Hatumiao, July 3, 1976, No. 84, leg. Ma Yuchuan, Liou Zhong-ling).

General distribution: endemic.

255. **A. hsinbaticus** P.Y. Fu et Y.A. Chen in Fl. pl. herb. Chinae bor.-or. 5 (1976) 175 and 103; Fl. Intramong. 3 (1977) 205.—*A. quasitesticulatus* Bar. et Chu in Liou et al., Claves pl. Chinae bor.-or. (1955) 176 nom. seminud.—*A. grubovii* auct. non Sancz.: H.C. Fu in Fl. Intramong. 2 ed. 3 (1989) 289, p. min. p.

—**Ic.:** Fl. pl. herb. Chinae bor.-or. 5 (1976) tab. 46, fig. 1–9; Fl. Intramong. 3 (1977) tab. 104, fig. 1–9.

Described from Inner Mongolia (Dalai-nor). Type in Shen'yan town. Map 5.

In sandy steppes, along plains and trails.

IA. Mongolia: ***East. Mong.*** (steppe southward of Kerulen river, on sandy soil, June 10, 1889—Pot. and Sold.; Dalai lake, steppe, No. 968, June 27, 1951—S.H. Li; Shilin-gol, desert steppe, No. 16, June 16, 1958—Yu-ch. Ma [HIMC]; 70 km south-east of Choibalsan town, steppe, July 26, 1971—Karam. and Safronova; Matad somon, valley of Tsagan-Temetiin-gobi valley, June 21, 1987—Gub. and Dariima; "Khulun buir"—H.C. Fu l.c.), ***Ordos*** (duke Dzhungor camp, on sandy soil, Aug. 11, 1884—Pot.).

General distribution: endemic.

256. **A. hebecarpus** Cheng f. ex S.B. Ho in Bull. Bot. Research, 3, 1 (1983) 53.

—**Ic.:** ib. tab. 8, fig. 1–10.

Described from Sinkiang (Junggar). Type in Beijing (PE).

On sand in desert.

IIA. Junggar: ***Jung. Gobi*** ("Shawan Xian, Shawan ad Potai, in arena viatica, June 10, 1957, No. 785, leg. K.J. Kuan—typus !; ib. Xiayedi, in desertis, June 13, 1957, No. 872, leg. id. (?)).

General distribution: endemic.

Section 31(75). **Macrotrichoides** Ulzij.

257. **A. monophyllus** Bunge ex Maxim. in Mel., Biol. 10 (1880) 642; Pavl. in Byul. Mosk. obshch. ispyt. prir., otd. biol. 38, 1–2 (1929) 93; Grub. Konsp. fl. MNR (1955) 185; Sanczir in Grub. Opred. rast. Mong. [Key to Plants of Mongolia] (1982) 160; Ulzij. in Tr. Inst. bot. AN MNR, 8 (1920) 36, p. max. p.: Opred. rast. Tuv. ASSR [Key to Plants of Tuva Autonomous Soviet Socialist Republic] (1984) 145; Ulzij. and Gub. in Byul. Mosk. obshch. ispyt prir., otd. biol. 92, 5 (1987) 117; Fl. Intramong. 3 (1989) 271, p.p.

—**Ic.:** Grub. Opred. rast. Mong. [Key to Plants of Mongolia] (1982), Plate 84, fig. 386.

Described from Mongolia (East. Gobi). Type in St.-Petersburg (LE). Plate VII, fig. 4.

In desert-steppe and desert rocky and rubbly slopes and trails along gullies and rocks.

IA. Mongolia: ***Mong. Alt.*** (Khan-Taishir mountain range and Dzhamtyr-yavar pass, from Beger-nur basin, gully, floor, June 17, 1971—Grub., Ulzij., et al.; Daribi-nuru mountain range, 45 km south-east-east of Dariba settlement, Aug. 16; [MW]; Dzhargalant-ula, 40 km north-east of Mankhan settlement, July 24—1984, Gub. [MW]), ***East. Mong.*** (Mongolia chinensis in reditu e China 1841—Kirilov; "Shilin-gol, Eren khot"—H.C. Fu et Cheng l.c.), ***Depr. Lakes*** (south. fringe of Khara-Usu-nur lake basin, along road to Khobdo, among old irrigation canals, in desert, June 27, 1971—Grub., Ulzij. et al.), ***Val. Lakes*** (on cliffs around Tsakhir-bulak spring, July 19; in valley to the south of Tsakhir-Ol, July 19—1894, Klem.; Udzhyum well, 1987 m, Aug. 16; Tuin-gol river, 1446 m, Sep. 4—1886, Pot.; pebble bed steppe in basin of Orok-nor lake, Sep. 6; pebbly talus of mountain left of Tuin-gol river bank in lowland, Sep. 12—1924, Pavl.; short-grass meadow on first terrace of Ongiin-gol river, July 18, 1926—Gus.; Dzhinst somon, right bank of Nariin-gol river, upstream river terrace, rubbly-rocky plateau, Aug. 18, 1949—Kal.; Dzapkhyn-gol valley 30 km before Tsagan-Oloma, Aug. 3, 1950—Kuznetsov; south of Ulan-nur lake, sandy desert—July 2, 1970—Kazantseva; valley of Dzapkhyn river 2 km beyond Taishiri somon centre, rocky slope, desert, Aug. 8, 1979—Grub. et al.), ***Gobi-Alt.*** (Leg river valley, on rubble, Aug. 28, 1886—Pot.; in Burgustai-ama creek valley [west. Bayan-Leg valley], Aug. 5, 1894—Klem.; Bayan-Tukhum area, rubbly semidesert, in arid river bed, Aug. 3, 1931—Ik.-Gal.; south. trail of Arts-Bogdo-nuru, on road to Leg, somon 5 km west of Dzhargalant-khuduk collective, desert steppe, 1948—Grub.; Dzhinst-ula hills 15 km south of Shine-Dzhinst settlement, Aug. 14 1979—Gub. [MW]), ***East. Gobi*** (Tsagan-tugurik—road station nor. of pass to Ude-Shine-Dzhinst workshop, Aug. 14, 1979—Gub. [MW]), ***East. Gobi*** (Tsagan-tugurik—workshop north of pass to Ude workshop on Darkhansk road, June 7 [1857]—Fisher, typus !; road to Urga from Alashan, along road to Unyugute area from Kharmyktai well, June 2, 1909—Napalkov and Davydenko; Shabarakh-Usu, Outer Mongolia, on sandy ridge at 3000 ft, No. 48, 1925—Chaney; Delger-Khangai somon, Khoir-Ul'tszeitu area and Sharangad, between Luus and Kholt somons, desert steppes, Aug. 15, 1930—Kuznetsov; Dalan-Dzadgad town, solonchak meadows along brook 1 km east of town, June–July 1939—Surmazhab; Mandal-Obo somon, old Ulan-Bator—Dalan-Dzadgad road, 2 km nor. of Talain-Bulak, steppe along somewhat ridgy plain, Oct. 20, 1947—Grub. and Kal.; Kholt somon, plain south of Oldakhu-Khid monastery, desert steppe, July 5, 1950—Kal.; from basin of Beger-nur lake to Khalyun, June 17; Beger-nura basin, south-west of fringe, canyon in red-coloured formations nor.-west of Khatakhyn-gol spring, along canyon floor, June 17—1971, Grub., Ulzij. et al.; Bulgan somon, bindweed-saxaul-Russian thistle desert, June 7, 1972—Kazantseva; "Ulan-Tsad"—H.C. Fu et Cheng l.c.), ***West. Gobi*** (Khukhu-us area 15–20 km south-east of Atas-Bogdo mountains, hillocky area, rocky desert, Aug. 11, 1943; Tukhumyin-khundei area west of Alzhi-Bogdo, desert slope, Aug. 3, 1947—Yun.; south. bend of road to Chonoin-Bom area; rocky hillocky area, among rocks of hillock slopes on sand at foothill, Aug. 18; hillock 1399 eight km nor.-west of Chonoin-Bom area on road to Ekhiin-gol, rocky slope, Aug. 19—1948, Grub.; 15 km east-nor.-east of Talyn-Bilgekh-bulak spring, in gully, July 18; south. part of Atas-Bogdo-ula trail, in gully, July 21—1973, Isach. and Rachk.; Tsagan-Bogdo-ula mountain range, rocky slope of mountain, Aug. 14, 1976—Rachk.; same locality, nor. macro slope under main summit near Sudzhiin-bulak spring, steep rocky slope, 2000–2380 m, in rock crevices, Aug. 29, 1979—Grub., Muldashev et al.).

IB. Kashgar: ***South.*** (nor. foothill of Russky mountain range, vicinity of Kopa, about 2134 m, on pebble, June 20, 1890—Rob.).

IIA. Junggar: ***Jung. Gobi*** (90 km south of Beidashan' mountain range, No. 2447a, Sep. 30, 1957—Shen-Tyan'; 10 km west of Bulgan somon, June 29, 1980—Kerzhner; "Bodonchin-gol-Niederung 13 km sudlich Altaj-sum, trockene Kiesterrasse, Wuste, 1982"—E.J. Jager et al.).

General distribution: endemic.

Note. The species is strictly edemic in Central Asia although it enters the desert-steppe south of Tuva (Ubsa lake basin).

258. **A. gubanovii** Ulzij. in Bull. Soc. Natur. Moscou, ser. biol. 92, 5 (1987) 112. Map 3.

Described from Mongolia (Depr. Lakes). Type in Moscow (MW), isotype in St.-Petersburg (LE).

On rubbly desert slopes of hillocky regions and in taro deserts.

IA. Mongolia: ***Mong. Alt.*** (Sagsai river lowland at its confluence with Khobdo river, desert valleys, July–Aug.; same locality, Sagsai river, steppe valley, near Nikiforov trading station, Aug. 1—1909, Sap.), ***Depr. Lakes*** (south. fringe of Ubsanur basin, hillocky area south-east of Ulangom town, 10 km along road to Malchin somon, steppified desert along trail of hillock, July 19, 1971—Grub., Ulzij. et al.; Ubsanur basin 14 km south-east of Ulangom town, rubbly desert on slopes of hillocky area, about 1000 m, No. 9290, Sep. 1, 1984—Gub., typus !; nor.-east. bank of Khirgis-nur lake, desert steppe 40 km south-south-west of Khirgis settlement, 1200 m, Sep. 7, 1985—Gub. [MW]).

General distribution: endemic.

259. **A. macrotrichus** Peter-Stib. in Acta Horti Gotoburg. 12 (1937–38) 67; Wang and Tang in Ill. treatm. princip. pl. China, Legum. (1955) 373; Fl. Intramong. 3 (1977) 205, p. max. p.; S.B. Ho in Bull. Bot. Research, 3, 1 (1983) 54; C.Y. Yang in Claves pl. Xinjiang, 3 (1985) 168; Ulzij. and Gub. in Byul. Mosk. obshch. ispyt. prir., otd. biol. 92, 5 (1987) 113; Liou fil. in Fl. desert Sin. 2 (1989) 285.—*A. monophyllus* auct. non Bunge: Sanczir in Grub. Opred. rast. Mong. [Key to Plants of Mongolia] (1982) 160, p. min. p.; Fl. Intramong. 2 ed., 3 (1989) 271, p.p.

—**Ic.:** Fl. Intramong. 3 (1977) tab. 105, fig. 1–9; Fl. desert sin. 2, tab. 100, fig. 7–12.

Described from North China (nor. Shan'si). Type in Munich (?). Plate VII, fig. 3. Map. 3.

In deserts, on rocky-rubbly and sandy slopes and trails of hillocky areas.

IA. Mongolia: ***Mong. Alt.*** (Bulgan river basin, Nariin-gol river, middle and lower courses, July 16, 1984—Kam., Dariima), ***East. Gobi*** (on way to Urgu from Alashan, Khara-Teg area, June 25, 1909—Czet.; Dzamyn-Ude, on granite rocks, Aug. 26, 1931—Pob.; Bailinmyao town, desert steppe, 1959—Ivanov; hillocky massif south-south-east of Khan-Bogdo somon, 10 km nor.-west of Bosgony-khuduk well, trail of granite hillocky area, July 20, 1974—Rachk. and Volk.; along south. macro slope of Nariin-ula mountain, 1200 m, June 21, 1980 [MW]; nor. fringe of Galbyn-Gobi 50 km east of Khan-Bogdo settlement, desert, 900 m, July 11, 1982 [MW]; 10 km nor.-west of Dalan-Dzadagad town on road to Bulgan, in steppe, July 26, 1984—Gub. [MW]), ***West. Gobi*** (Bayan-Gobi somon, Shara-Khulusuni area, along gully floor, Aug. 8; 20 km south of Maikhan-bulak spring, toward Atas-Bogdo, desert along hillocks, Aug. 16—1943, Yun.; foothill of Adzhi-Bogdo mountain range, about 1700 m, ridgy desert near Dzamyn-Shanda-bulak camp, 35 km east of Altay somon, July 28 [MW]; 40 km south-west of Shara-Khulusni-bulak, hillocky desert near Dzamyn-Bilgekhu camp, Aug. 4—1978, Gub. [MW]), ***Alash. Gobi*** (Bordzon-Gobi desert, sand nor. of Khaldzan-ula, 10 km south of Shine-Gune-khuduk well on sand, July

28, 1970—Grub., Ulzij. et al.; Bayan-chzhao [Bainchzaner], on sand, June 13, 1978—Yun Shi-pen [HIMC]; Bichikte-Usny-khuduk area 25 km south-west of Tsagan-Deris border post, 900–1000 m, July 6, 1981—Gub. [MW]), *Khesi* (nor. foremontane plain of Nanshan, on pebble, 1524–1829 m, May 14, 1894—Rob.; 30 km south of Tszyutsyuan town, pebble bed in Nanshan foothills, July 15, 1958—Peter.; "Mintsin"—Liou fil. l.c.).

IB. Kashgar: *East.* ("Khami"—C.Y. Yang l.c.).

IIA. Junggar: *Jung. Gobi* (30 km south-west of Bidzhi-Altay settlement, 1600 m sand mounds in rubbly desert, July 25, 1978 [MW]; Baitag-Bogdo mountain range, July 27 [MW]; east. macro slope of Baitag-Bogdo mountain range, Budun-Khargaityn-gol valley near border, along arid slopes, 1950 m, July 29—1979 [MW]; Khaldzan-ula mountain range 50 km south-east-east of Altay settlement, Sep. 2, 1983—Gub. [MW]; "Urumchi, Fukan, Tsitai"—C.Y. Yang l.c.).

IIIA. Qinghai: *Nanshan* (encampment on Kuku-usu river, 2438 m, July 11, 1879—Przew.).

IIIC. Pamir (Tashkurgan river valley, 3 km west of Tashkurgan town toward Sarykol' mountain range, debris cone, June 13, 1959—Yun. and I-f. Yuan'; "Tashkurgan"—Liou fil. l.c.).

General distribution: China (north-west: Shen'si).

Section 32 (76). **Borodiniana** B. Fedtsch.

260. **A. baischanticus** Ulzij., Novosti sist. vyssh. rast. 33 (2001) 144.

Described from Inner Mongolia (Alash. Gobi). Type in St.-Petersburg (LE).

On sand.

IA. Mongolia: *Alash. Gobi* (Tengeri sand, Baishinte area, on plain, on sandy soil, No. 372, July 6, 1909—S.S. Czetyrkin, typus !).

General distribution: endemic.

261. **A. borodinii** Krassn. in Spisok rast. Vost. Tyan'-Shanya [List of Plants of East. Tien Shan] (1887) 46; id. in Scripta Bot. Horti Univ. Petrop. 2 (1889) 15; O. et B. Fedtsch. Konsp. fl. Turk. 2 (1909) 228; Gontsch. and Boriss. in Fl. SSSR, 12 (1946) 581 excl. syn. *A. muschketovii* B. Fedtsch.; Fl. Kirgiz. 7 (1957) 311, p.p.; Fl. Kazakhst. 5 (1961) 235, p.p.; Bait. Astrag. Tyan'-Shanya (1977) 70; Opred. rast. Sr. Azii [Key to Plants of Mid. Asia] 6 (1981) 227; S.B. Ho in Bull. Bot. Research, 3, 1 (1983) 54; Golosk. Fl. Dzhung. Alat. (1984) 73; C.Y. Yang in Claves pl. Xinjiang, 3 (1985) 159; Ulzij. and Gub. in Byul. Mosk. obshch. ispyt. prir., otd. biol. 92, 5 (1987) 111.—*A. projecturus* Sumn. in Animadv. Syst. Herb. Univ. Tomsk. 9–10 (1936) 6; Gontsch. and Boriss. in Fl. SSSR, 12 (1946) 579; Fl. Kirgiz. 7 (1957) 308.

—**Ic.:** Fl. SSSR, 12, Plate 35, fig. 1; Fl. Kazakhst. 5, Plate 31, fig. 1.

Described from Kirghizstan (Charyn river). Type in St.-Petersburg (LE). Plate VII, fig. 5.

On rocky and rubbly slopes of mountains, variegated beds, along desert-steppe terraces of montane rivers and on pebble bed formations, along banks of lakes in mountains.

IA. Mongolia: *Mong. Alt.* (valley of Bulgan-gol river 5 km beyond meander of Ulyasutai-gol river, left flank of valley, terrace, windblown sand with saxaul, Aug. 18, 1979—Grub., Muldashev et al.; Narin-gol river valley, middle and lower courses, July 16, 1984—Kam. and Dariima).

IB. Kashgar: *Nor.* (valley of Taushkan-dar'ya river near Akchit post 35 km south-west and above Uch-Turfan oasis, desert along II terrace, Sep. 19, 1958—Yun. and I-f. Yuan'; Zigdeichak in Kel'pin, terrace of arid river bed, No. 7476, Sep. 9, 1958—A.R. Lee 1958, ***West.*** (8 km east of Ken-su spring, along road to Irkeshtam from Kashgar, desert, 2200 m, gully fringe, June 17; same locality, 30 km east of Ulugchat settlement along road to Kashgar from Irkeshtam, intermontane valley, steppified desert, June 18; Baikurt settlement 83 km on highway to Turugart from Kashgar, 2300 m, on steppified desert along rubbly slope of hillock, June 19; same locality, left flank of valley, steppified desert, June 19—1959, Yun. and I-f. Yuan').

IIA. Junggar: *Tien Shan* (Borborogusun, 914–1219 m, April 20; Irenkhaberga, Taldychuelle, nor. Borborogusun, 1219 m, April 27—1879, A. Reg.; 20 km south-east of Urumchi, along road to Davanchin-daban, desertified mountain range, June 2, 1957—Yun. and I-f. Yuan'), ***Jung. Gobi*** (hillocky area on fringe of Khaldzan-ula mountain range, 50 km south-east-east of Altay settlement, Sep. 2, 1983—Gub. [MW]; South. slope of Sertengiin-Khubchu mountain near junction with Khaldzan-ula mountains, July 30, 1984, Kam. and Dariima), ***Zaisan*** ("Burchum"—S.B. Ho l.c., C.Y. Yang l.c.), ***Dzhark.*** ("Ili"—C.Y. Yang l.c.).

IIIC. Pamir ("Tashkurgan"—C.Y. Yang l.c.).

General distribution: Jung.-Tarb. (Jung. Ala Tau), Nor. and Cen. Tien Shan; Mid. Asia (Pamiro-Alay).

262. **A. pseudoborodinii** S.B. Ho in Bull. Bot. Research, 3, 1 (1983) 54.

—**Ic.:** ib. tab. 9, fig. 1–10.

Described from Sinkiang (Jung. Gobi). Type in Beijing (PE).

On arid montane slopes.

IIA. Junggar: *Tien Shan* (?), ***Jung. Gobi*** (Urumqi, Hongyanchi, in declivitatibus, June 2, 1957, leg. K.J. Kuan, No. 591—typus ! [PE]; ib. Yanerwo, in declivitatibus aridis, May 17, 1962, leg. Inst. Bio-Pedo psamm. Xinjiang, Ac. Sin., No. 3508; ib. Ziwobu, 1000 m, in glareosis, July 21, 1964, leg. Coll. 45543—S.B. Ho l.c.).

General distribution: endemic.

263. **A. efolialatus** Hand.-Mazz. in Oesterr. Bot. Zeitschr. 85 (1936) 215; Peter-Stib. in Acta Horti Gotoburg, 12 (1937–38) 68; Wang and Tang in Ill. treatm. princip. pl. China, Legum. (1955) 373; Fl. Intramong. 3 (1977) 200 and 2 ed., 3 (1989) 271; S.B. Ho in Bull. Bot. Research, 3, 1 (1983) 52; Liou fil. in Fl. desert Sin. 2 (1987) 284.

—**Ic.:** Fl. Intramong. 3, tab. 96, fig. 8–14 and 2 ed., 3 tab. 105, fig. 1–5; Fl. desert Sin. 2, tab. 100, fig. 1–6.

Described from North-West China (Gansu). Type in Münich (MU).

In low hills, along hillocks.

IA. Mongolia: *East. Mong.* ("Shilin-gol: Shulun-khukhu-khoshu, Shulun-tsagan-khoshu"—H.C. Fu l.c.), ***Alash. Gobi*** ("Bayan-nur: Oirad"—H.C. Fu l.c.), ***Ordos*** (Polochala, 1400 m, No. 3865, Ts. Ch. Syui [MC], "Ike-Chzhao: Uushin, Otog", "Khubchiin-elis", "Ninsya: Linu"—Liou fil. l.c.), ***Khesi*** (Uvei, 15 km nor.-west of Tadzhin town, rocky low hills of Chan Lin-Shan' mountain range, along hillocks, June 24, 1958— Petr.; "Gulang, Dajing"—Liou fil. l.c.).

General distribution: China (North-West: Shensi nor., Gansu).

264. **A. muschketovii** B. Fedtsch. in Bull. Herb. Boiss. Ser. 2, VII, 11 (1899) 825; O. Fedtsch. Tr. SPb. bot. sada, 21, 3 (1903) 318; O. et B. Fedtsch. Konsp. fl. Turk. 2 (1909) 228; Fl. Tadzhik. 5 (1937) 426; Opred. rast. Sr. Azii [Key to Plants of Mid. Asia] 6 (1981) 227; Fl. Tadzhik. 6 (1981) 266.—*A. borodini* auct. non Krassn.: Gontsch. and Boriss. in Fl. SSSR, 12 (1946) 581, p.p.; Fl. Kirgiz. (1957) 311, p.p.; Fl. Kazakhst. 5 (1961) 235, p.p.; Ikonn. Opred. rast. Pam. [Key to Plants of Pamir] (1963) 162.

—**Ic.:** Fl. Tadzhik. 6 (1981) Plate 44, fig. 13–18.

Described from Pamir. Type in St.-Petersburg (LE).

In alpine cryophilic steppes and deserts, on rubbly and rocky slopes, on sand along river valleys and banks of lakes at 3600–4100 m.

IB. Kashgar: *West.* (upper Kizil-Su river beyond Kashgar, between Simkhane and Egin town, rocky slopes, July 1, 1929—Pop.).

IIIC. Pamir ? (reported from and common in adjoining territories of Tajikistan like the vicinity of Kara-Kul' along Kara-Su river, Rang-Kul' lake, vicinity of Murgab and others).

General distribution: East. Pamir; Mid. Asia (Pamiro-Alay).

265. **A. alberti** Bunge in Acta Horti Petrop. 7 (1880) 375; O. et B. Fedtsch. Konsp. fl. Turk. 2 (1909) 227; Gontsch. and Boriss. in Fl. SSSR, 12 (1946) 581; Fl. Kirgiz. 7 (1957) 308; Fl. Kazakhst. 5 (1961) 234; Bait. Astrag. Tyan'-Shanya (1977) 70; Opred. rast. Sr. Azii [Key to Plants of Mid. Asia] 6 (1981) 227; Golosk. Fl. Dzhung. Alat. (1984) 73; C.Y. Yang in Claves pl. Xinjiang, 3 (1985) 159.

Described from East. Kazakhstan (Jung. Ala Tau: Altyn-Emel'). Type in St.-Petersburg (LE).

On rocky slopes, along river valleys in midbelt of mountains.

IIA. Junggar: *Dzhark.* (Ili river valley west of Kul'dzha, April 1879—A. Reg.; "Ili"—C.Y. Yang l.c.).

General distribution: Jung.-Tarb. (south-west. spurs), Cen. Tien Shan.

266. **A. vallestris** R. Kam. in Novit. Syst. Pl. Vasc. 15 (1978) 173; Ulzij. in Tr. Inst. bot. AN MNR, 8 (1982) 36; Grub. Opred. rast. Mong. [Key to Plants of Mongolia] (1982) 163; Grub. in Novosti sist. vyssh. rast. 21 (1984) 207; Ulzij. and Gub. in Byul. Mosk. obshch. ispyt. prir., otd. biol. 92, 5 (1987) 118; F. Nemeth in Studia Bot. Hungarica, 21 (1989) 45, 47.—*A. alberti* auct. non Bunge: Pavl. in Byul. Mosk. obshch. ispyt. prir., otd. biol. 38, 1–2 (1929) 92; Grub. Konsp. fl. MNR (195) 182.

—**Ic.:** Grub. Opred. rast. Mong. [Key to Plants of Mongolia] Plate 82, fig. 378.

Described from Mongolia (Gobi-Altay). Type in St.-Petersburg (LE). Map 2.

On gravelly, garavelly-clayey slopes, sandy-pebbly terraces, along flanks and floors of gorges.

IA. Mongolia: ***Mong. Alt.*** (nor.-east. bank of Tonkhil-nur lake, July 17, 1974—Shreter; "Tonkhil village, Aug. 18, 1989"—F. Nemeth l.c.), ***Depr. Lakes*** ("Khovd, flat semidesert on sand and debris and granitic hills in northern foreground of Khovd city, July 28, 1989"—F. Nemeth l.c.), ***Val. Lakes*** (arid bed in ridge on left bank of Tuin-gol river in low lands, Sep. 12; clayey precipices of plateau between Tuin- and Tatsyn-gol rivers, Sep. 14—1924, Pavl.; Beger-nur lake basin, south-west fringe, canyon in red beds toward north-west of Khatakhyn-gol springs, on sand along canyon floor, June 17; hillocky area 26 km west of Bu-Tsagan somon along the road, desert, Aug. 25—1972, Grub., Ulzij. et al.; between Bayan-Leg and Orok-nur lake, trail nor.-east of gorge tip, June 25, 1974— Shreter), ***Gobi-Alt.*** (nor. slope of Nemegtu mountain range, Aug. 22, 1886—Pot.; nor. foothill of Ikhe-Bogdo mountain range, rocky semidesert, May 15, 1924—E. Kozlova; Baga-Bogdo, exposed slopes, alt. 6000–8500 ft, No. 30, 1925—Chaney; Dzhinst-ula 15 km south of Shine-Dzhinst settlement, July 14, 1979—Gub. [MW]), ***East. Gobi*** (Outer Mongolia, Shabarakh Usu, on sandy slopes, No. 47, 1925—Chaney; Dalan-Dzadgad town, solonchak meadows, along brook 1 km east of town, May–July, 1939—Surmazhab; 28–30 km south of Tsogt-Tsetsii somon, desert steppe, Oct. 4, 1940—Yun.; Kholt somon, Dagshikhuin-khuduk, outcrops of red clays on nor.-west. flank of basin, July 21; same locality, Ulan-Osh, red clay outcrops south-west of somon, along trails, Aug. 4—1950, Kal.; Bulgan somon, 16 km nor.-west of Den brigade, plain, May 28, 1970—Sanczir; 20 km nor. of Bulgan somon, desert steppe on plain, June 8, 1971—Borissova; 70 km south of Mandal-Gobi, in melkozem areas, between marmorised limestone platforms, June 3, 1972 —Rachk. and Volk.; Bayan-Boro-nuru mountain range, 115 km east-north-east of Bulgan somon, in gully, July 2, 1972—Guricheva and Rachk., typus !; Bayan-Dzag area 17 km from Bulgan somon centre toward north-east, basin with different types of red sand-stones, on precipices and talus, Sep. 13, 1979—Grub., Muldashev et al.).

IIA. Junggar: ***Jung. Gobi*** (nor. extremity of Maikhan-Ulan hill 28 km south-west of Bugat somon, Aug. 1, 1984—Kam. and Dariima).

General distribution: Nor. Mong. (cen. Hang.: Ikhe-Tamir).

Subgenus 9. **Calycocystis** Bunge

1. Shrub or subshrub with well-developed caudex and annual stems .... 2.
+ Perennial with greatly shortened surface caudex .... 11.
2. Branched shrubs; flowers in dense capitate or subumbellate inflorescence; calyx vesicularly-inflated toward end of anthesis (section 2 (78). **Cysticalyx** Bunge) .... 3.
+ Subshrubs; flowers in rather lax, short ovate inflorescence; calyx slightly inflated and shedding with pod toward end of anthesis; calyx teeth lanceolate, 1/4–1/3 as long as tube. Bracts ovate, acuminate (section 1 (77). **Cystodes** Bunge) .... 267. **A. medius** Schrenk ex C.A. Mey.

3. Calyx toward end of anthesis and in fruit, large, 15–18 mm long. Standard 20–25 mm long .... 4.
+ Calyx toward end of anthesis and in fruit, calyx small, 8–13 (14) mm long .... 5.
4. Annual branches white-hairy. Leaflets 3–4 (5) pairs, linear or linear-lanceolate, 10–20 (21) mm long, 1–3 mm broad, acute .... 268. **A. leucocladus** Bunge
+ Annual branches with appressed white and less abundant black hairs. Leaflets 4–6 pairs, lanceolate or oblong-elliptical, rarely elliptical or oval, 8–9 (25) mm long, acute. Calyx 11–12 (later 15–16) mm long, with teeth 1/2 as long as tube. Corolla yellow, standard 20–21 mm long, wings 18–20 mm long. Pods about 12 mm long .... 269. **A. melanocladus** Lipsky
5. Leaflets linear or linear-lanceolate. Corolla rather lurid .... 6.
+ Leaflets elliptical, oblong-elliptical or oblong, rarely lanceolate. Corolla of different colours .... 7.
6. Standard 13–14 mm long; somewhat shorter than calyx, limb bandore-shaped. Leaflets linear-lanceolate, 1.5–5 cm long, 2–6 mm broad, acute, glabrous above, diffusely appressed-pilose beneath. Pods 8–10 mm long, 3–4 mm broad, oblong .... 270. **A. kopalensis** Lipsky ex R. Kam.
+ Standard 17–20 mm long, considerably longer than calyx, limb oblong-oval. Leaflets linear, (10) 12–20 mm long, 2–4 mm broad, diffusely pilose above, densely-appressed pilose beneath. Pods 5 mm long, 2.5 mm broad, oblong-ovate .... 271. **A. tytthocarpus** Gontsch.
7. Limb of standard oblong, slightly narrowed in upper part. Corolla blue (greenish-yellow on drying). Leaflets 4–5 pairs, ovate or elliptical, 8–17 (24) mm long, with short cusp, diffusely appressed-pilose on both surfaces or subglabrous above. Pods oblong, 9–11 mm long, coriaceous. Racemes cylindrical, dense, 3–7 cm long .... 272. **A. dendroides** Kar. et Kir.
+ Limb of standard obovate or oblong-obovate, narrowed in lower part. Corolla yellow, brownish-yellow .... 8.
8. Annual branches white- and black-hairy .... 9.
+ Annual branches white-hairy .... 10.
9. Stipules lanceolate, 3–5 mm long, acuminate, with appressed black and white hairs. Pods about 8 mm long, narrowed into subulate beak about 1 mm long. Corolla pale-yellow .... 273. **A. majevskianus** Kryl.

\+ Stipules deltoid, oblong-ovate, 6–8 mm long, acuminate, pubescent mainly with appressed black or white hairs. Pods 6–8 (10) mm long, abruptly narrowed at tip into 1.5–2 mm long subulate beak. Corolla lurid. .... 274. **A. intermedius** Kar. et Kir.

10\. Leaflets 4–5 pairs, oval or oblong-elliptical, (13) 25–35 mm long, acute. Corolla lurid; standard 19–20 mm long. Peduncle 1.5–2 times longer than leaves. Pods with dense white pubescence .... 275. **A. cysticalyx** Ledeb.

\+ Leaflets 5–10 pairs, oblong, obtuse or lanceolate, short-acuminate, 10–28 mm long, (3) 4–7 mm broad. Corolla yellow; standard 15–16 mm long. Peduncles as long as leaves, more rarely exceeding them. Pods with black and very faint white pubescence .... 276. **A. scleropodius** Ledeb.

11 (1). Leaflets pubescent with semipatent or nearly appressed forked, double-ended hairs. Pods completely enclosed in calyx, more rarely piercing, erect (section 3 (79). **Chaetodon** Bunge) .... 12.

\+ Leaflets pubescent with appressed double-ended hairs .... 16.

12\. Bracts as long as calyx tube or nearly so, 7–10 mm long, linear-lanceolate. Corolla light-purple, standard oblong-rhomboid, 20–24 mm broad. Plant 10–30 cm tall, with 2–6 cm tall stem .... 277. **A. tekesensis** S.B. Ho

\+ Bracts distinctly shorter than calyx tube .... 13.

13\. Mature pods 5–6 mm long, globose-ovate, semibilocular. Racemes capitate, with 3–5 flowers. Calyx teeth slender, as long as tube or slightly shorter. Standard 9–13 mm long .... 278. **A. gracilidentatus** S.B. Ho

\+ Mature pods longer than 10 mm, rather oblong or lanceolate-linear, smoothly attenuated into beak, subsessile or on distinct stalk, bilocular or subbilocular. Inflorescence oblong, lax or ovate, dense. Toward end of anthesis, calyx oblong or broadly ovate inflated .... 14.

14\. Stems generally long, slender, weak, appressed- or semiappressed-pilose. Toward end of anthesis, inflorescence lax with flaccid flowers. Pods sessile, bilocular. Plant 10–40 cm tall .... 15.

\+ Stems very short, with patent, tomentose pubescence. Inflorescence dense, with erect flowers. Peduncles 1–2.5 cm long. Pods subsessile, oblong, subbilocular. Plant dwarf, 6–12 cm tall. Stipules 5–6 mm long .... 279. **A. breviscapus** B. Fedtsch.

15. Leaflets oblong-elliptical. Stipules 3–4 mm long. Pods 11–13 mm long, 2.5–3 mm broad, linear-oblong, with short, 0.5–1 mm long, recurved beak. Peduncles 2–5 (8) cm long .... 280. **A. suidunensis** Bunge.

\+ Leaflets elliptical. Stipules 2–3 mm long. Pods 12–16 mm long, lanceolate-linear, narrowed into erect, 3–4 mm long beak. Peduncles 2.5–3 mm long .... 281. **A. saccocalyx** Schrenk.

16. Plant with well-developed stems. Stipules connate but not adnate to petiole. Petals of corrolla caducous (section 4 (80). **Hypsophilus** Bunge) .... 17.

\+ Plant acauline, densely-caespitose, woody at base. Stipules not connate or slightly connate but adnate to petiole at base. Petals of corolla persistent .... 19.

17. Plant 20–40 cm tall, with 15–35 cm long stems. During fruiting, calyx 14–16 mm long in fruit. Leaflets 7–10 pairs, 8–17 mm long, 4–9 mm broad, oblong-ovate or oblong. Pods 8–9 mm long, semiorbicular-oblong. Flowers large, pale-pink or lilac; standard 21–28.5 mm long. Bracts 5–7 mm long .... 282. **A. burchan-buddaicus** Ulzij.

\+ Plant 8–25 cm tall with 5–15 cm long stems. Calyx 10–12 mm long in fruit. Standard up to 21 mm long. Stipules 4–6 mm long .... 18.

18. Leaflets 5–8 pairs, 4–10 mm long, elliptical or oval. Pods 5–8 mm long, 5–5.5 mm broad, asymmetrically-broadly-ovate. Corolla violet or blue-violet. Bracts 2–3 mm long, ovate .... 283. **A. nivalis** Kar. et Kir.

\+ Leaflets (6) 8–11 pairs, 2–5 mm long, oblong. Pods 9–10 mm long, 3–3.5 mm broad, semiorbicular-oblong. Corolla light-lilac, pale-pink or white with violet tip of keel. Bracts 4–5 mm long, oblong-ovate .... 284. **A. kukunoricus** Ulzij.

19. Corolla violet, pink, pale-purple or, rarely white or yellowish with purple keel. Stipules free, i.e. not connate (section 5 (81). **Laguropsis** Bunge) .... 20.

\+ Corolla pale-yellow, yellow or sulphureous. Stipules somewhat connate (section 6 (82). **Sphaerocystis** Bunge) .... 30.

20. Calyx patently hispid, 11–18 mm long. Corolla violet, 15–22 mm long. Pods unilocular, oblong, (6) 7–8 mm long .... 21.

\+ Calyx appressed-pilose .... 24.

21. Mats large. Peduncles usually 1.5–2 times longer than leaves. Inflorescence globose-capitate, dense, 2–4 cm long. Leaflets 4–9 pairs, elliptical or oblong-elliptical, 5–10 (12) mm long, 3–5 (7)

mm broad. Calyx 11–15 mm long, with patent or semi-patent dense hairs, teeth 2–4 mm long, usually black-hairy .... 285. **A. ochrias** Bunge.

\+ Mats small. Peduncles not longer than leaves .... 22.

22. Inflorescence globose or ovate. Leaflets oblong, narrowly-elliptical or lanceolate, 3–4 (6) mm broad. Calyx 11–14 mm long in fruit .... 23.

\+ Inflorescence oblong-cylindrical, dense, (2.5) 3–8 cm long. Leaflets broadly-elliptical or oblong-obovate, more rarely suboval, 10–20 (25) mm long, (4) 7–10 (12) mm broad. Calyx (13) 14–18 mm long in fruit, teeth 4–6 mm long. Standard 15–19 (20) mm long, slightly constricted .... 286. **A. gobi-altaicus** Ulzij.

23. Leaflets lanceolate or narrowly-elliptical, 10–20 mm long; stipules ovate-lanceolate, 6–7 mm long; bracts linear, 5–7 mm long. Standard 18–22 mm long, slightly constricted in lower third; calyx teeth 3–4 mm long .... 287. **A. laguroides** Pall.

\+ Leaflets oblong or oblong-elliptical, 8–11 (14) mm long; stipules deltoid, 4–5 (5.5) mm long; bracts lanceolate, 4–5 mm long. Standard 15–17.5 mm long, slightly constricted at middle; calyx teeth 2.5–3 mm long .... ***A. tamiricus** Ulzij.

24. Pods unilocular. Leaflets 3–5 pairs, with stiff silvery-white pubescence or densely appressed, canescent white hairs on both surfaces .... 25.

\+ Pods bilocular. Leaflets usually many pairs; if (2) 3–5 pairs, canescent-green, sometimes with silvery pubescence .... 26.

25. Leaflets elliptical or oblong-obovate. Corolla pink-violet or purple-violet, caerulescent on drying. Peduncles 2–4 times longer than leaves. Calyx ovate-vesicular in fruit, 11–13 mm long .... 288. **A. schrenkianus** Fisch. et Mey.

\+ Leaflets lanceolate, oblong-obovate. Corolla purple-red (var. *obtusifoliolus* S.B. Ho). Peduncles as long as leaves or slightly longer. Calyx globose-vesicular in fruit, 14–20 mm long .... 289. **A. nobilis** Bunge ex B. Fedtsch.

26. Corolla purple-red. Calyx usually 5–8 mm long .... 27.

\+ Corolla of different colours. Calyx larger .... 28.

27. Leaves 5–7 cm long, leaflets 2–3 (4) pairs, oblong, 15–25 mm long, 4–7 mm broad. Racemes compact. Bracts deltoid. Calyx cupulate-campanulate, 5–7 mm long, teeth subulate, (1.5) 2–2.5 mm long. Standard oblong, broader at base. Pods lanceolate or oblong-lanceolate .... 290. **A. cupulicalycinus** S.B. Ho

+ Leaves 2–3 cm long, leaflets 3–4 pairs, linear or linear-lanceolate, 8–23 mm long, 1.5–2.5 mm broad. Racemes lax. Bracts linear. Calyx tubular, 7–8 mm long, teeth filiform, 1–1.5 mm long. Standard obovate, cuneate at base. Pods ovate, 10–11 mm long .... 291. **A. habaheensis** Liou f.

28. Calyx 10–14 mm long in fruit. Corolla pink, pale-purple or yellowish with purple tip of keel .... 29.

+ Calyx 14–18 mm long in fruit, globose-vesicular, uniformly black- and white-hairy. Corolla lilac-violet, 18–20 mm long. Petiole not rigescent; leaflets 5–7 (9) pairs, elliptical, lanceolate or linear-oblong, 5–11 (12) mm broad, with silvery pubescence on both surfaces. Loosely-caespitose plant .... 292. **A. grum-grshimailoi** Palib.

29. Calyx with appressed white hairs; corolla pinkish. Leaflets 5–9 pairs, lanceolate, more rarely narrowly-obovate or elliptical, 7–16 (22) mm long, 3–7 (9) mm broad, acute. Pods oblong, obtuse-trigonous, 9–11 mm long, 3 mm broad, with densely appressed hairs, abruptly narrowed into erect subulate 1–2 mm long beak. Pod somewhat longer than calyx tube, piercing it under tip. Plant acauline not forming mat, 7–20 cm tall .... 293. **A. sabuletorum** Ledeb.

+ Calyx white- and black-hairy; corolla pale-purple or yellowish with purple keel; standard 17–20 mm long. Leaflets 4–6 pairs, elliptical, oblong-elliptical or obovate, 5–12 mm long. Pods ovate or oblong-lanceolate, 8–9 mm long, 3–3.5 mm broad, patently white- and stiff-hairy, enclosed in inflated calyx and not piercing it. Plant acauline, forming small, 3–10 cm thick mats .... 294. **A. dilutus** Bunge.

30 (19). Calyx patently-pubescent .... 34.

+ Calyx appressed-pubescent .... 31.

31. Calyx with white pubescence, sometimes with sparse black hairs on teeth, latter up to 15 mm long. Corolla yellow, standard (20) 24–26 mm long. Pods bilocular, not exserted from calyx, patently yellow-hairy. Leaflets oblong-obovate, obtuse, 10–30 mm long, 6–12 mm broad .... 295. **A. petropylensis** Bunge.

+ Calyx with white- and black-pubescence; generally densely pilose. Corolla sulphureous. Pods not entirely bilocular or subbilocular .... 32.

32. Leaflets 3–5 pairs. Standard 20–22 mm long, elliptical, constricted in upper part. Calyx pubescent with white and black hairs. Bracts ovate-lanceolate, acuminate, 2–3 (3.5) mm

long. Pod on slender stalk, appressed-pubescent, lanceolate, ancipital, not entirely bilocular ...... 296. **A. zaissanensis** Sumn.

\+ Leaflets (4–5) 8–11 pairs. Calyx pubescent with black hairs mixed with some white .... 33.

33. Calyx 13–14 mm long, teeth 1/4 as long as tube. Standard 18–24 mm long, wings nearly bilobed at tip. Bracts lanceolate, acute, 2.5–5 (7) mm long, 1/5–1/3 as long as calyx, with black and white pubescence. Peduncles nearly as long as leaves. Pods on 1–1.5 mm long stalks, elliptical, laterally compressed, keeled, 11–13 mm long, 1.5 mm broad, villous due to long white hairs .... 297. **A. kurtschumensis** Bunge.

\+ Calyx 10–12 mm long in fruit, teeth 1/2 as long as tube. Standard 16–20 mm long, wings somewhat emarginate. Bracts membranous, glabrous, ovate-lanceolate, acuminate, nearly as long as calyx or barely shorter. Peduncles longer than leaves. Pods sessile, oblong, 6–8 mm long, 2 mm broad, with white pubescence .... 298. **A. follicularis** Pall.

34. Leaflets 1–2 pairs .... 35.

\+ Leaflets (3) 4–14 pairs .... 36.

35. Leaflets 10–18 mm long, oblong-obovate or oblong-elliptical. Stipules lanceolate, with dense and semiappressed white hairs. Racemes globose-ovate. Corolla yellow .... 299. **A. kazymbeticus** Saposhn. ex Sumn.

\+ Leaflets 4–6 mm long, obovate or elliptical. Stipules deltoid, white-ciliate along margin. Racemes subcapitate. Corolla white .... 300. **A. wenquanensis** S.B. Ho

36. Inflorescence ovate or oblong, (3.5) 4–7 (8) cm long. Limb of standard oblong-obovate. Pods oblong-oval, unilocular .... 37.

\+ Inflorescence globose or globose-oval, 3–6 cm long, more rarely oblong, upto 10 cm long, but then bracts oblong-ovate or lanceolate, 3–4 mm long. Limb of standard oblong-elliptical or almost oblong. Pods bilocular .... 38.

37. Stipules ovate, acuminate, 6–8 mm long. Leaflets 4–6 (8) pairs, 7–20 (25) mm long. Bracts linear, acuminate. Calyx initially about 10–13 mm long, teeth lanceolate-subulate, 1.5–2.5 mm long. Plant 5–20 cm tall .... 301. **A. lupulinus** Pall.

\+ Stipules narrowly-deltoid, 10–17 mm long. Leaflets 3–5 (6) pairs, 10–30 (35) mm long. Bracts lanceolate. Calyx initially about 10 mm long, teeth linear-lanceolate, 5–6 mm long. Plant 15–30 cm tall .... 302. **A. baotouensis** H.C. Fu

38. Bracts oblong-ovate or broadly-lanceolate. Pods oblong-oval, 5–8 mm long, up to 3 (4) mm broad, with nearly appressed hairs .... 39.

\+ Bracts linear-lanceolate. Pods oblong or oblong-oval, (8) 9–15 mm long, with dense downy-hairs .... 40.

39. Calyx 8–11 mm long in fruit, white- and black-hairy. Peduncles as long as leaves or up to 1.5 times longer. Inflorescence ovate or subglobose, 2.5–4 cm long, more rarely oblong, up to 8 cm long. Leaflets (3) 4–6 pairs, elliptical or oblong-obovate, 5–10 mm long, silvery-white on both surfaces due to dense appressed hairs .... 303. **A. sphaerocystis** Bunge.

\+ Calyx 12–15 mm long in fruit, with dense patent and long white hairs, mixed with sparse black hairs on teeth. Peduncles distinctly shorter than leaves or nearly as long. Inflorescence elongated, compact, usually oblong or elongated-cylindrical, up to 10 cm long. Leaflets 2–7 pairs, oblong-elliptical or broadly-ovate, tip rounded with short cusp, 10–25 (26) mm long, 5–9 mm broad, with diffuse appressed hairs on both surfaces .... 304. **A. koslovii** B. Fedtsch. et N. Basil. ex Ulzij.

40. Peduncles 1.5–2 times longer than leaves. Inflorescence globose or globose-oval, 3–4 cm long. Stipules adnate to petiole to a high level and connate at base. Leaflets (5) 8–14 pairs, oblong-elliptical or oblong-obovate, (4) 5–8 (10) mm long, (1.5) 2–3 (3.5) mm broad, acute, more rarely subobtuse but then with very short cusp. Calyx teeth 2.5–3 mm long. Pods 9–12 mm long. Perennial, 6–15 cm tall .... 305. **A. arkalycensis** Bunge.

\+ Peduncles as long as leaves, slightly shorter or longer. Inflorescence oval, more rarely globose-oval, (4) 5–6 cm long. Stipules adnate to petiole only at base and also connate. Leaflets (3) 4–8 pairs, broadly-elliptical or obovate, 8–15 (20) mm long, usually acute, more rarely obtuse. Calyx teeth 4–5 mm long. Pods 12–15 mm long. Perennial, 13–30 cm tall, loosely-caespitose .... 306. **A. ellipsoideus** Ledeb.

Section 1 (77). **Cystodes** Bunge

267. **A. medius** Schrenk ex C.A. Mey. in Bull. Phys.-math. Ac. Sci. Petersb. 2 (1844) 196; Bunge Gen. Astrag. Sp. Geront. 1 (1868) 131 and 2 (1869) 231; id. Astrag. Turk. (1880) 308; O. et B. Fedtsch. Konsp. fl. Turk. 2 (1909) 242; Kryl. Fl. Zap. Sib. 7 (1933) 1703; Gontsch. and M. Pop. in Fl. SSSR, 12 (1946) 783; Fl. Kazakhst. 5 (1961) 303; Opred. rast. Sr. Azii [Key to Plants of Mid. Asia] (1981) 188.—*A. albicaulis* auct. non DC.: Ledeb. Fl. Ross. 1, 3 (1843) 628.

—**Ic.:** Fl. Kazakhst. 5, Plate 39, fig. 1.

Described from Cen. Kazakhstan (Ulutau hills). Type in St.-Petersburg (LE).

In clayey steppes, native rocks and Tertiary clays, more rarely in pebble beds.

IIA. Junggar: ***Balkh.-Alak.*** (Stugelland am fl. Taldy, Nidergungen, No. 781, May 28, 1842—Schrenk ?).

General distribution: Aralo-Casp., Fore Balkh.; West. Sib. (Irt., south).

Section 2 (78). **Cysticalyx** Bunge

268. **A. leucocladus** Bunge in Bull. Soc. Natur. Moscou, 39, 3 (1866) 27; id. Gen. Astrag. Sp. Geront. 1 (1868) 136 and 2 (1869) 233; id. Astrag. Turk. (1880) 312; O. et B. Fedtsch. Konsp. fl. Turk. 2 (1909) 244; Gontsch. and M. Pop. in Fl. SSSR, 12 (1946) 832; Bait. Astrag. Tyan'-Shanya (1977) 93; Opred. rast. Sr. Azii [Key to Plants of Mid. Asia] 6 (1981) 189; S.B. Ho in Bull. Bot. Research, 3, 1 (1983) 55; C.Y. Yang in Claves pl. Xinjiang, 3 (1985) 166.

Described from East. Kazakhstan (Kungei Ala Tau). Type in Moscow [MW].

On montane slopes.

IIA. Junggar: ***Tien Shan*** (Chapchal pass, 2438 m, June 25, 1878—A. Reg.; Inin "Kul'dzha]"—C.Y. Yang l.c.), ***Jung. Gobi*** ("Chingil river basin"—C.Y. Yang l.c.), ***Dzhark.*** ("Ili river valley"—C.Y. Yang l.c.).

General distribution: Nor. Tien Shan (Kungei Ala Tau mountain range).

Note. Yang (C.Y. Yang l.c.) indicates a very wide distribution range for this species from Ili to Chingil' river basin.

269. **A. melanocladus** Lipsky in Acta Horti Petrop. 26 (1907) 272; Gontsch. and M. Pop. in Fl. SSSR, 12 (1946) 831; Fl. Kazakhst. 5 (1961) 314; Bait. Astrag. Tyan'-Shanya (1977) 93; Opred. rast. Sr. Azii [Key to Plants of Mid. Asia] 6 (1981) 189; C.Y. Yang in Claves pl. Xinjiang, 3 (1985) 168.

Described from East. Kazakhstan (Saur mountain range). Type in St.-Petersburg (LE).

Among shrubs and on grassy slopes in middle and upper mountain belts.

IIA. Junggar: ***Tarb.*** ("Dachen, Saur"—C.Y. Yang l.c.).

General distribution: endemic.

270. **A. kopalensis** Lipsky ex R. Kam. in Consp. fl. Asiae Mediae, 6 (1981) 355 and 191; Lipsky in Acta Horti Petrop. 37 (1924) 69, nomen; Gontsch. and M. Pop. in Fl. SSSR, 12 (1946) 839; Fl. Kazakhst. 5 (1961) 320; Bait. Astrag. Tyan'-Shanya (1977) 94; Golosk. Fl. Dzhung. Alat. (1984) 74; C.Y. Yang in Claves pl. Xinjiang, 3 (1985) 166.

Described from East. Kazakhstan (Jung. Ala Tau). Type in St.-Petersburg (LE).

On rubbly and rubbly-rocky slopes, in valleys of montane rivers.

IIA. Junggar: ***Cis-Alt.*** ("Chingil', Fukhai"—C.Y. Yang l.c.), ***Jung. Ala Tau*** ?

General distribution: Jung.-Tarb. (Jung. Ala Tau).

271. **A. tytthocarpus** Gontsch. in Not. Syst. (Leningrad), 9 (1946) 148; Gontsch. and M. Pop. in Fl. SSSR, 12 (1946) 837; Fl. Kirgiz. 7 (1957) 344; Fl. Kazakhst. 5 (1961) 319; Opred. rast. Sr. Azii [Key to Plants of Mid. Asia] 6 (1981) 190; C.Y. Yang in Claves pl. Xinjiang, 3 (1985) 165.—*A. woldemari* Juz. in Fl. SSSR, 12 (1946) 888 and 837; Fl. Kirgiz. 7 (1957) 344.—*A. woldemari* var. *atrotrichocladus* S.B. Ho in Bull. Bot. Research, 3, 1 (1983) 56.

—**Ic.:** S.B. Ho l.c. tab. 4, fig. 1–7 (var. *atrotrichocladus* S.B. Ho).

Described from Kirghizstan (Chulek-Kaindy gorge along bank of B. Kubin river). Type in St.-Petersburg (LE).

On rocky and rocky-melkozem slopes in juniper groves in middle and upper mountain belt.

IIA. Junggar: ***Cis-Alt.*** ("Altay"—S.B. Ho l.c.), ? ***Tarb., Tien Shan*** ("south. Tien Shan slope"—C.Y. Yang l.c.), ***Zaisan*** ("Habahe Xian, Hujiliti lingchang, in declivitatibus glareosis, alt. 1600 m, No. 11208, July 3, 1977, leg. Inst. Bio-Pedol. Psamm. Xinjiang Ac. Sin., typus ! var. *atrotrichocladus* S.B. Ho [XJBI]"—S.B. Ho l.c.).

General distribution: Nor. Tien Shan; Mid. Asia (Pamiro-Alay).

272. **A. dendroides** Kar. et Kir. in Bull. Soc. Natur. Moscou, 15 (1842) 339; Bunge Gen. Astrag. Sp. Geront. 1 (1868) 135 and 2 (1869) 233; id. Astrag. Turk. (1880) 309; id. in Acta Horti Petrop. 7 (1880) 379; O. et B. Fedtsch. Konsp. fl. Turk. 2 (1909) 243; Fl. Tadzhik. 5 (1937) 474; Gontsch. and M. Pop. in Fl. SSSR, 12 (1946) 838; Fl. Kirgiz. 7 (1957) 347; Fl. Kazakhst. 5 (1961) 319; Bait. Astrag. Tyan'-Shanya (1977) 94; Opred. rast. Sr. Azii [Key to Plants of Mid. Asia] 6 (1981) 191; S.B. Ho in Bull. Bot. Research, 3, 1 (1983) 56; Golosk. Fl. Dzhung. Alat. (1984) 74; C.Y. Yang in Claves pl. Xinjiang, 3 (1985) 165; Liou fil. in Fl. desert Sin. 2 (1987) 290.—*A. komarovii* Lipsky in Acta Horti Petrop. 26 (1907) 186; p.p.; O. et B. Fedtsch. Konsp. fl. Turk. 2 (1909) 243, p.p.

—**Ic.:** Fl. SSSR, 12, Plate 49, fig. 3; Fl. Kazakhst. 5, Plate 40, fig. 5.

Described from East. Kazakhstan (Jung. Ala Tau). Type in Moscow [MW], isotype in St.-Petersburg (LE).

Along steppe slopes in middle mountain belt.

IIA. Junggar: ***Cis-Alt.*** ("Fukhai"—C.Y. Yang l.c.); ***Tarb.*** (?), ***Jung. Ala Tau*** ("Ven'syan' [Arasan]"—C.Y. Yang l.c.), ***Dzhark.*** (Khuochen town—S.B. Ho l.c., Liou fil. l.c.).

General distribution: Jung.-Tarb.; Nor. and Cen. Tien Shan; Mid. Asia (Pamiro-Alay).

273. **A. majevskianus** Kryl. in Animadv. Syst. Herb. Univ. Tomsk. 3 (1932) 1; Kryl. Fl. Zap. Sib. 7 (1933) 1707; Gontsch. and M. Pop. in Fl. SSSR, 12 (1946) 835; Fl. Kazakhst. 5 (1961) 318; Grub. in Byul. Mosk. obshch. ispyt. prir., otd. biol. 87, 3 (1982) 127; S.B. Ho in Bull. Bot. Research, 3, 1 (1983) 56; C.Y. Yang in Claves pl. Xinjiang, 3 (1985) 168; Kam. et al. in Byul. Mosk. obshch. ispyt. prir., otd. biol. 90, 5 (1985) 115.

—**Ic.:** Animadv. Syst. (Tomsk), 3 (1932) 5; Claves pl. Xinjiang, 3, tab. 9, fig. 3.

Described from Altay (Narym mountain range). Type in Tomsk (TK). Map 6.

On steppe slopes of mountain, in scrubs.

IA. Mongolia: ***Mong. Alt.*** (upper Dzhelty river, Aug. 13, 1979—Gub. [MW]; valley of Nariin-gol river, middle and lower courses, July 16; Arshantyn-nuru, in Bilut-ula mountain area, July 21; Bulgan river basin, upper Bayan-gol river and watershed, July 23; same locality, middle and lower courses of Bayan-gol river, right bank, July 24—1984, Kam. and Dariima).

IIA. Junggar: ***Cis-Alt.*** (20 km nor.-west of Shara-Sume (on Kran river), shrubby meadow steppe, July 7; same locality, 20 km nor. of Kok-Togoi, right bank of Kairta river, valley of Kuidyn river, forest belt, steppe rocky slope, July 15—1959, Yun. and I-f. Yuan'; "Altay [Shara-Sume town], Qinhe [Chingil'], Fuyun' [Koktogai], Khabakhe [Kaba river]"—S.B. Ho l.c.).

General distribution: West. Sib. (Altay).

274. **A. intermedius** Kar. et Kir. in Bull. Soc. Natur. Moscou, 15 (1842) 340; Bunge Gen. Astrag. Sp. Geront. 1 (1868) 136 and 2 (1869) 234; id. Astrag. Turk. (1880) 313; O. et B. Fedtsch. Konsp. fl. Turk. 2 (1909) 244; Gontsch. and M. Pop. in Fl. SSSR, 12 (1946) 835; Fl. Kirgiz. (1957) 343; Fl. Kazakhst. 5 (1961) 317; Bait. Astrag. Tyan'-Shanya (1977) 93; Opred. rast. Sr. Azii [Key to Plants of Mid. Asia] 6 (1981) 190; Golosk. Fl. Dzhung. Alat. (1984) 74; C.Y. Yang in Claves pl. Xinjiang, 3 (1985) 168.

—**Ic.:** Fl. Kazakhst. 5, Plate 40, fig. 6.

Described from East. Kazakhstan (Jung. Ala Tau). Type in St.-Petersburg (LE).

On steppe slopes in lower and middle mountain belt.

IIA. Junggar: ***Cis-Alt.*** ("Chingil'"—C.Y. Yang l.c.), ***Tarb.*** ("Dachen [Chuguchak]"—C.Y. Yang l.c.), ***Jung. Ala Tau*** (?).

General distribution: Jung.-Tarb. (Jung.-Ala Tau), Nor. Tien Shan.

275. **A. cysticalyx** Ledeb. Fl. Ross. 1, 3 (1843) 643; Bunge Gen. Astrag. Sp. Geront. 1 (1868) 135 and 2 (1869) 234; id. Astrag. Turk. (1880) 313; O. et B. Fedtsch. Konsp. fl. Turk. 2 (1909) 244; Gontsch. and M. Pop. in Fl. SSSR, 12 (1946) 834; Fl. Kazakhst. 5 (1961) 317; Bait. Astrag. Tyan'-Shanya (1977) 93; Opred. rast. Sr. Azii [Key to Plants of Mid. Asia] 6 (1981) 190; S.B. Ho in Bull. Bot. Research, 3, 1 (1983) 57; Golosk. Fl.

Dzhung. Alat. (1984) 74; C.Y. Yang in Claves pl. Xinjiang, 3 (1985) 166.—*A. physocalyx* Kar. et Kir. in Bull. Soc. Natur. Moscou, 14 (1841) 409, non Fisch. (1837).

Described from East. Kazakhstan (Tarbagatai). Type in St.-Petersburg (LE).

In scrubs, along meadows in middle mountain belt.

IIA. Junggar: ***Tarb.*** ("Dachen [Chuguchak town]"—S.B. Ho l.c.; C.Y. Yang l.c.).

General distribution: Jung.-Tarb.

276. **A. scleropodius** Ledeb. Fl. Alt. 3 (1831) 326; id. Fl. Ross. 1, 3 (1843) 642; Bunge Gen. Astrag. Sp. Geront. 1 (1868) 136 and 2 (1869) 233; id. Astrag. Turk. (1880) 312; O. et B. Fedtsch. Konsp. fl. Turk. 2 (1909) 243; Kryl. Fl. Zap. Sib. 7 (1933) 1705; Gontsch. and M. Pop. in Fl. SSSR, 12 (1946) 836; Fl. Kazakhst. 5 (1961) 318; Opred. rast. Sr. Azii [Key to Plants of Mid. Asia] 6 (1981) 190; C.Y. Yang in Claves pl. Xinjiang, 3 (1985) 165.

—**Ic.:** Ledeb. Ic. pl. fl. Ross. 3 (1831) tab. 295.

Described from East. Kazakhstan (vicinity of Baty village on Irtysh). Type in St.-Petersburg (LE).

On steppe slopes of foothills.

IIA. Junggar: ***Tarb.*** (Saur mountain range, south. slope, valley of Karagaitu river near its exit from mountain range on to trail, south. rocky slope near forest, June 23, 1957—Yun. and I-f. Yuan') ***Tien Shan*** ? ("south. slopes of Tien Shan mountain range"—C.Y. Yang l.c.).

General distribution: Jung.-Tarb. (Saur.); West. Sib. (Altay, south).

Section 3 (79). **Chaetodon** Bunge

277. **A. tekesensis** S.B. Ho in Bull. Bot. Research, 3, 1 (1983) 53.

—**Ic.:** S.B. Ho in l.c. tab. 2, fig. 1–10.

Described from Sinkiang (East. Tien Shan). Type in Urumchi [XJBI].

Along banks of rivers, on meadows, at 1300 m.

IIA. Junggar: ***Tien Shan*** ("Tekes Xian, ad ripas fluriorum et in pratis, 1300 m, June 21, 1960, G.J. Liou, No. 793—typus ! [XJBI]"—S.B. Ho l.c.).

General distribution: endemic.

Note. According to the author of this species S.B. Ho, it is closely related to *A. excelsior* M. Pop. but, in our view, *A. tekesensis* S.B. Ho is possibly related to *A. breviscapus* B. Fedtsch.

278. **A. gracilidentatus** S.B. Ho in Bull. Bot. Research, 3, 1 (1983) 51.

—**Ic.:** S.B. Ho l.c. tab. 1, fig. 1–10.

Described from Sinkiang (Altay). Type in Urumchi (XJBI).

On meadows and steppe montane slopes.

IIA. Junggar: *Cis-Alt.* ("Fuyun Xian, Koktohai, in glareosis clivis, June 3, 1974, No. 939, leg. Inst. Bio.-Pedol. Psamm. Xinjiang-typus ! [XJBI]; Altay Xian, in aridis clivis prope urbem, May 10, 1976, No. 15, leg. id.; Qinghe [Chingil'] Xian, in pratis, May 31, 1973, No. 903, leg. id."—S.B. Ho l.c.).

General distribution: endemic.

279. **A. breviscapus** B. Fedtsch. in Acta Horti Petrop. 24 (1905) 234; O. et B. Fedtsch. Konsp. fl. Turk. 2 (1909) 240; Fl. Tadzhik. 5 (1937) 459; Gontsch. and M. Pop. in Fl. SSSR, 12 (1946) 822; Fl. Kirgiz. (1957) 341; Ikonn. Opred. rast. Pam. [Key to Plants of Pamir] (1963) 163; Bait. Astrag. Tyan'-Shanya (1977) 91; Opred. rast. Sr. Azii [Key to Plants of Mid. Asia] 6 (1981) 237.—*A. oophorus* Freyn in Bull. Herb. Boiss. 2 ser. 5 (1905) 1019; O. et B. Fedtsch. Konsp. fl. Turk. 2 (1909) 240.

Described from Kirghizstan (Cen. Tien Shan). Type in St.-Petersburg (LE).

On rocky-rubbly, more rarely sand-covered and solonetzic slopes in upper mountain belt.

IB. Kashgar: *West.* (submontane nor. trails, King-Tau mountain range 40 km southwest of Upal oasis, along road to Kosh-Kulak, desert on standing moraine, June 9, 1959—Yun. and I-f. Yuan').

IIA. Junggar: *Tien Shan* (in Aksu river region, on pass of Talak-gol-daban river, on sun-exposed slope, 2350 m, No. 8905, Sep. 25, 1958—A.R. Lee (1958)).

General distribution: Nor. and Cen. Tien Shan, East. Pamir; Mid. Asia (Pamiro-Alay).

280. **A. suidunensis** Bunge in Acta Horti Petrop. 8 (1880) 378; Gontsch. and M. Pop. in Fl. SSSR, 12 (1946) 821; Fl. Kazakhst. 5 (1961) 311; S.B. Ho in Bull. Bot. Research, 3, 1 (1983) 54; C.Y. Yang in Claves pl. Xinjiang, 3 (1985) 169; Liou fil. in Fl. desert Sin. 2 (1987) 292, p.p.—*A. saccocalyx* auct. non Schrenk ex Fisch. et Mey.: Opred. rast. Sr. Azii [Key to Plants of Mid. Asia] 6 (1981) 236, p.p.

Described from Sinkiang (vicinity of Suichun). Type in St.-Petersburg (LE). Plate VIII, fig. 3. Map 4.

On rocky and rubbly slopes of mountains.

IIA. Junggar: *Dzhark.* (Kuldscha, May 3, 1877; Aktube prope Kuldscha 3000 ft, May 13, 1877, Iliufer ostl. von Kuldscha, May 14, 1877; Kuldscha, June 12, 1877; Iliufer sudlich von Kuldscha, June 30, 1877, A. Reg.; fl. Talki prope Suidun, May 4, 1878; between Suidun and Ili, May 4, 1878, No. 384, A. Regel—typus !; Station Bajandai oder Langer, May 5, 1878, No. 431; Station Bajandai 2000 ft, May 5, 1878, Kuldscha, July 1878—A. Reg.; Togustarau W von Kuldscha, April 1879, A. Reg.), "along Ili river"—S.B. Ho l.c.; "Inin [Kul'dzha]"—Liou fil. l.c.; "Khuochen [Huochang]"—Liou fil. l.c., C.Y. Yang l.c.).

General distribution: Dzhark.

Note. Report possible in Sinkiang section of Junggar Ala Tau.

281. **A. saccocalyx** Schrenk ex Fisch. et Mey. Enum. pl. nov. 1 (1841) 83; Ledeb. Fl. Ross. 3 (1843) 628; Bunge Gen. Astrag. Sp. Geront. 1 (1868) 135 and 2 (1869) 234; id. Astrag. Turk. (1880) 308; O. et B. Fedtsch. Konsp. fl. Turk. 2 (1909) 242; Gontsch. and M. Pop. in Fl. SSSR, 12 (1946) 820; Fl. Kazakhst. 5 (1961) 310; Bait. Astrag. Tyan'-Shanya (1977) 90;

Opred. rast. Sr. Azii [Key to Plants of Mid. Asia] 6 (1981) 236, p.p.; Golosk. Fl. Dzhung. Alat. (1984) 74; C.Y. Yang in Claves pl. Xinjiang, 3 (1985) 169.—*A. suidunensis* auct. non Bunge: Liou fil. in Fl. desert Sin. 2 (1987) 292, p.p.

Described from East. Kazakhstan (Jung. Ala Tau). Type in St.-Petersburg (LE).

On arid rocky and rubbly slopes and clay exposures and variegated rocks in foothills.

IIA. Junggar: ***Jung. Gobi*** ("Shufu [Shikho]"—S.B. Ho l.c.; "Urumchi, Manas, Savan, Kuitun"—Liou fil. l.c.). ? ***Tien Shan*** ("Aksu"—S.B. Ho l.c.).

General distribution: endemic.

Section 4 (80). **Hypsophilus** Bunge

282. **A. burchan-buddaicus** Ulzij. in Novit. syst. pl. vasc. 30 (1996) 104.

Described from Tibet (Weitzan). Type in St.-Petersburg (LE). Map 4.

Along sandy-pebbly, clayey slopes and loessial cliffs, along arid river beds.

IIIA. Qinghai: ***Nanshan*** (Machan-ula, July 26, 1879—Przew.; Humboldt mountain range, Ulan-bulak spring, along loessial cliffs, 3353–4267 m, June 2; Sharagol'dzhin river, Paidza-tologoi area, on sandy-pebbly steppe, 3353–3658 m [11,000–12,000 ft], No. 314a, June 11; Humboldt mountain range, nor. slope, Ulan-daba pass, 3505 m, on stones around springs, June 17, 1894; nor. slope, Chan-Sai gorge, 3048 m, along clayey slopes, June 23, 1895—Rob.), ***Amdo*** (on Huang He river alongside of Churmyn river estuary, 2591–2743 m, under rocks, May 19, 1880—Przew.).

IIIB. Tibet: ***Weitzan*** (Burkhan-Budda mountain range, south. slope, June 14, 1900; same locality, nor. slope, Khatu gorge, 3048–3962 m [10,000–13,000 ft], along rocky arid river bed, No. 215, July 12, 1901—Lad., typus !).

General distribution: endemic.

283. **A. nivalis** Kar. et Kir in Bull. Soc. Natur Moscou, 15 (1842) 341; Bunge Gen. Astrag. Sp. Geront. 1 (1868) 137 and 2 (1869) 234; id. Astrag. Turk. (1880) 301; Lipsky in Acta Horti Petrop. 26 (1906) 200; O. et B. Fedtsch. Konsp. fl. Turk. 2 (1909) 239; Ulbr. in Hedin S. Tibet, 6, 3 (1922) 59; Fl. Tadzhik. 5 (1937) 454; Gontsch. and M. Pop. in Fl. SSSR, 12 (1946) 824; Fl. Kirgiz. 7 (1957) 342; Fl. Kazakhst. 5 (1961) 312; Bait. Astrag. Tyan'-Shanya (1977) 92; Podlech et Deml in Mitt. Bot. Staatssamml. München, 13 (1979) 411; Opred. rast. Sr. Azii [Key to Plants of Mid. Asia] 6 (1981) 261; Fl. Tadzhik. 6 (1981) 331; Golosk. Fl. Dzhung. Alat. (1984) 74; C.Y. Yang in Claves pl. Xinjiang, 3 (1985) 169; Li et Ni in Fl. Xizang, 2 (1985) 809.—*A. orthanthus* Freyn in Bull. Herb. Boiss. ser. 2, May, 11 (1905) 1018, non Gray (1864).—*A. orthanthoides* Boriss. in Fl. SSSR, 12 (1946) 825; Ikonn. Opred. rast. Pam. [Key to Plants of Pamir] (1963) 164.

—**Ic.:** Fl. Kazakhst. 5, Plate 40, fig. 3.

Described from East. Kazakhstan (Jung. Ala Tau). Type in Moscow (MW), isotype in St.-Petersburg (LE).

On rocky and rubbly slopes, pebbly and sandy shoals of montane rivers, on talus and moraine in middle and upper mountain belt, at 3700–5000 m.

IB. Kashgar: *Nor.* (Uch-Turfan, Karagailik gorge, May 18, 1908—Divn.).

IIA. Junggar: *Tien Shan* (Sairam, Kyzemchek, 3048 m, July; Talki-Bash, July—1877; Kyzemchek, Sairam, 2042 m, July; Borotala, 2591 m, July—1878; Dzusalan-Kash, 3048–3353 m, Aug. 12, 1879—A. Reg.; Sairam-nor, July 12, 1878—Fet.; Danyu river, on slope, 2900 m, No. 2076, July 21; 6–7 km south of Danyu, rubbly slope, No. 478, July 22—1957, Kuan; on road to Kashgar from Urumchi, on sun-exposed slope, 2350 m, No. 6234, July 22; Malyi Luitsigen in Khomote alongside water, 3100 m, in Bagrashkul' lake region, No. 7178, Aug. 9—1958, A.R. Lee; Manas river basin, upper Danu river on ascent to Se-daban pass, alpine meadow, July 21; same locality, 6–7 km beyond Se-daban pass from summit to Danu pass, alpine belt, along talus, July 22—1957; intermontane basin of Bol'shoi Yuldus, 1 km south-west of Bain-bulak settlement, along arid pebble beds, Sep. 9; same locality, steppe, Sep. 9—1958, Yun. and I-f. Yuan'), ***Tarb.*** ("Dachen"—C.Y. Yang l.c.).

IIIB. Tibet: ***Weitzan*** (Nor. Tibet, No. 186, 1884—Przew.), ***Chang Tang*** (nor. slope of Russky mountain range, Aksu river, 3658 m, June 16, 1890—Rob.; Khotan, along Molbdzha-su river, 2200 m [7200 ft], July 23—1885, Przew.).

IIIC. Pamir (Ulug-Rabat, pass, along clayey-rocky descent, July 23, 1909—Divn.; Tynnen-daban pass, 4000–4200 m., June 26, 1942—Serp.).

General distribution: Jung.-Tarb., Nor. and Cen. Tien Shan, East. Pamir; Mid. Asia (Pamiro-Alay), Himalayas (west., Kashmir).

284. **A. kukunoricus** Ulzij. in Novit. syst. pl. vasc. 30 (1996) 107.

Described from Qinghai (Kuku-nor lake). Type in St.-Petersburg (LE). Map 9.

On coastal pebble beds and sand of rivers and lakes.

IIIA. Qinghai: *Nanshan* (bank of Kukunor lake, 3108 m, June 9, 1880—Przew.; Kukunor lake, along bank on sand, 3658 m [12,000 ft], No. 708, Aug. 29, 1908—Czet., typus !; Kukunor lake, east. bank, coastal strip, 3200 m, Aug. 5, 1959—Petr.).

IIIB. Tibet: ***Weitzan*** (left bank of Dychyu river, tributary of Yangtze river, on pebble beds, 3962 m, June 28, 1884—Przew.; Amnen-kor mountain range, nor. slope, 3962 m, arid rocky river bed leading to pass, No. 101; Yan'tszytszyan river basin, around Nyam-tso, 4115 m, July 14—1900; Russkoe lake, east. bank, 4115 m, on sandy-rocky banks, May 31, 1901—Czet.).

General distribution: endemic.

Section 5 (81). **Laguropsis** Bunge

285. **A. ochrias** Bunge in Bull. Ac. Sci. St.-Petersb. 24 (1877) 33; Maxim. in Mel. Biol. 10 (1878) 53.—*A. ellipsoideus* auct. non Ledeb.: Peter-Stib. in Acta Horti Gotoburg, 12 (1937–38) 68; Sanczir in Grub. Opred. rast. Mong. [Key to Plants of Mongolia] (1982) 162, p. min. p.; S.B. Ho in Bull. Bot. Research, 3, 1 (1983) 59, p.p.; H.C. Fu in Fl. Intramong. 3 (1989) 297; Liou fil. in Fl. desert Sin. 2 (1987) 291, p.p.

Described from Inner Mongolia (East. Mongolia), Type in St.-Petersburg (LE). Plate VIII, fig. 1. Map. 7.

On sandy, rocky and rubbly mountain slopes and hillocky areas in deserts.

IA. Mongolia: ***East. Mong.*** (Muni-ula mountain in Huang He river basin, No. 25, mid-May 1872—Przew., typus !), ***East. Gobi*** (on way to Urgu from Alashan, Kharmyktei-khuduk area, May 9, 1909—Czet.; nor. fringe of Galbyn-Gobi, Undain-gol near Tabun-Obo, valley between hillocks, rubbly desert, Sep. 29, 1940; Undur-Shili somon, 7–8 km nor.-west of Unegetu-khuduk, sand gullies among granite outcrops, June 3; Mandakh somon hillocky area 10–15 km south-east of Tszagiin-khuduk, rocky slope of hillock, June 5—1946, Yun.; 40 km south-south-east of Sain-Shanda town, along fringe of sandy gully, July 20; 60 km south-south-east of Khubsugyl somon, Khutag-ula hill, nor. rocky slope, July 28—1971, Isach. and Rachk.; 118 km south-east of Mandal-Gobi, plateau scarp, on weathered crust, June 18; 85 km south of Mandal-Gobi, along south. slope of mountain, July 4—1972, Gurcheva and Rachk.; 35 km south of Dzun-Bayan town, on slopes of Takhyat-ula mountain, 900 m, July 7; Khutag-ula mountain range, July 10—1982, Gub. [MW]; "Bayan-nur"—H.C. Fu l.c.), ***West. Gobi*** (Atas-Bogdo-ula town, west. slope, Aug. 3, 1978—Ogureeva), ***Alash. Gobi*** (Alashan mountain range, June 20—July 10, 1873—Przew.; Alashan mountain range, Tszosto gorge, southern slope, lower and middle belts, May 12, 1908—Czet.; Bordzon-Gobi area, nor.-east. fringe of Khaltszan-ula mountain, along upper part of trail and hillocky desert, Sep. 8, 1950—Lavr., Yun. and Kal.; same locality, Dubnig-ula hill 35 km south-south-west of Ulan-Ergiin-khure, rocky montane slopes, Sep. 9, 1950—Yun.; "Alashan mountain range"—H.C. Fu l.c. (sub nom. *A. kurtshumensis* auct. non. Bunge; "Ukhai, Chintunshia"—Liou f. l.c.), ***Ordos*** (Ordos, 1872—Przew.), "Nin'sya"—H.C. Fu l.c.).

IIA. Junggar: ***Tien Shan*** (Nan-shan-kou, on rocky soil, June 10, 1977—Pot.), ***Jung. Gobi*** (Khukhu-Syrkhe mountain, May 20, 1879—Przew.; in Baityk-Bogdo mountains, Aug. 6, 1898—Klem.).

General distribution: endemic.

Note. Junggar plant differs slightly from type in the following respects: calyx with patent long white hairs, inflorescence subcapitate, standard larger, almost without constriction, leaflets (3) 4–9 pairs, appressed-pilose on both surfaces.

*__A. psilolobus__ Putschk. Vidy sekts. Chaetodon [Species of section Chaetodon] (1967) 48; Bait. Astrag. Tyan'-Shanya (1977) 92; Tsukervanik in Opred. rast. Sr. Azii [Key to Plants of Mid. Asia] 6 (1981) 243.—*A. chaetodon* auct. non Bunge: Gontsch. and M. Pop. in Fl. SSSR, 12 (1946) 821, quo ad pl. e reg. Pribalch.; A. Vassiljeva in Fl. Kazakhst. 5 (1961) 311, quo ad pl. e reg. Betpakd., Balch.-Alak. et Tshuilien.

—**Ic.:** Putschk. (Puchkova) l.c. fig. 9.

Described from East. Kazakhstan (Jung. Ala Tau). Type in Tashkent (TAK) ?

On rocky, rubbly steppified slopes of foothills.

IIA. Junggar: ***Jung. Ala Tau*** (distributed in adjoining territories of Kazakhstan in Junggar Ala Tau).

General distribution: Fore Balkh., Jung. Tarb., Nor. Tien Shan.

286. **A. gobi-altaicus** Ulzij. in Bull. Soc. Natur. Moscou, ser. biol. 95, 2 (1990) 83.—*A. laguroides* Pall. var. *micranthus* S.B. Ho in Bull. Bot. Research, 3, 1 (1983) 57; H.C. Fu in Fl. Intramong. 2 ed. 3 (1989) 295.

—**Ic.:** S.B. Ho l.c. (1983) tab. 5, fig. 1–9. Fl. Intramong. 3 (1989) tab. 115, fig. 6–10.

Described from Mongolia (Gobi Altay). Type in St.-Petersburg (LE), isotype in Ulan Bator [UBA].

On hill-steppy and desert-steppe slopes and mountain trails.

IA. Mongolia: ***Gobi-Alt.*** (Gurban-Saichan, Altay mountains, open slopes near summit, 7500 ft [2286 m], No. 131, 1925—Chaney; Tsakhe mountains, near Arshan-khural temple, in ravines, Sep. 11, 1925—Glag.; Ikhe-Bogdo mountain, foothill and lower belt, Aug. 18, 1926—Tug.; on way to Gurban-Saikhan from Sain-usu, Tabun-Khobote, May 31, 1929—Kondrat'ev; Bayan-Tukhum area, rubbly semidesert, Aug. 4; Tszolin mountains, on nor. rubbly slope, Aug. 8; Dund-Saikhan hills, on rubbly slope, Aug. 18—1931, Ik.-Gal.; Bayan-Tsagan mountain range, montane slopes and trails up to upper belt, July–Aug. 1933—Khurlat and Simukova; pass between Dundu- and Dzun-Saikhan, steep rocky slope toward gully 1 km nor. of pass, July 22; Ikhe-Bogdo mountain range, south. slope, upper course of left bank tributaries of Icheru-gol, arid steppe, Sep. 10; same locality, nor. slope, Bityuten-ama creek valley, shrubby subalpine steppes, Sep. 12—1943, Yun.; hillocky region south of Ikhe-Bayan-ula in Tavun-Khobur-khuduk well area and 1703 m, along rocky slopes of hillock, Aug. 2; Tostu-nuru mountain range, Sharga-Morite main peak, 2300–2565 m, on summit and along nor.-west slope, Aug. 15; large gully along road to Bayan-Undur and Leg somon near exit from gorge, on rubbly slope, Aug. 25—1948, Grub.; central part of Gurvan-Saikhan ridge along road to Khushu-khural, steppe, July 19, 1950—Kal.; Ikhe-Nomgon-ula mountain range, nor. slope, gully under main summit, rubbly trail, July 25, 1970—Grub., Ulzij. et al.; 30 km east-nor.-east of Bayan-Dalai somon, Dund-Saikhan-ula mountain range, 2300 m, steppe on south. slope, July 22, 1972—Guricheva and Rachk.; 15 km south of Shine-Dzhinst somon, south. slope of Tsagan-Khalgyn-Tsakhir-ula mountains, among rocks, July 27; 25 km nor.-east of Shine-Dzhinst somon, hillocky massif on rubbly-stony slope of hillock, Aug. 6—1973; Gurban-Saikhan mountain range, Khabtsagaitu-gol area, montane steppe, on nor. slope, July 10—1974, Rachk. and Volk.; Noën-Bogdo-ula mountain, montane slope near summit, nor. exposure, 2200 m above sea level, tansy-wheat grass steppe, No. 1964, Sep. 8, 1979—Grub., Muldashev and Dariima-typus !; Dzhinst-ula mountains 15 km south of Shine-Dzhinst settlement, July 14, 1979 [MW]; Khurkhu-ula hills, June 28, 1981 [MW]; Dzolen-ula mountain range 40 km east of Sevrei settlement, Aug. 26 [MW]; 90 km south-south-east of Dalan-Dzadgad town, Khachig-ula mountain range foothills, Sep. 1—1982, Gub. [MW]; ***East. Gobi*** ("Baganmaotasum [Baga-Mod-sume], No. 2147, May 29, 1931—T.N. Liou.—*A. laguroides* Pall. var. *micranthus* S.B. Ho l.c."; "Bayan-nur: Uradyn-khoid-khoshu—*A. laguroides* Pall. var. *micranthus* S.B. Ho l.c."—H.C. Fu l.c.).

General distribution: endemic.

287. **A. laguroides** Pall. Reise, 3 (1825) Anh. 750; DC. Prodr. 2 (1825) 300; Ledeb. Fl. Ross. 1 (1842) 646; Bunge Gen. Astrag. Sp. Geront. 1 (1868) 138 and 2 (1869) 236; Kryl. Fl. Zap. Sib. 7 (1933) 1709; Gontsch. and Boriss. in Fl. SSSR, 12 (1946) 855; Boriss. in Fl. Zabaik. 6 (1954) 588; Grub. Konsp. fl. MNR (1955) 185, p. max. p.; M. Pop. Fl. Sr. Sib. 1 (1957) 336; Fl. Krasnoyar. kr. 6 (1960) 41; Fl. Tsentr. Sib. 2 (1979) 601; Sanczir in Grub. Opred. rast. Mong. [Key to Plants of Mongolia] (1982) 161; Ulzij. in Tr. Inst. bot. AN MNR, 8 (1982) 31; Opred. rast. Tuv.

ASSR [Key to Plants of Tuva Autonomous Soviet Socialist Republic] (1984) 146; Ulzij. and Gub. in Byul. Mosk. obshch. ispyt. prir., otd. biol. 92, 5 (1987) 117.—*A. lagurus* Pall. Astrag. (1800) 18, non Willd. (1794).—*A. lupulinus* Pall. var. *laguroides* (Pall.) N. Basil., in Not. Syst. (Leningrad) 3 (1922) 116; Pavl. in Byul. Mosk. obshch. ispyt. prir., otd. biol. 38, 1–2 (1929) 93.

—**Ic.:** Pall. Reise, 3 (1776) tab. C, e., fig. 3; id. Astrag. (1800) tab. 16.

Described from East. Siberia (Transbaikal). Type in London (BM). Plate VIII, fig. 5.

On rubbly and rocky steppe slopes, trails, pebble beds, along flanks of gullies, on rock talus and rocks, more often in sandy steppes.

IA. Mongolia: ***Khobd.*** (Khatu river, along exit from gorge on to steppe valley of Bukon'-bere river [Bukhu-Muren], on arid pebble bed, June 17; steppe east of Ulan-daba, along exit from gorge, on floor, June 28—1879, Pot.; plain 7 km south of Khobd brigade, steppe, Aug. 1, 1977—Karam., Sanczir et al.; 27 km nor. of Bukhu-Muren somon, fringe of lacustrine plain, steppe, 1600 m, July 9, 1978—Karam., Beket. et al.; 30 km nor.-west of Ulangom town, floodplain of Turgen-gol river, Aug. 18, 1984—Gub. [MW], ***Mong. Alt.*** (Tsitsirin-gol river, on arid pebble bed, July 10, 1877—Pot.; on Altyn-khadasu cliff between Shara-bulak springs and Kosheta brook, July 13; on cliffs around a spring of Tsakhir-bulak, July 19—1894; around a cliff of Bichigin-nuru, on rock talus, July 18; various sites in steppe between Tunkul' lake and Kharatei hills before Khulmu lake, Aug. 2—1896; mountains between Uruktu and Kobdo rivers, July 2, 1898—Klem; steppe near Khobdo town, July 18, 1906—Sap.; south-east of Karaganat ridges and south of Argalante, on rocky slope, Aug. 9, 1926—Glag.; east. slopes of Tonkilnursk basin, montane desert steppe, Aug. 13, 1945—Yun.; west. fringe of basin of Tsetseg-nur,Temitiin-Khukh-ula, pass on road to Must somon, 2350 m, steppe, June 26, 1971—Grub., Ulzij. et al.; Ushgiin-Barun-khoolai valley 6 km north of pass on Tonkhil somon—Tsetseg-nur road, slope of spur, steppe, Aug. 11; Ulan-Ergiin-gol valley near Must somon centre, Mu-ulan-tologoi granite hillock, gravelly-rocky slope and rocks, Aug. 12—1979, Grub., Muldashev et al.; 35 km south-west-west of Khalyun settlement, Aug. 13 [MW]; Sutai-ula mountain range, 12 km south-south-west of Dariv settlement, Aug. 18 [MW]; 10 km east of Ulgii town, Aug. 26—1984, Gub. [MW]), ***Cen. Khalkha*** (nor. bank of Ugei-nur lake, near Khure [small monastery], on rocks, June 15; on hill among rocks, between Khar-tologoi lake, Togon-us well and Tsagan-deli lake, July 30—1893; 7–8 versts (1 verst = 1.067 km) up along Kharukha river bank, June 27—1895; steppe in Shara-Shorotai area, Aug. 13, 1897, Klem.; on way to Urgu from Alashan, along road to Khara-Tologoi area from Mandalyn-Gobi area, June 8, 1909—Czet.; Gangy-bulak, rocky slopes, July 3, 1925—Glag.; vicinity of Ikhe-Tukhum-nor lake, Ubur-Bulagain-ama ravine, June; same locality, Tarandag mountain, June, 1926—Zam.; rocky steppe and rocks near Choiren, July 1, 1926—Pavl.; Khukhu-khoshun, rocky slope, July 24; Ikhe-Dzara mountain, rocky slope, Aug. 25—1926, Lis.; Choiren-ula hill, 1940—Sanzha, Damdin; 5 km nor.-east of Choiren, steppe along hillocky area, Aug. 22, 1940; valley of Orkhon-gol river near Erdeni-Dzu monastery, rocky hillock on left bank above river bed, June 21, 1948—Yun.; 15 km nor. of Mandalyn-Gobi, rock faces, June 5, 1949—Yun.; Delger-Tsogt somon, rocky hillocks, June 15, 1950—Kal.; Bayan-Undur somon, Dagan-del' area along road to Arbai-khere from ulan Bator, rocky slopes of hillock, June 19; 8–10 km nor.-east of Buridu somon on right bank of Mukhryn-gol river, steppe, July 14—1952, Davazamc; 20 km east-south-east of Dzhargalt-khana, steppe along slope, June 18; 26 km south-east of Undurkhan town, hill and Bayan-khuduk well, 1580 m, steppe on hill summit, June 19; 30 km south-west of Munkh-khan somon, high hillock, steppe along hillock summits, June 20; around old Choiren, 35 km south-

south-east of new Choiren, on granite outcrops, June 14—1971, Karam., Isach., Rachk. et al.; rock exposures along gully nor.-west of Undzhul somon, montane steppe, June 27; same locality, Bayasgalant mountain, trail, along gully, July 4; Munkhkhan-ula hill, 1607 m, hilly steppe, July 25; Darkhan-ula mountain, 1610 m, steppe, July 27—1974, Golubkova and Tsogt), ***East. Mong.*** (Sharotu, July 16, Borokhudzhir, June 17, 1850—Fisher), ***Depr. Lakes*** (Ulan-gom area, on ploughed farm, June 26; Ulyasutai river, July 9; Torkholik river, Ubsa tributary, on ploughed farms, weed, Sep. 24—1879, Pot.; around an irrigation canal 10 versts (1 verst = 1.067 km) from Ubsa lake, July 3, 1892—Kryl.; on sandy left bank of Dzapkhyn river, July 11, 1894—Klem.; 8 km nor.-west of Sagila, desert steppe, July 13, 1977; 32 km nor.-east of Sagil somon, spur of Barun Termiz-ula mountain, shrubby desert steppe, 1250 m, June 27, 1978—Karam. et al.), ***Val. Lakes*** (Tuin-gol river south of Khangai mountain range, Sep. 4; Tui river, between Ulan-Erge and Udzhyum localities, Sep. 6—1886, Pot.; steppe between Dzapkhyn river and Geulykh [Guilin]-bulak spring, on cliff, June 29, 1894—Klem.; nor. creek valley running from Buur mountain to floor, Aug. 17; along rocky hill slope in Tuin-gol ring valley, in lower courses, Sep. 3; along rocky summits of Naryn-Khara mountain nor. of Orok-nor lake, Sep. 7—1924, Pavl.; basin of Orok-nor lake, Naryn-Khara mountains, Aug. 12, 1926—Tug.; 40 km south-west of Khairkhan-Dulan somon, on road to Bayan-Khongor, June 27, 1941, steppe—Tsatsenkin; 20 km nor.-nor.-west of Delger somon on road, steppe in the vicinity of hillocky area, Aug. 30, 1948—Grub.; Dzhinst somon terrace above lake, Aug. 17, 1949—Kal.; valley of Dzapkhyn-gol river, 20 km beyond Tsagan-Oloma, Aug. 2, 1950—Kuznetsov; interfluvine zone of Tatsiin-gol and Tuin-gol in Abzag-ula region and Adagiin-Khara-khuduk well, Luugaryn-ama, rocky slope of canyon, June 13, 1971—Grub., Ulzij. et al.; 65 km from Teeg spring west-south-west of road to Bogdo somon, aeolian sand on basalt exposures on slopes, June 25, 1972—Banzragch and Karam.), ***Gobi-Alt.*** (depression between Nemegtu and Tsomtso mountains, nor. slope of Nemegtu mountain range, Aug. 22; south. slope of Ubten-daban pass, Aug. 30—1886, Pot.; nor. foothills of Ikhe-Bogdo mountain range, rocky semidesert, May 13, 1926—Kozlova), ***East. Gobi*** (Daying Gol, edge of fan in wash of broad valley at 5000 ft [1524 m], No. 5288, 1925—Chaney; Delger-Hangay, on rubbly slope, Aug. 1; same locality, in eastern section of mountain range, Aug. 1—1931, Ik.-Gal., 90 km nor. of Saikhan-Dulan somon, hillocky area along west. bank of Dzhargalag-nur lake, on rubbly summit of hillock, Aug. 16; 10 km west-south-west of Saikhan-Dulan somon, along rubbly slope of hillock, Aug. 3—1971, Isach. and Rachk.).

General distribution: West. Sib. (Alt. south-east.), East. Sib. (Sayans, South, Daur.), Nor. Mong. (Hent., Hang., Mong. Daur.).

288. **A. schrenkianus** Fisch. et Mey. in Bull. Phys.-Math. Ac. Sci. Petersb. 2 (1844) 197; Bunge Gen. Astrag. Sp. Geront. 1 (1868) 138 and 2 (1869) 235; id. Astrag. Turk. (1880) 307, excl. syn. *A. holargyreus*; O. et B. Fedtsch. Konsp. fl. Turk. 2 (1909) 241, p.p.; Gontsch. and M. Pop. in Fl. SSSR, 12 (1946) 862, excl. syn. *A. holargyreus* Bunge; Fl. Kirgiz. 7 (1957) 349, p.p.; Fl. Kazakhst. 5 (1961) 329, p.p.; Bait. Astrag. Tyan'-Shanya (1977) 97; Opred. rast. Sr. Azii [Key to Plants of Mid. Asia] 6 (1981) 246; Fl. Tadzhik. 6 (1981) 335; Golosk. Fl. Dzhung. Alat. (1984) 74.—*A. dshanbulakensis* B. Fedtsch. in Acta Horti Petrop. 24 (1904) 236; O. et B. Fedtsch. Konsp. fl. Turk. 2 (1909) 242.—*A. turlanicus* Bajt. et Myrzak. in Not. Syst. (Alma Ata) 10 (1977) 29.

—**Ic.:** Fl. Kazakhst. 5, Plate 42, fig. 5.

Described from Cen. Kazakhstan (Arganaty mountains) and from Ters-akkan valley. Type in St.-Petersburg (LE).

On rocky and rocky-rubbly montane slopes and on rubble talus.

IA. Mongolia: ***Mong. Alt.*** (12 km nor. of Tamchi somon, steppe, on granite hillocky area, July 16; 15 km nor.-west of Tamchi-daban pass, steppe along ravines between hillocks, July 16; east. slopes of Tonkhil-nur basin, hilly-desert steppe, Aug. 13—1945, Yun.).

General distribution: Aralo-Casp., Fore Balkh., Nor. Tien Shen; Mid. Asia (West. Pamiro-Alay).

289. **A. nobilis** Bunge ex B. Fedtsch. in Acta Horti Petrop. 24 (1905) 236; Gontsch. and A. Korol. in Fl. Tadzhik. 5 (1937) 465; Gontsch. and M. Pop. in Fl. SSSR, 12 (1946) 867; Fl. Tadzhik. (1981) 337; Opred. rast. Sr. Azii [Key to Plants of Mid. Asia] 6 (1981) 248.—*A. nobilis* var. *obtusifoliolus* S.B. Ho in Bull. Bot. Research, 3, 1 (1983) 58.

—**Ic.:** Fl. Tadzhik. 5 (1937) Plate 54 and 6 (1981) Plate 39, fig. 15–21; Fl. SSSR, 12, Plate 50, fig., 1; S.B. Ho l.c., tab. 6, fig. 1–11.

Described from Mid Asia (Turkest. mountain range). Type in St.-Petersburg (LE).

On arid rocky and rubbly slopes in low and middle mountain belts.

IB. Kashgar: ***Nor.*** ("Wuqia Xian, Jigen, Ximuhana alt. 3000 m, in pratis, July 29, 1978, No. 2128, leg. Exped. Xinjiang Inst. Bot. bor.-occ.—typus *A. nobilis* var. *obtusifoliolus* S.B. Ho [NWBI]; ib, Kaladaban, alt. 2300 m, in inundatis, May 29, 1973, No. 7352, leg. Exped. Xinjiang Ac. Sin."—S.B. Ho l.c.).

IIA. Junggar: ***Jung. Ala Tau*** ("Wenquan Xian, Aug. 24, 1957, leg. K.J. Kuan, No. 4617" —S.B. Ho l.c.).

General distribution: Mid. Asia (Pamiro-Alay).

290. **A. cupulicalycinus** S.B. Ho ex Y.C. Ho in Bull. Bot. Research, 3, 1 (1983) 47; Liou fil. in Fl. desert Sin. 2 (1987) 290.

—**Ic.:** S.B. Ho l.c. tab. 3, fig. 1–10; Fl. desert Sin. 2, tab. 102, fig. 5–9.

Described from Sinkiang (Zaisan). Type in Urumchi [XJBI].

In sandy deserts, on slopes of hillocks.

IIA. Junggar: ***Zaisan*** ("Habahe Xien, Yu Chang, in desertis arena, alt. 550 m, June 17, 1976, leg. Inst. Bio.-Psammo, Xinjiang, No. 10095—typus ! (XJBI); Burgin Xian, in declivitate, June 12, 1974, leg. id. No. 7274"—S.B. Ho l.c., Liou fil. l.c.).

General distribution: endemic.

Note. The author of this species S.B. Ho ex Y.C. Ho (1983) at first included it erroneously in section **Helima** of subgenus *Cercidothrix*.

291. **A. habaheensis** Liou f. in Fl. desert Sin. 2 (1987) 445 and 291.

—**Ic.:** Liou fil. l.c. tab. 102, figs. 15–19.

Described from Sinkiang (Zaisan). Type in Urumchi (Herb. Xinjiang, Aug. 1, Agr. Coll.).

In desert steppes, on sand.

IIA. Junggar: ***Zaisan*** ("Habahe, in desert-steppe, alt. 550 m in arenosis, June 17, 1976, C.Y. Yang, No. 10097—typus !"—Liou fil. l.c.).

General distribution: endemic.

292. **A. grum-grshimailoi** Palib. in Bull. Herb. Boiss. 2, 8 (1908) 3; Ulzij. in Tr. Inst. bot. AN MNR, 8 (1982) 33.—*A. bulganicus* Ulzij. in Prir. usl. rast. pokrov i zhivotn. mir Mong. (1988) 223 nom. nodum.

—**Ic.:** Palib. l.c. tab. 3, fig. 1.

Described from Sinkiang (Cis-Alt.). Type in St.-Petersburg (LE). Plate VIII, fig. 2. Map 5.

On rocky slopes of mountains.

IA. Mongolia: *Mong. Alt.* (Bulgan river basin, upper Bayan-gol river and waterdivide, July 23, 1984—Kam. and Dariima).

IIA. Junggar: *Cis-Alt.* (Bugotor river, high Altay plateau between Burchum and Kran, June 11, 1903—Gr.-Grzh., typus !).

General distribution: endemic.

293. **A. sabuletorum** Ledeb. Fl. Alt. 3 (1831) 321; id. Fl. Ross. (1842) 645; Bunge Gen. Astrag. Sp. Geront. 1 (1868) 138 and 2 (1869) 235; id. Astrag. Turk. (1880) 307; O. et B. Fedtsch. Konsp. fl. Turk. 2 (1909) 242; Kryl. Fl. Zap. Sib. 7 (1933) 1708; Gontsch. and Boriss. in Fl. SSSR, 12 (1946) 859; Grub. Konsp. fl. MNR (1955) 186; Fl. Kazakhst. 5 (1961) 327; Opred. rast. Sr. Azii [Key to Plants of Mid. Asia] 6 (1981) 245; Sanczir in Grub. Opred. rast. Mong. [Key to Plants of Mongolia] (1982) 161; Ulzij. in Tr. Inst. bot. AN MNR, 8 (1982) 31; Grub. in Novosti sist. vyssh. rast. 21 (1984) 213; C.Y. Yang in Claves pl. Xinjiang, 3 (1985) 172.

—**Ic.:** Ledeb. Ic. pl. fl. Ross. 3 (1831) tab. 298; Fl. Kazakhst. 5, Plate 42, fig. 2.

Described from East. Kazakhstan (Zaisan). Type in St.-Petersburg (LE).

Along hummocky sand, on rubbly desert-steppe slopes, in sandy desert steppes, along flanks of gorges and on slopes of hillocky regions.

IA. Mongolia: *Mong. Alt.* (Adzhi-Bogdo mountain range, Dzusylan gorge, on gravelly soil, June 29, 1877—Pot.; along road toward exit of Bodonchin-gol, Sep. 25, 1930—Bar.; 12 km nor. of Tamchi somon, steppe on hillocky area, July 16, 1947—Yun.; Burun-khoolai valley along road to Tsetseg somon near Yamatu-ula, sandy steppe, June 25, 1971—Grub., Ulzij. et al.; 8 km south of Bugat somon in hilly desert soil, July 31, 1977—Volk. and Rachk.; valley of Bulgan river, between Bayan-gol and Nariin-gol river estuaries, along rocky slopes, July 17, 1984—Kam. and Dariima), ***West. Gobi*** (Atas-Bogdo-ula, nor. macro slope, montane steppe, 2600 m, Aug. 24, 1973—Isach. and Rachk.; Tsagan-Bogdo mountain range, rocky slope, Aug. 14; same locality, montane steppe, Aug. 21—1976, Rachk. and Damba; hillocky area 24 km east of Khatyn-Suudlyn-bulak spring, waterdivide plateau, semidesert, Aug. 27; Tsagan-Bogdo mountain range, nor. macro slope near Sudzhiin spring, upper part of trail, 1840 m, rubbly hamada, Aug. 28—1979, Grub., Muldashev et al.).

IIA. Junggar: *Cis-Alt.* (?), *Jung. Gobi* (45 km west of Bugat somon, on slopes of hillocky area, Aug. 1, 1977—Volk. and Rachk.; Sertengiin-Khubchi mountain range, 25 km south-east of Altay somon, July 6, 1984—Kam. and Dariima), ***Tien Shan*** (Nan-Shan-Kou, on rocky soil, June 7, 1877—Pot.), ***Zaisan*** ("Bruchum, Kaba river; Zimunai"—C.Y. Yang l.c.).

General distribution: Fore Balkh. (Zaisan); West. Sib. (Alt.).

294. **A. dilutus** Bunge in Del. Sem. Horti Dorpat. (1840) 7; Ledeb. Fl. Ross. 1 (1842) 644; Bunge Gen. Astrag. Sp. Geront. 1 (1868) 138 and 2 (1869) 236; Kryl. Fl. Zap. Sib. 7 (1933) 1709; Gontsch. and Boriss. in Fl. SSSR, 12 (1946) 850; Grub. Konsp. fl. MNR (1955) 183; Fl. Kazakhst. 5 (1961) 321; Fl. Intramong. 3 (1977) 208 and 2 ed., 3 (1989) 293, p.p.; Sanczir in Grub. Opred. rast. Mong. [Key to Plants of Mongolia] (1982) 161; Ulzij. in Tr. Inst. bot. AN MNR, 8 (1982) 31; S.B. Ho in Bull. Bot. Research, 3, 1 (1983) 57; Opred. rast. Tuv. ASSR [Key to Plants of Tuva Autonomous Soviet Socialist Republic] (1984) 146; Grub. in Novosti sist. vyssh. rast. 21 (1984) 213; C.Y. Yang in Claves pl. Xinjiang, 3 (1985) 172; Liou fil. in Fl. desert Sin. 2 (1987) 291; Ulzij. and Gub. in Byul. Mosk. obshch. ispyt. prir., otd. biol. 92, 5 (1987) 116.

—**Ic.:** Fl. Kazakhst. 5, Plate 41, fig. 4; Fl. Intramong. 3 (1977) tab. 105, fig. 10–17 and 2 ed. 3, tab. 115, fig. 1–5.

Described from Altay (Chui river basin). Type in St.-Petersburg (LE).

On rocky and sandy trails, rubbly montane slopes, on pebble beds and thin riverine and lacustrine sand.

IA. Mongolia: ***Khobd.*** (steppe east of Ulan-daba mountain passage (Ubsa lake plain), on rocky soil, June 23, 1879—Pot.; 65 km east-nor.-east of Bayan-Ulgii, knolls, desert steppe along mountain trails, July 28, 1977—Karam., Sanczir et al.), ***Mong. Alt.*** (Adzhi-Bogdo mountain range, Urten-gol, June 30; Tsitsirin-gol, between rocks, July 10—1877, Pot.; on Altyn-khadasu cliff between Shara-bulak and Koshety brook springs, July 3, 1894; mountains between Uruktu and kobdo rivers, July 2, 1898—Klem., Tsagan-gol river valley, July 16, 1909; along barren steppes of entire east. slope of Altay at Kobdo river source [undated]—Sap.; 12 km nor. of Tamchi somon, steppe along hillocky region, July 16, 1947—Yun.; Bugun-daba pass, 22 km south-east of Bugat somon, in ravine, Sep. 2, 1973—Isach. and Rachk.; Uertiin-Khuren-ula mountains 20 km nor.-east of Bugat somon and 5 km from pass, 2543 m, July 5, 1984—Kam. and Dariima), ***Depr. Lakes*** (Ulangom area, on sandy soil, June 26, 1879—Pot.), ***Gobi-Alt.*** (on nor. slope of one of Baga-Bogdo mountains, Aug. 11, 1894—Klem.; central section of Gurban-Saikhan ridge along road to Khushu-khural, steppe, July 19, 1950—Kal.), ***East. Gobi*** (40 km south-south-west of Sain-Shanda town, along road to Ulgii, Aug. 2, 1974—Rachk. and Volk.; "Bayan-nur, northern section"—H.C. Fu l.c.; "Lan-shan'"—H.C. Fu l.c., Liou fil. l.c.), ***West. Gobi*** ("Gansu: Minshui"—Liou fil. l.c.), ***Alash. Gobi*** ("Ninsya: Shizuishan'"—Liou fil. l.c.), ***Ordos*** ("Ike-Chzhao: Arvas-ula hill"—H.C. Fu l.c., Liou fil. l.c.).

IIA. Junggar: ***Cis-Alt.*** ("Altay"—S.B. Ho l.c., C.Y. Yang l.c.), ***Tien Shan*** (on road to Chzhaosu from Aksu, No. 1589, Aug. 15, 1957—Shen'-Tyan'; "Tien Shan"—S.B. Ho l.c.), ***Jung. Gobi*** (Baitag-Bogdo mountain range, Budun-Khargaityn-gol valley, July 29, 1979—Gub. [MW]; in Khabtag-ula mountain range, east. Khar-tologin-bulak, montane slopes, 2200–2400 m, Aug. 21, 1981—Rachk.; west. part of hillocky area near Khubchiin-ula hill, July 31; nor. extremity of Maikhan-ula hill 28 km south-west of Bugat somon, Aug. 1—1984, Kam. and Dariima).

General distribution: West. Sib. (Alt. south-east.).

Section 6 (82). **Sphaerocystis** Bunge

295. **A. petropylensis** Bunge Gen. Astrag. Sp. Geront. 1 (1868) 139 and 2 (1869) 237; Kryl. Fl. Zap. Sib. 7 (1933) 1712; Gontsch. and M. Pop. in Fl. SSSR, 12 (1946) 851; Fl. Kazakhst. 5 (1961) 322; Opred. rast. Sr. Azii [Key to Plants of Mid. Asia] 6 (1981) 243; C.Y. Yang in Claves pl. Xinjiang, 3 (1985) 171.—*A. ellipsoideus* α *intermedius* Ledeb. Fl. Alt. 3 (1831) 319; id. Fl. Ross. 1, 3 (1843) 645.

—**Ic.:** Fl. Kazakhst. 5, Plate 41, fig. 6.

Described from East. Kazakhstan (vicinity of Ust'-Kamenogorsk). Type in St.-Petersburg (LE).

On rocky, rocky-rubbly and rocky-clayey slopes of foothills.

IIA. Junggar: ***Tarb.*** ("Saur"—C.Y. Yang l.c.), ***Zaisan*** ("Kaba river, Zimunai"—C.Y. Yang l.c.).

General distribution: Fore Balkh. (Zaisan), Jung. Tarb. (Saur, Monrak); West. Sib. (Alt.: vicinity of Ust'-Kamenogorsk).

296. **A. zaissanensis** Sumn. in Animadv. Syst. Herb. Univ. Tomsk, 2–3 (1934) 4; Gontsch. and M. Pop. in Fl. SSSR, 12 (1946) 858; Fl. Kazakhst. 5 (1961) 327; Opred. rast. Sr. Azii [Key to Plants of Mid. Asia] 6 (1981) 245; S.B. Ho in Bull. Bot. Research, 3, 7 (1983) 61; C.Y. Yang in Claves pl. Xinjiang, 3 (1985) 171.—*A. kurtschumensis* auct. non Bunge: Sanczir in Grub. Opred. rast. Mong. [Key to Plants of Mongolia] (1982) 161, p. min. p.

Described from East. Kazakhstan (Altay). Type in Tomsk (TK). Along rocky and rubbly montane slopes.

IA. Mongolia: ***Mong. Alt.*** (cen. lower course of Turgen-gol river, left bank tributary of Bulgan-gol, arid meadow, July 1947—Yun.).

IIA. Jungger: ***Cis-Alt.*** ("Altay, Fuyun', in hills to 1200 m alt."—S.B. Ho l.c.), ***Zaisan*** ("Burchum; Kaba river; Zimunai"—C.Y. Yang l.c.).

General destribution: West. Sib. (Alt. South.).

297. **A. kurtschumensis** Bunge Gen. Astrag. Sp. Geront. 1 (1868) 139 and 2 (1869) 236; id. Astrag. Turk. (1880) 303; O. et B. Fedtsch. Konsp. fl. Turk. 2 (1909) 240; Kryl. Fl. Zap. Sib. 7 (1933) 1711; Gontsch. and M. Pop. in Fl. SSSR, 12 (1946) 852; Fl. Kazakhst. 5 (1961) 323; Opred. rast. Sr. Azii [Key to Plants of Mid. Asia] 6 (1981) 244; Sanczir in Grub. Opred. rast. Mong. [Key to Plants of Mongolia] (1982) 161; Ulzij. in Tr. Inst. bot. AN MNR (1982) 32; Grub. in Novosti sist. vyssh. rast. 21 (1984) 213; C.Y. Yang in Claves pl. Xinjiang, 3 (1985) 171; Ulzij. and Gub. in Byul. Mosk. obshch. ispyt. prir., otd. biol. 92, 5 (1987) 117; H.C. Fu in Fl. Intramong. 2 ed., 3 (1989) 299.

—**Ic.:** Fl. Intramong. 2 ed., 3 (1989) tab. 115, fig. 11–15.

Described from East. Kazakhstan (Altay). Type in Paris (P), isotype in St.-Petersburg (LE).

On steppe rocky and rubbly slopes of mountains.

IA. Mongolia: ***Mong. Alt.*** (Khasagtu-Khairkhan mountain range, east. extremity, on Gobi Altay—Daribi lateral creek valley (with springlet) road to nor.-west of Chandmani-ula, rocky slopes, June 30; west. fringe of Tsetseg-nura basin, Temetiin-Khukh-ula, south-west. slope on road to Must somon from Tsetseg somon, 2150–2200 m, desertified steppe slopes, June 26, 1971—Grub., Ulzij. et al.; Ulyastai-gol river gorge 10 km south-west of Bugat somon, rocky slopes and rocks, May 5, 1984—Kam. and Dariima; Sutai-ula mountain range, 12 km south-south-west of Dariba settlement, Aug. 18, 1984—Gub. [MW], ***Depr. Lakes*** (right bank of Khungui river 7 km east of Ikhe-Margats-ula, on road to Urgamal somon, steppe, Aug. 18, 1972—Grub., Ulazij. et al.), ***East. Gobi*** ("Bayan-nur: Urdyn-Khoid-khoshu"—H.C. Fu l.c.), ***Alash. Gobi*** ("Alashan mountain range"—H.C. Fu l.c.).

IIA. Junggar: ***Zaisan*** ("Burchicm; Kaba river"—C.Y. Yang l.c.).

General distribution: West. Sib. (Altay, south: Kurchum river estuary).

298. **A. follicularis** Pall. Astrag. (1800) 16; DC. Prodr. 2 (1825) 301; Ledeb. Fl. Alt. 3 (1831) 322; id. Fl. Ross. 1 (1842) 644; Bunge Gen. Astrag. Sp. Geront. 1 (1868) 139 and 2 (1869) 236; id. Astrag. Turk. (1880) 303; O. et B. Fedtsch. Konsp. fl. Turk. 2 (1909) 240; Kryl. Fl. Zap. Sib. 7 (1933) 1710; Gontsch. and M. Pop. in Fl. SSSR, 12 (1946) 857; Fl. Kazakhst. 5 (1961) 327; Bait. Astrag. Tyan'-Shanya (1977) 96; Opred. rast. Sr. Azii [Key to Plants of Mid. Asia] 6 (1981) 245; Golosk. Fl. Dzhung. Alat. (1984) 74; C.Y. Yang in Claves pl. Xinjiang, 3 (1985) 171.—*A. kalguttensis* Sumn. in Animadv. Syst. Herb. Univ. Tomsk. 5–6 (1933) 4.

—**Ic.:** Pall. 1800 l.c. tab. 14.

Described from Altay. Type in London (BM).

On sandy banks of lakes, rocky and steppe slopes.

IIA. Junggar: ***Tarb.*** ("Saur; Dachen"—C.Y. Yang l.c.), ***Zaisan*** ("Kaba river; Burchum"—C.Y. Yang l.c.).

General distribution: Fore Balkh., Jung.-Tarb.; West. Sib. (Irt. south-east., Alt.), Nor. Mong. (Hang.: Oigon-nur lake).

299. **A. kazymbeticus** Saposch. [Sap.] ex Sumn. in Animadv. Syst. Herb. Univ. Tomsk. 5–6 (1933) 6; Gontsch. and M. Pop. in Fl. SSSR, 12 (1946) 854; Fl. Kazakhst. 5 (1961) 324; Bait. Astrag. Tyan'-Shanya (1977) 96; Opred. rast. Sr. Azii [Key to Plants of Mid. Asia] 6 (1981) 244; Golosk. Fl. Dzhung. Alat. (1984) 74; C.Y. Yang in Claves pl. Xinjiang, 3 (1985) 170.

Described from East. Kazakhstan (Jung. Ala Tau). Type in St.-Petersburg (LE).

On rocky and rubbly slopes in upper mountain belt.

IIA. Junggar: ***Tarb.*** ("Dachen"—C.Y. Yang l.c.). ***Jung. Ala Tau*** (?), ***Jung. Gobi*** ("Chingil' river"—C.Y. Yang l.c.).

General distribution: endemic, Jung Ala Tau.

300. **A. wenquanensis** S.B. Ho in Bull. Bot. Research, 3, 1 (1983) 58.

—**Ic.:** S.B. Ho l.c. tab. 7, fig. 1–8.

Described from Sinkiang (Jung. Ala Tau). Type in Urumchi (in Herb. Coll. Agric. Aug. 1, Xinjiangense).

IIA. Junggar: ***Jung. Ala Tau*** ("Wenquan [Arixang], Haxia ligchan, in collibus pascuisque, alt. 1700 m, June 17, 1978, leg. S.Q. Huang, No. 8—typus !"—S.B. Ho l.c.).

General distribution: endemic.

301. **A. lupulinus** Pall. Reise, 3 (1776) Anh. 750; id. Astrag. (1800) 17; DC. Astrag. (1802) 180; Ledeb. Fl. Ross. 1 (1842) 646; Bunge Gen. Astrag. Sp. Geront. 1 (1868) 139 and 2 (1869) 238; Gontsch. and Boriss. in Fl. SSSR, 12 (1946) 856; Boriss. in Fl. Zabaik. 6 (1954) 588; M. Pop. Fl. Sr. Sib. 1 (1957) 336; Fl. Tsentr. Sib. 2 (1979) 602; Sanczir in Grub. Opred. rast. Mong. [Key to Plants of Mongolia] (1982) 161; Ulzij. in Tr. Inst. bot. AN MNR, 8 (1982) 32; Ulzij. and Gub. in Byul. Mosk. obshch. ispyt. prir., otd. biol. 92, 5 (1987) 117.—*A. baicalensis* Bunge l.c. 1 (1868) 139 and 2 (1869) 238.

—**Ic.:** Fl. Zabaik. 6, fig. 302.

Described from East. Siberia (Transbaikal area). Type in St.-Petersburg (LE).

On steppe rocky, rubbly and sandy montane slopes, pebble beds and trails, in steppes.

IA. Mongolia: ***Mong. Alt.*** (south-east: 35 km south-west-west of Khalyun settlement [Khara-Adzargyn-nuru mountain range], July 13, 1984—Gub. [MW], ***Val. Lakes*** (Delger somon, east. Fringe of Guilin-tall area, feather grass steppe, Aug. 26, 1943—Yun.), ***Gobi-Alt.*** (Gurban-Saikhan mountain range, June 29, 1981—Gub. [MW], ***East. Gobi*** (rocky ridge facing Delger-Khangai mountain range from nor., July 29, 1924—Pakhomov; Ondai Sair, on ridges and sandy wash borders at 5700 ft, No. 181, 1925—Chaney; 30 km south of old Gurban-Saikhan somon, nor. slope of hillocky massif, June 17, 1972—Guricheva and Rachk.; 75 km nor.-west of Sain-Shanda town along road to Khara-Airag, hillocky area near Ulan-nur lake, steppe, July 31; 70 km west-nor.-west of Sain-Shanda town near Ulan-khuduk well and Arshantyn-khure ruins, along slopes of hillock, Aug. 11—1974, Rachk. and Volk.; Khutag-ula hill, June 19—1980—Gub [MW]), ***Alash. Gobi*** (25 km nor.-west-west of Tsagan-ula border post, July 7, 1981—Gub. [MW]).

IIA. Junggar: ***Jung. Gobi*** (Ikhe-Khabtag-ula mountain range, nor. macro slope, 2300 m, hilly steppe, Aug. 12, 1977—Volk. and Rachk.).

General distribution: West. Sib. (Alt.: desert-steppe Tuva), East. Sib. (Sayans: west. bank of Baikal lake, Daur.), Nor. Mong. (Hang., Mong.-Daur.).

302. **A. baotouensis** H.C. Fu in Fl. Intramong. 2 ed. 3 (1989) 670 and 295.

—**Ic.:** ib. tab. 116, fig. 1–6.

Described from Inner Mongolia (vicinity of Baotou town). Type in Khukh-khote (HIMC).

On meadow montane slopes.

IA. Mongolia: ***East. Mong.*** (Baotoushi, Baiynobo [Baotou town, Bayan-Obo], Aug. 28, 1979, Lei Xi-ting, No. 1922—typus ! [HIMC]).

General distribution: endemic.

303. **A. sphaerocystis** Bunge Beitr. Kenntn. Fl. Russl. Stepp. Cen. As. (1852) 97 in adnot. (seors. impr.); id. in Mém. Ac. Sci. Petersb. Sav. Etrang. 7 (1854) 273 in adnot.; id. Gen. Astrag. Sp. Geront. 1 (1868) 139 and 2 (1869) 306; id. Astrag. Turk. (1880) 306; O. et B. Fedtsch. Konsp. fl. Turk. 2 (1909) 241; Gontsch., M. Pop. and Boriss. in Fl. SSSR, 12 (1946) 854; Grub. Konsp. fl. MNR. (1955) 187; Fl. Kirgiz. 7 (1957) 348; Fl. Kazakhst. 5 (1961) 326; Bait. Astrag. Tyan'-Shanya (1977) 96; Opred. rast. Sr. Azii [Key to Plants of Mid. Asia] 6 (1981) 244; Sanczir in Grub. Opred. rast. Mong. [Key to Plants of Mongolia] (1982) 162; Ulzij. in Tr. Inst. bot. AN MNR, 8 (1982) 32; S.B. Ho in Bull. Bot. Research, 3, 1 (1983) 60; Golosk. Fl. Dzhung. Alat. (1984) 74; C.Y. Yang in Claves pl. Xinjiang, 3 (1985) 170.—*A. nanodes* Bunge in Acta Horti Petrop. 7 (1880) 377.—*A. baisensis* Sumn. in Animadv. Syst. Herb. Univ. Tomsk. 1–2 (1933) 8.

—**Ic.:** Grub. Opred. rast. Mong. [Key to Plants of Mongolia] (1982) Plate 84, fig. 388.

Described from East. Kazakhstan (Jung. Ala Tau). Type in St.-Petersburg (LE).

On rocky slopes of mountains and along river valleys in montane-steppe belt.

IA. Mongolia: *Mong. Alt.* (upper valley of Bulgan river, July 27, 1906—Sep.; upper Bulgan river, valley of Ulagchin-gol on road to Khudzhirtu, left bank 1 km before Khudzhirlag-gol estuary, lateral creek valley, steppe, July 3, 1971—Grub., Ulzij. et al.), ***East. Gobi*** (hillocky massif south-south-east of Khan-Bogdo somon, 10 km nor.-west of Bosgony-khuduk well, in gully—Rachk. and Isach.), ***West. Gobi*** (35 km west of Segseg-Tsagan-Bogdo post, nor. Slope, low granite hillocks, Aug. 20, 1973—Isach. and Rachk.; Atas-Bogdo mountain range, nor. macro slope, 2350 m, montane steppe, Aug. 21, 1976—Rachk. and Damba).

IIA. Junggar: ***Cis-Alt.*** ("Qinhe"—C.Y. Yang l.c.), ***Tarb.*** ("Dachen"—S.B. Ho l.c., C.Y. Yang l.c.), ***Jung. Alt.*** ("Dzhair mountain range"—S.B. Ho l.c.).

General distribution: Jung.-Tarb., Cen. Tien Shan; Mid. Asia (Pamiro-Alay).

Note. Plants from East. Gobi and West. Gobi require a detailed scrutiny with more abundant material.

304. **A. koslovii** B. Fedtsch. et N. Basil. ex N. Ulzij. in Bull. Soc. Natur Moscou, ser. biol. 95, 2 (1990) 85.

Described from Mongolia (Gobi Altay). Type in St.-Petersburg (LE). Plate VIII, fig. 4.

In arid beds of gullies and mountain trails.

IA. Mongolia: *Gobi Alt.* (nor. foothills of Ikhe-Bogdo mountain range, rocky-clayey-sandy soil, May 27, 1926—Kozlova; Ikhe-Bogdo hill, foothill and lower belt of mountains, Aug. 18, 1926—Tug., typus!; between Bayan-Leg and Orok-nur lake, pebble bed of gully 3 km nor.-west of gorge tip, June 25, 1974—Shreter).

General distribution: endemic.

305. **A. arkalycensis** Bunge Gen. Astrag. Sp. Geront. 1 (1868) 139 and 2 (1869) 238; id. Astrag. Turk. (1880) 305; O. et B. Fedtsch. Konsp. fl. Turk. 2 (1909) 241; Kryl. Fl. Zap. Sib. 7 (1933) 1713; Gontsch. and M. Pop. in Fl. SSSR, 12 (1946) 852; Fl. Krasnoyar. kr. 6 (1960) 41; Fl. Kazakhst. 5 (1961) 323; Opred. rast. Sr. Azii [Key to Plants of Mid. Asia] 6 (1981) 244; Sanczir in Grub. Opred. rast. Mong. [Key to Plants of Mongolia] (1982) 162; Ulzij. in Tr. Inst. bot. AN MNR (1982) 32; S.B. Ho in Bull. Bot. Research, 3, 1 (1983) 60; Opred. rast. Tuv. ASSR [Key to Plants of Tuva Autonomous Soviet Socialist Republic] (1984) 146; C.Y. Yang in Claves pl. Xinjiang, 3 (1985) 170; Pl. vasc. Helanshan (1986) 154; Ulzij. and Gub. in Byul. Mosk. obshch. ispyt. prir., otd. biol. 92, 5 (1987) 116; H.C. Fu in Fl. Intramong. 3 (1989) 299.—*A. ellipsoideus* γ *abbreviatus* Ledeb. Fl. Alt. 3 (1831) 320; id. Fl. Ross. 1, 3 (1843) 645.—*A. tricolor* Bunge l.c. 1 (1868) 139 and 2 (1869) 237.

—**Ic.:** Fl. Kazakhst. 5, Plate 41, fig. 7.

Described from East. Kazakhstan (Chingiztau mountains). Type in St.-Petersburg (LE).

On rocky-rubbly slopes of mountains, on sand and in desert sandy steppes, sandy ravines, along floors and flanks of gullies.

IA. Mongolia: ***Mong. Alt.*** (14 km from pass, 2543 m, and 12 km nor.-east of Bugat somon, July 5, 1984—Kam. and Dariima; 40 km south-east of Ulegei town, Aug. 26, 1984, Gub. [MW]). ***East. Gobi*** (35 km east of Undur-Shili somon, on slopes of granite hillocks, Aug. 10, 1974—Rachk. and Volk.), ***Alash. Gobi*** ("Alashan mountain range"—S.B. Ho l.c.), ***Ordos*** ("Nin'sya"—S.B. Ho l.c.).

IIA. Junggar: ***Cis-Alt.*** ("west. part of Altay"—C.Y. Yang l.c.).

General distribution: Fore Balkh., Nor. Tien Shan; West. Sib. (Altay, south), East. sib. (Sayans: Minusinsk steppes).

306. **A. ellipsoideus** Ledeb. Fl. Alt. 3 (1831) 319; id. Fl. Ross. 1 (1842) 645; Bunge Gen. Astrag. Sp. Geront. 1 (1868) 139 and 2 (1869) 237; id. Astrag. Turk. (1880) 304; O. et B. Fedtsch. Konsp. fl. Turk. 2 (1909) 240; Kryl. Fl. Zap. Sib. 7 (1933) 1712; Peter-Stib. in Acta Horti Gotoburg, 12 (1937–38) 68; Gontsch. and M. Pop. in Fl. SSSR, 12 (1946) 850; Wang and Tang in Ill. treatm. princip. pl. China, Legum. (1955) 373; Fl. Kazakhst. 5 (1961) 322; Bait. Astrag. Tyan'-Shanya (1977) 95; Opred. rast. Sr. Azii [Key to Plants of Mid. Asia] 6 (1981) 243; Sanczir in Grub. Opred. rast. Mong. [Key to Plants of Mongolia] (1982) 162; S.B. Ho in Bull. Bot. Research, 3, 1 (1983) 59; C.Y. Yang in Claves pl. Xinjiang, 3 (1985) 170; Pl. vasc. Helanshan (1986) 154; Liou f. in Fl. desert Sin. 2 (1987) 291; Ulzij. and Gub. in Byul. Mosk. obshch. ispyt. prir., otd. biol. 92, 5 (1987) 116; H.C. Fu in Fl. Intramong. 2 ed., 3 (1989) 297.—*A. transiliensis* Gontsch. in Not. Syst. (Leningrad), 10 (1947) 41; Gontsch. and M. Pop. in Fl. SSSR, 12 (1946) 853, descr. ross.; Fl. Kazakhst. 5

(1961) 324; Bait. Astrag. Tyan'-Shanya (1977) 95.—*A. transiliensis* var. *microphyllus* S.B. Ho in Bull. Bot. Research, 3, 1 (1983) 59.—*A. dilutus* auct. non Bunge: Fl. Intramong. 3 (1977) 208.

—**Ic.:** Fl. Kazakhst. 5, Plate 41, fig. 5; Fl. Intramong. 2 ed., 3 (1989) tab. 117, fig. 6–10.

Described from East. Kazakhstan (Altay). Type in St.-Petersburg (LE).

On desert rocky slopes of low mountains, in rocky-rubbly desert steppes.

IA. Mongolia: ***Mong. Alt.*** (sand on waterdivide of Tuguryuk and Dzergin rivers, Aug. 17, 1930—Bar.; Ulyastain-gol river gorge 10 km south-west of Bugat somon, on pebble beds, Aug. 5; Bulgan-gol river basin, upper course of Ulyastain-gol river, left bank, July 9—1984, Kam. and Dariima), ***East. Gobi*** ("Bayan-nur: Uradyn-dund-khoshu"—H.C. Fu l.c.), ***West. Gobi*** (30 km south-south-east of Dzakhoi oasis, nor. fringe of Ederengiin-nuru mountain, on slope, Aug. 16, 1973—Isach. and Rachk.), ***Ordos*** ("Nin'sya"—S.B. Ho l.c., Liou fil. l.c.).

IIA. Junggar: ***Tarb.*** (10 km nor. of Kosh-Tologoi settlement on Khobuk river, on road to Altay, pass through hillocky ridge, desert rocky steppe, July 4, 1959—Yun. and I-f. Yuan'; "Dachen"—C.Y. Yang, l.c.), ***Tien Shan*** (upper course of Taldy river, 1219 m, Irenkhaberga, May 15, Irenkhaberga, Taldy, 2438 m, May 17 and 24; Tarlagan, 2743 m, Kunges, Aug. 2—1879, A. Reg.; "Ili"—C.Y. Yang l.c.), ***Zaisan*** (valley of Ch. Irtysh river, Mai-Kapchagai area east of Zaisan, June 1, 1903—Gr.-Grzh.; "Burchum"—C.Y. Yang l.c.).

General distribution: Fore Balkh., Jung.-Tarb., Nor. Tien. Shan; West. Sib. (Alt., Irtysh region).

Plate I.

1—*A. chinensis* L. fil.; 2—*A. mongolicus* Bunge; 3—*A. przewalskii* Bunge; 4—*A. lithophilus* Kar. et Kir.

Plate II.

1—*A. imetensis* Boriss.; 2—*A. puberulus* Ledeb.; 3—*A. pavlovii* B. Fedtsch. et N. Basil.; 4—*A. versicolor* Pall.; 5—*A. melilotoides* Pall.

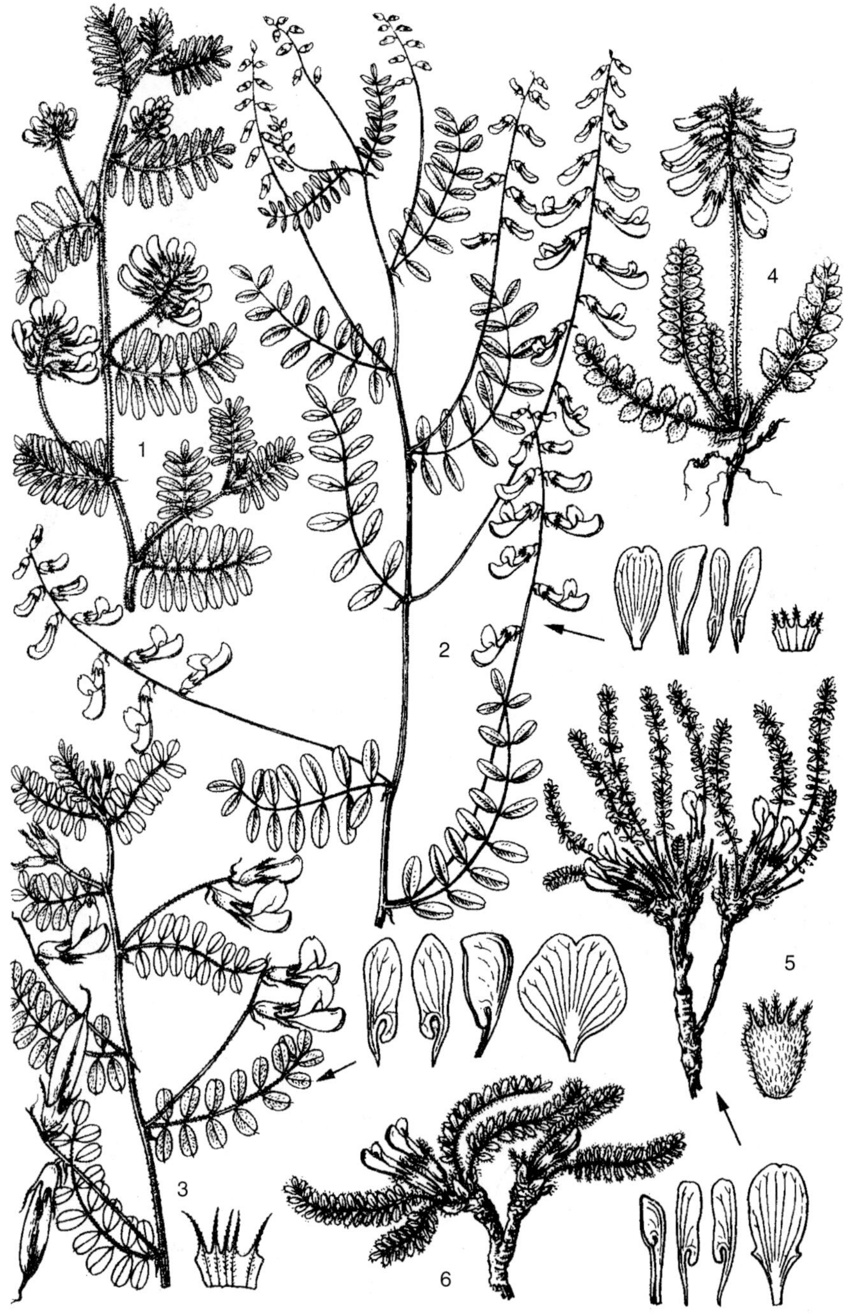

Plate III.

1—*A. tanguticus* Bat.; 2—*A. chrysopteris* Bunge.; 3—*A. pastorius* Tsai et Yu; 4—*A. licentianus* Hand.-Mazz.; 5—*A. alatavicus* Kar. et Kir.; 6—*A. przewalskianus* Podl. et Ulzij.

Plate IV.

1—*A. karkarensis* M. Pop.; 2—*A. scoparius* Schrenk.; 3—*A. chorogossicus* Lipsky; 4—*A. hamiensis* S.B. Ho; 5—*A. arbuscula* Pall.

Plate V.

1—*A. kuldshensis* Bunge; 2—*A. adsurgens* Pall.; 3—*A. angustissimus* Bunge; 4—*A. petracus* Kar. et Kir.; 5—*A. inopinatus* Boriss ; 6—*A. austrosibiricus* Schischk.

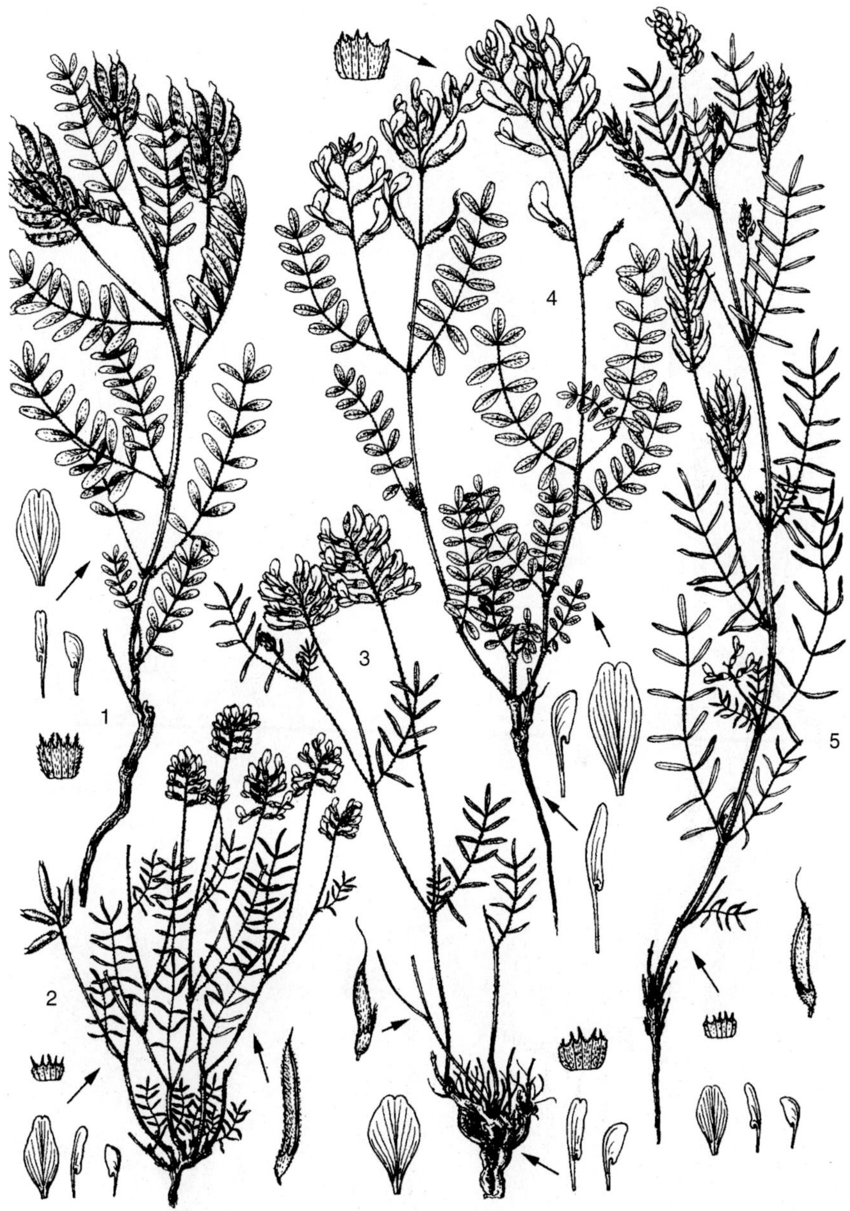

Plate VI.

1—*A. variabilis* Bunge ex Maxim.; 2—*A. miniatus* Bunge; 3—*A. brachybotrys* Bunge; 4—*A. discolor* Bunge; 5—*A. sulcatus* L.

Plate VII.

1—*A. grubovii* Sancz.; 2—*A. scaberrimus* Bunge; 3—*A. macrotrichus* Peter-Stib.; 4—*A. monophyllus* Bunge; 5—*A. borodinii* Krassn.

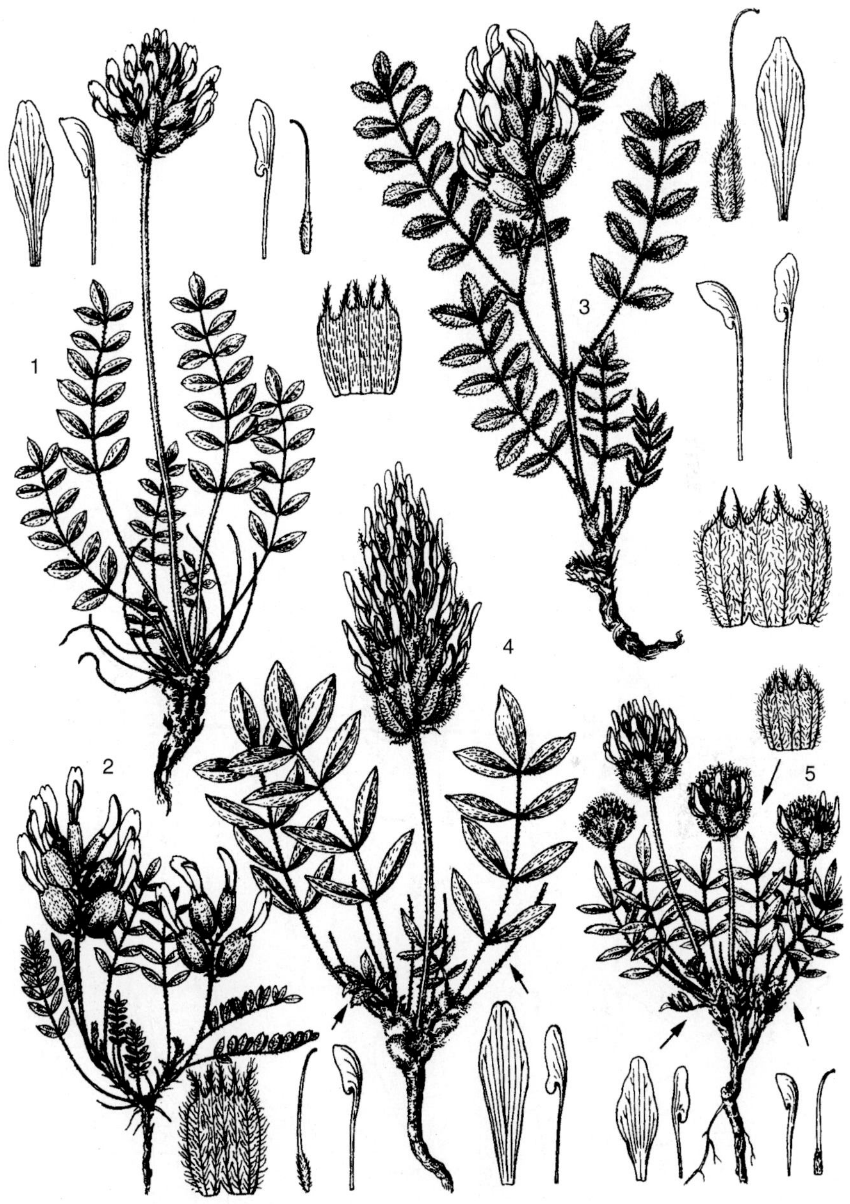

Plate VIII.

1—*A. ochrias* Bunge; 2—*A. grum-grshimailoi* Palib.; 3—*A. suidunensis* Bunge; 4—*A. koslovii* B. Fedtsch. et N. Basil. ex Ulzij.; 5—*A. laguroides* Pall.

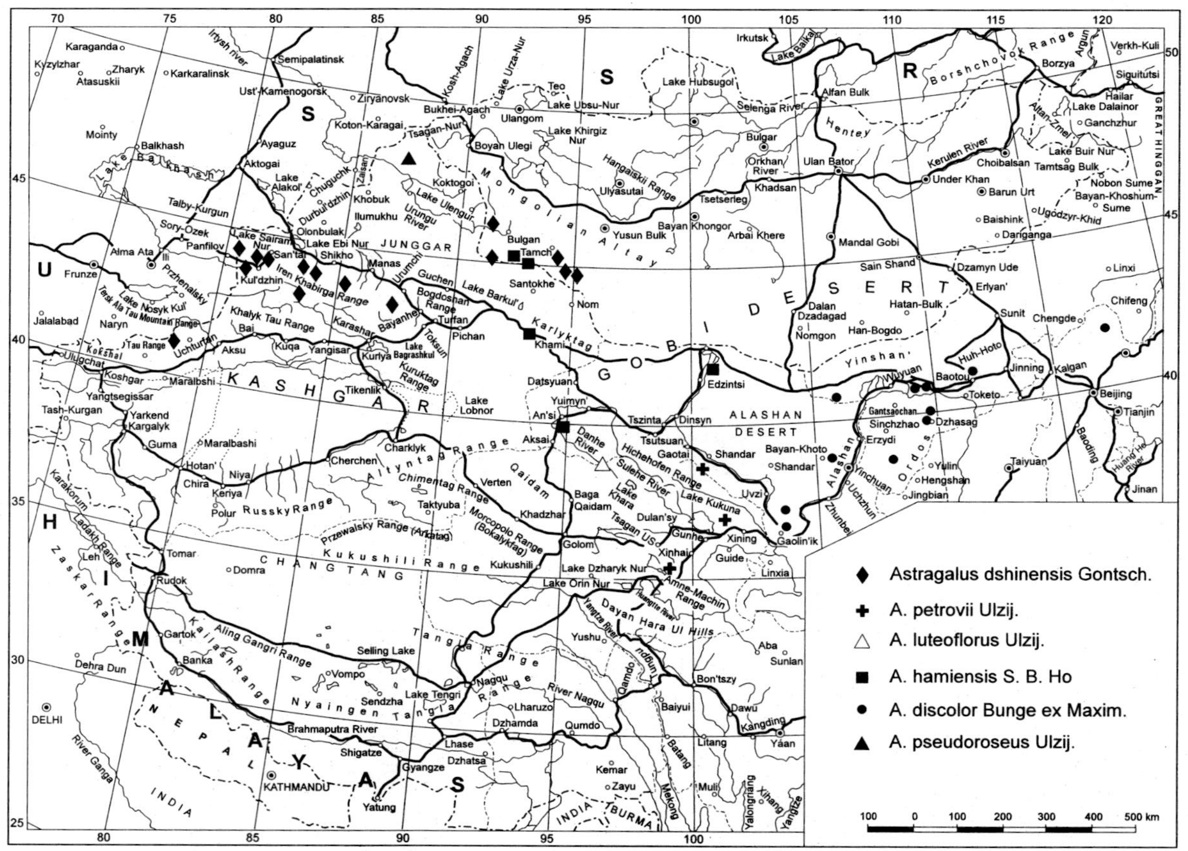
◆ Astragalus dshinensis Gontsch.
✚ A. petrovii Ulzij.
△ A. luteoflorus Ulzij.
■ A. hamiensis S. B. Ho
● A. discolor Bunge ex Maxim.
▲ A. pseudoroseus Ulzij.
100 0 100 200 300 400 500 km

Map 1.

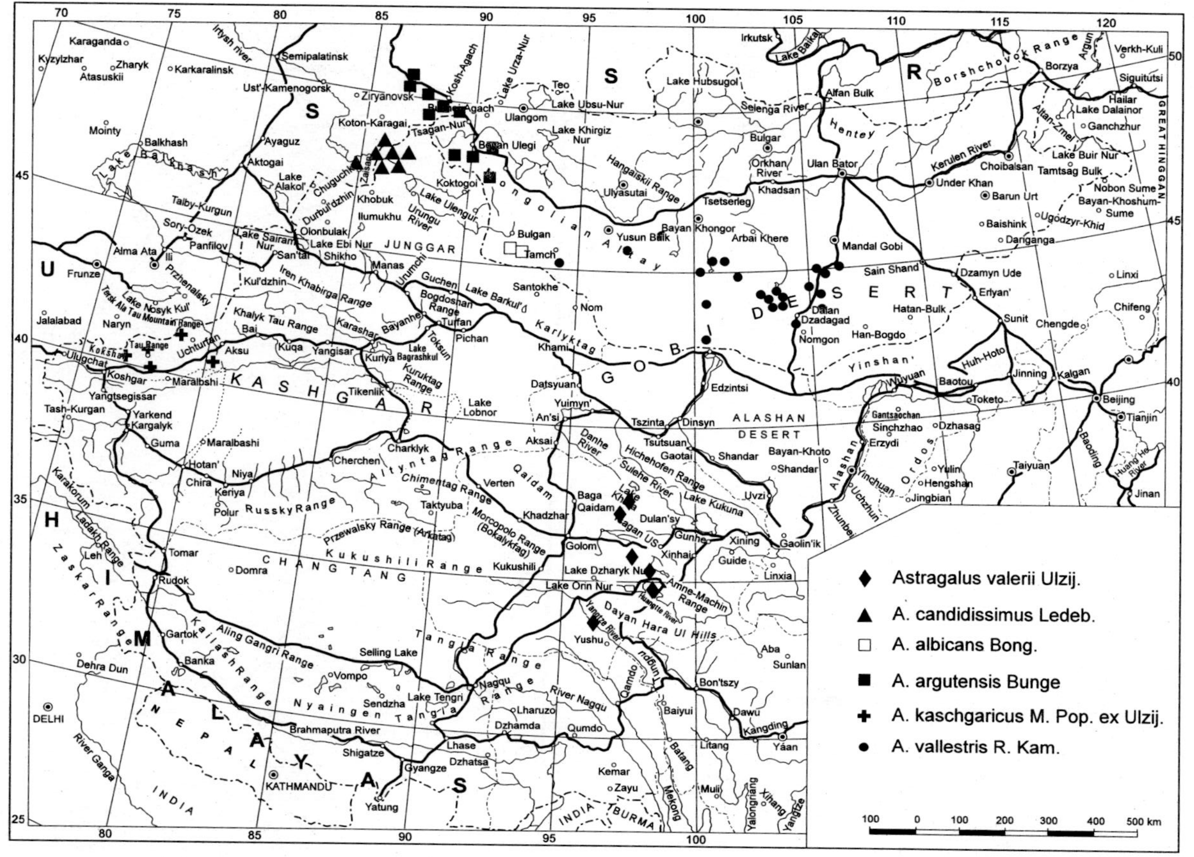

Astragalus valerii Ulzij.
A. candidissimus Ledeb.
A. albicans Bong.
A. argutensis Bunge
A. kaschgaricus M. Pop. ex Ulzij.
A. vallestris R. Kam.
100 0 100 200 300 400 500 km

Map 2.

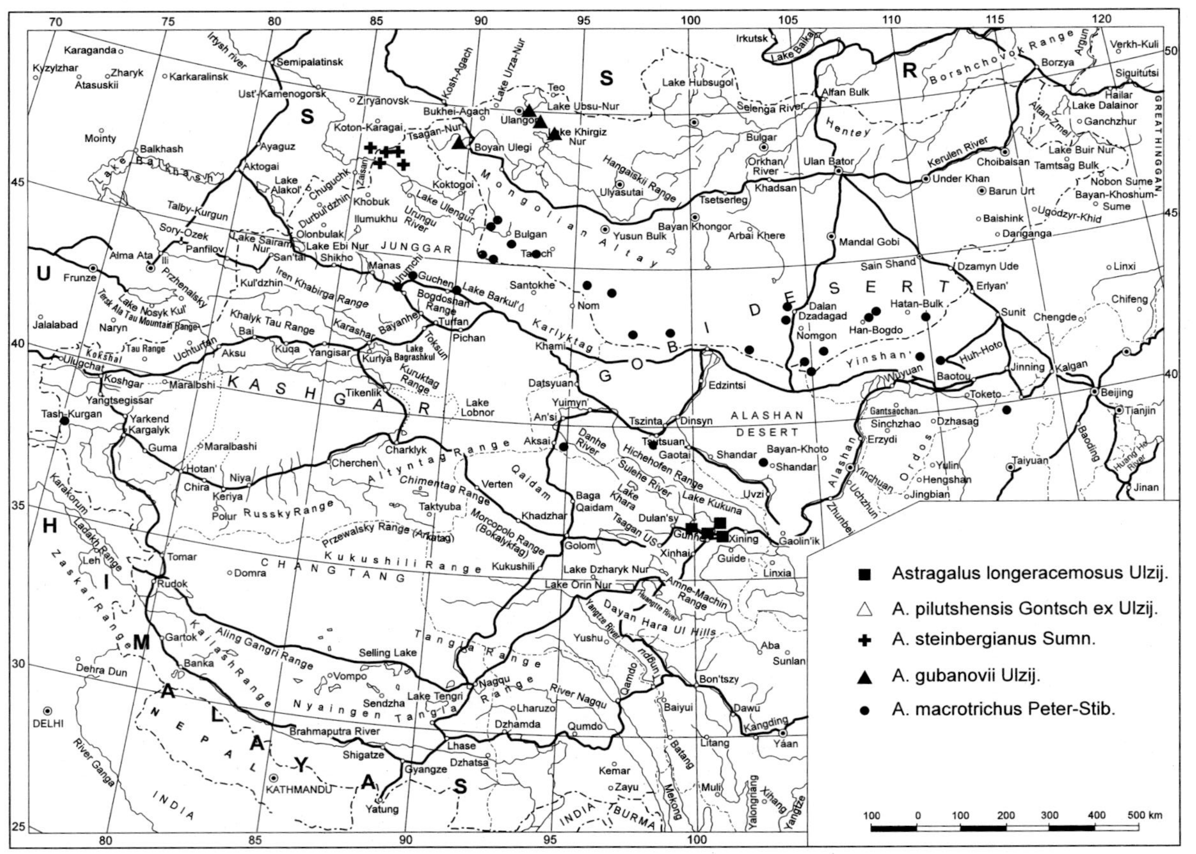
■ Astragalus longeracemosus Ulzij.
△ A. pilutshensis Gontsch ex Ulzij.
✚ A. steinbergianus Sumn.
▲ A. gubanovii Ulzij.
● A. macrotrichus Peter-Stib.
100 0 100 200 300 400 500 km

Map 3.

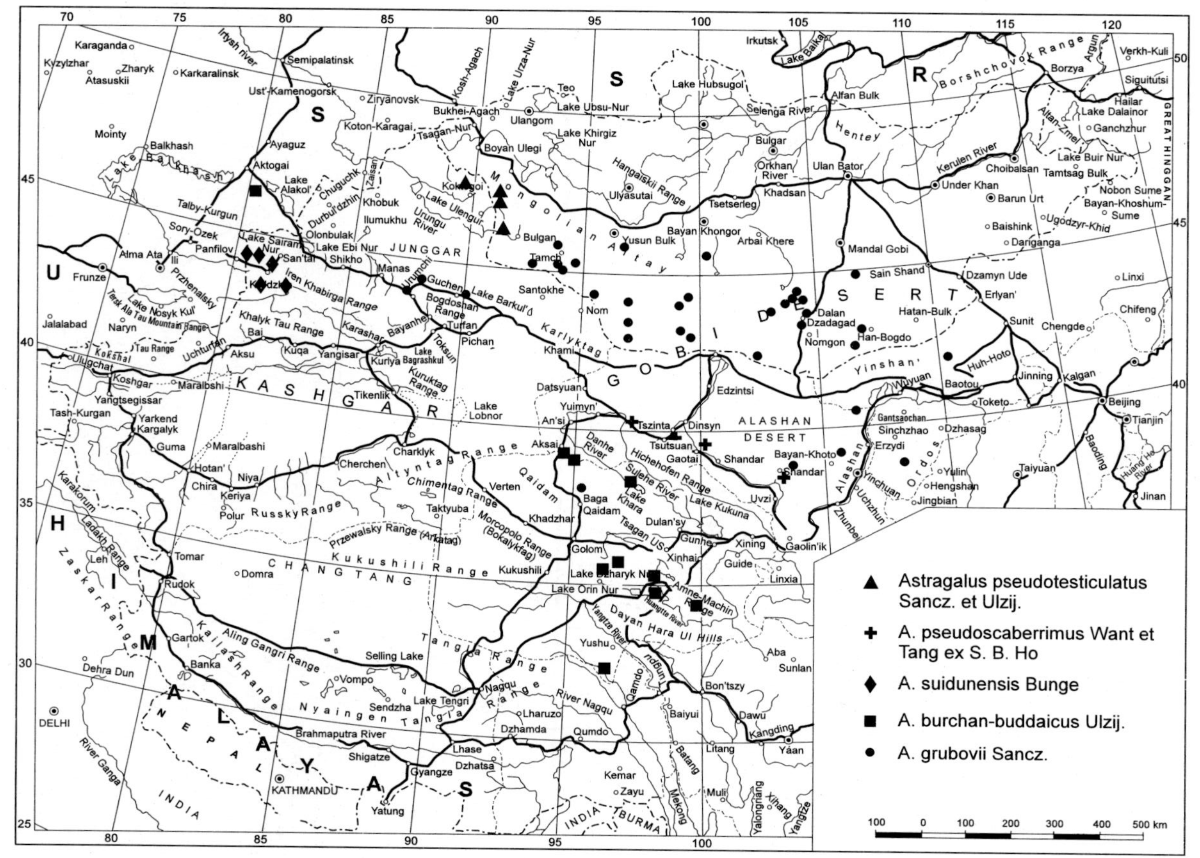
▲ Astragalus pseudotesticulatus Sancz. et Ulzij.
✚ A. pseudoscaberrimus Want et Tang ex S. B. Ho
◆ A. suidunensis Bunge
■ A. burchan-buddaicus Ulzij.
● A. grubovii Sancz.
100 0 100 200 300 400 500 km

Map 4.

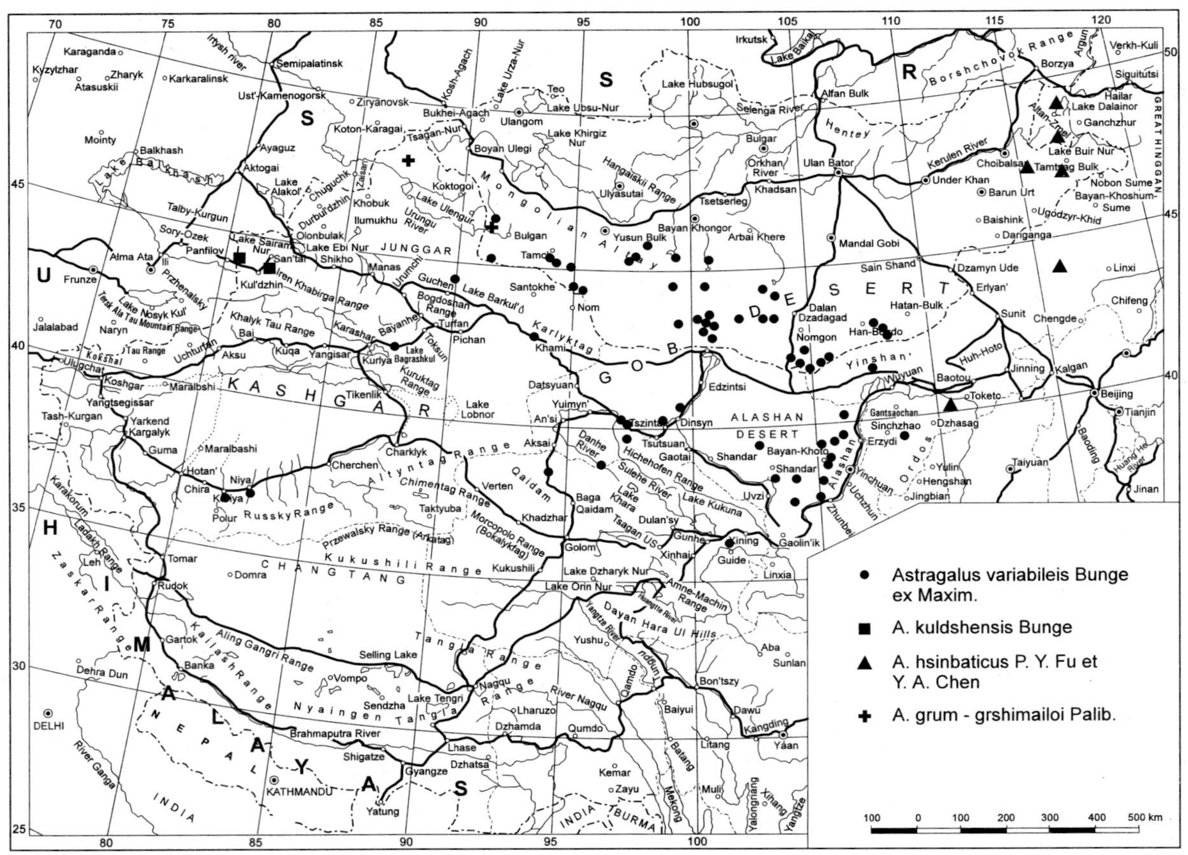
Astragalus variabileis Bunge ex Maxim.
A. kuldshensis Bunge
A. hsinbaticus P. Y. Fu et Y. A. Chen
A. grum - grshimailoi Palib.
100 0 100 200 300 400 500 km

Map 5.

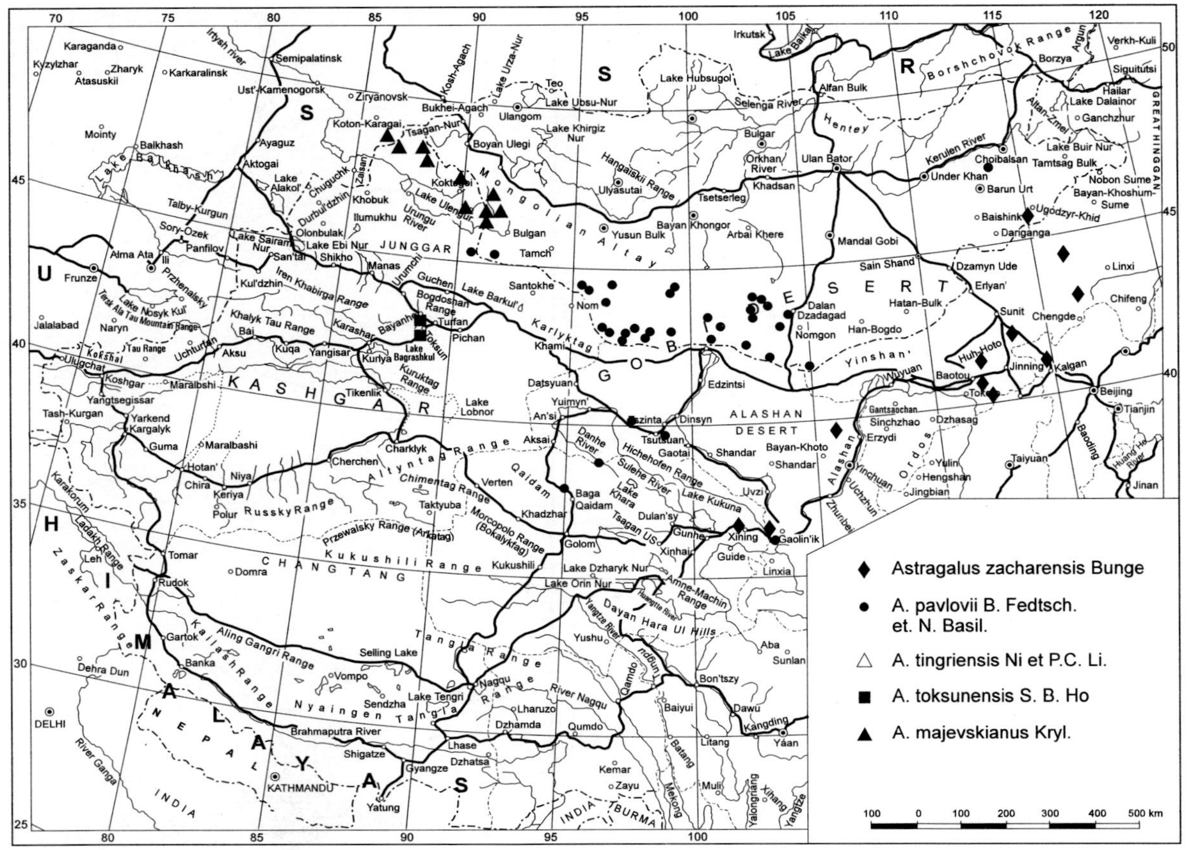

♦ Astragalus zacharensis Bunge
● A. pavlovii B. Fedtsch. et. N. Basil.
△ A. tingriensis Ni et P.C. Li.
■ A. toksunensis S. B. Ho
▲ A. majevskianus Kryl.
100 0 100 200 300 400 500 km

Map 6.

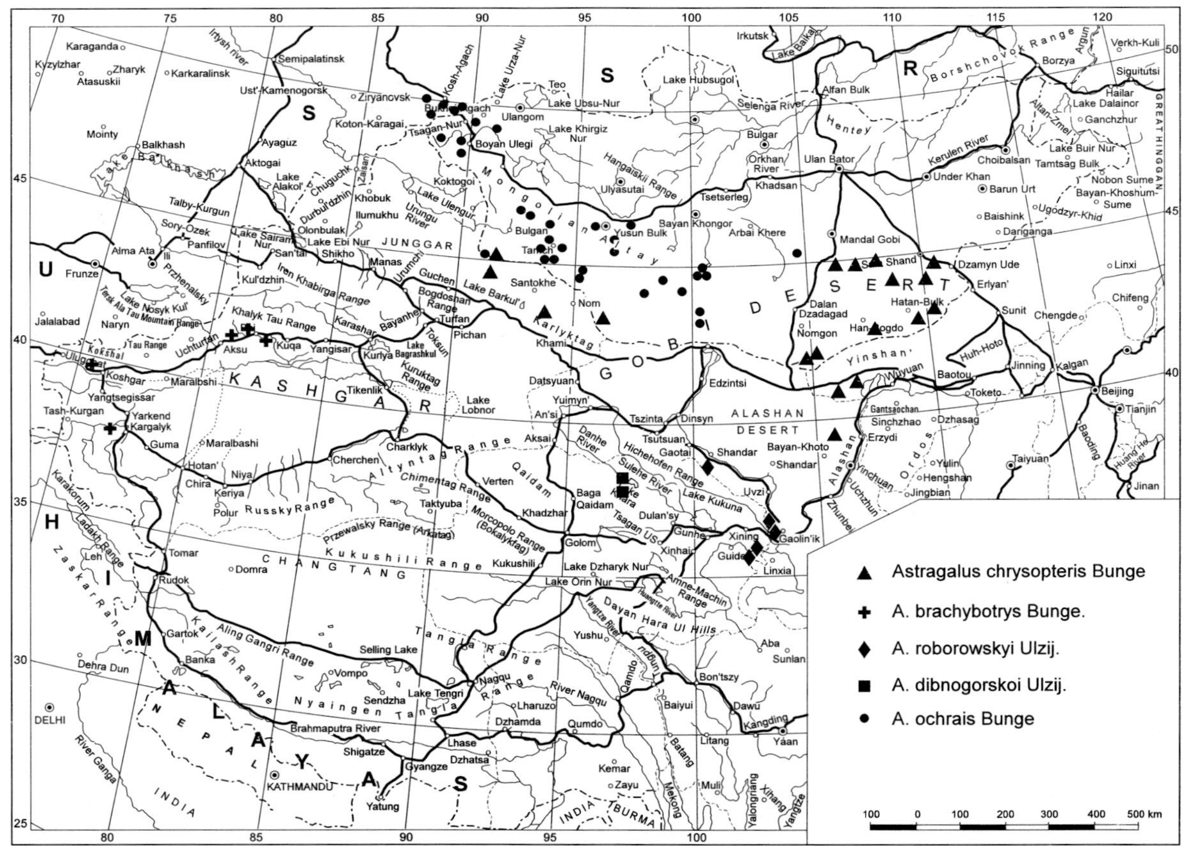
▲ Astragalus chrysopteris Bunge
✚ A. brachybotrys Bunge.
◆ A. roborowskyi Ulzij.
■ A. dibnogorskoi Ulzij.
● A. ochrais Bunge
100 0 100 200 300 400 500 km

Map 7.

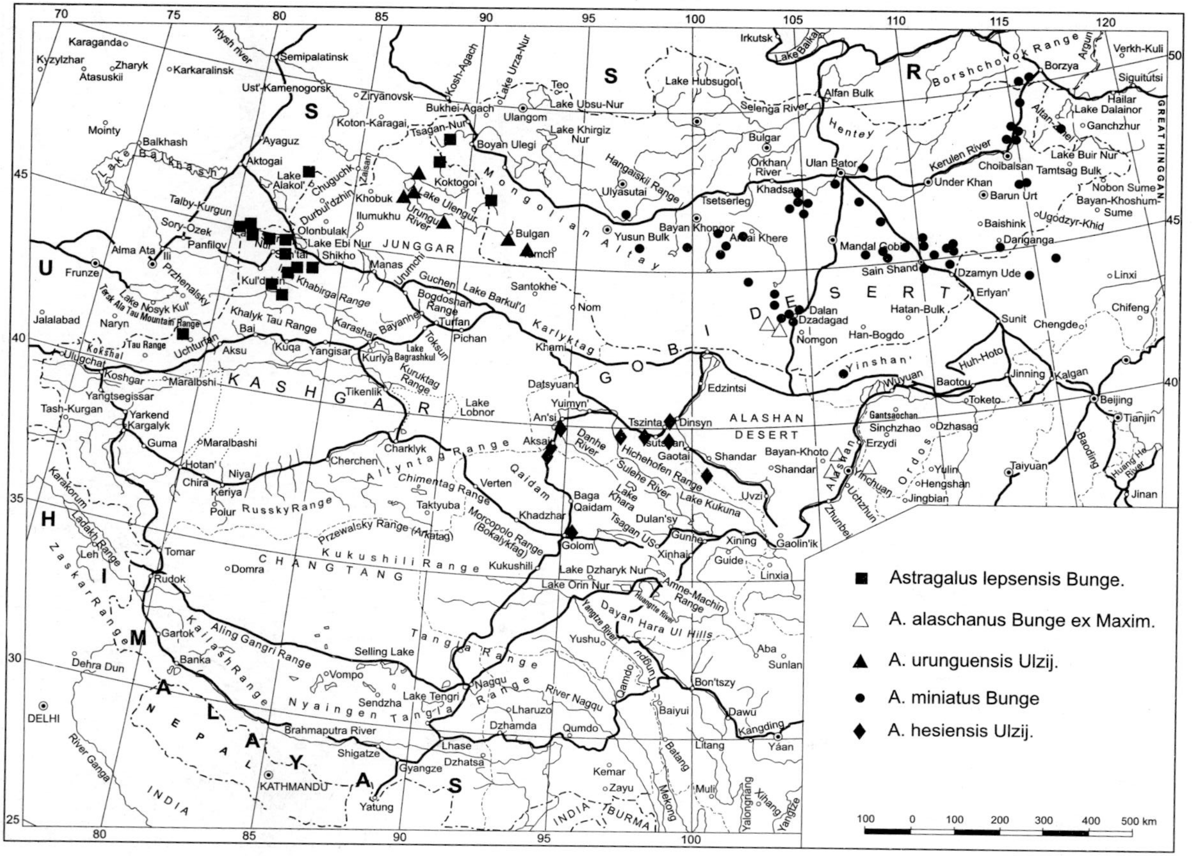
■ Astragalus lepsensis Bunge.
△ A. alaschanus Bunge ex Maxim.
▲ A. urunguensis Ulzij.
● A. miniatus Bunge
◆ A. hesiensis Ulzij.
100 0 100 200 300 400 500 km

Map 8.

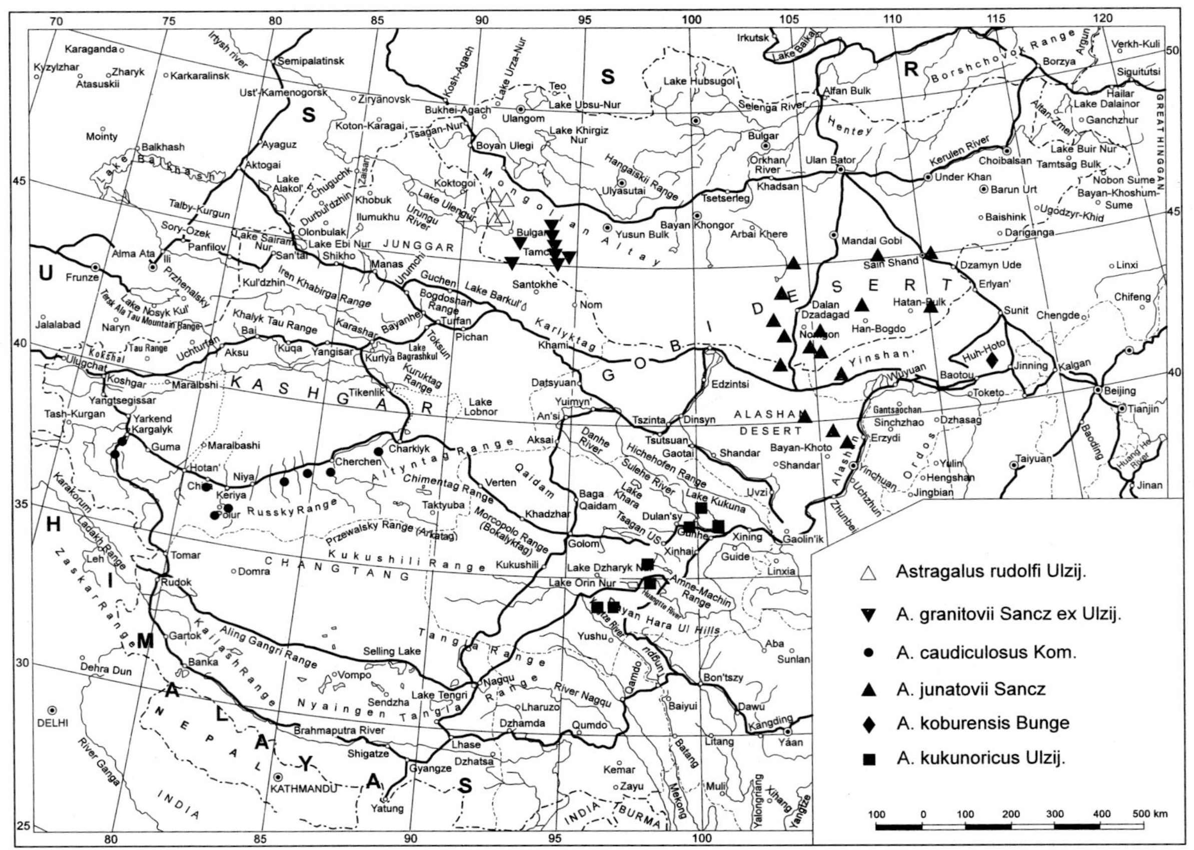
△ Astragalus rudolfi Ulzij.
▼ A. granitovii Sancz ex Ulzij.
● A. caudiculosus Kom.
▲ A. junatovii Sancz
◆ A. koburensis Bunge
■ A. kukunoricus Ulzij.
100 0 100 200 300 400 500 km

Map 9.

INDEX OF LATIN NAMES OF PLANTS

INDEX OF PLANT DISTRIBUTION RANGES

INDEX OF PLANT ILLUSTRATIONS

A. sulcatus L.	VI	5
A. tanguticus Bat.	III	1
A. variabilis Bunge ex Maxim.	VI	1
A. versicolor Pall.	II	4